and nodules. At other sites, the original evaporites were replaced selectively with celestite, which preserved both the shape and the internal features of the replaced crystals, nodules, and beds (Kahle and Floyd, 1971; Carlson, 1987c; Richards and Chamberlain, 1987).

Bedded halite (rock salt) is well crystallized, granular, and colorless or white. The coarse-grained halite of the channel-shaped bodies is colorless and transparent, and some cleavage surfaces exceed 6 inches in length (fig. 7). (See Chapter 4 for explanation of cleavage.) Hopper-shaped crystal molds of halite (see fig. 40B) occur in dolostones of the Salina and Detroit River Groups in Lucas, Ottawa, and Wyandot Counties (Gilbert, 1873; Kraus, 1905a; Kahle and Floyd, 1971, 1972; Janssens, 1977).

Anhydrite typically occurs in finely crystalline, granular, bluish-white to gray nodules and beds. The occurrences of this mineral are restricted to subsurface evaporitic rocks encountered in drill cores and underground mines.

Flint and chert are related types of sedimentary rocks that are composed chiefly of microcrystalline quartz. For this reason, the data for flint and chert are listed under quartz in the catalog (Chapter 7). There is no mineralogical difference between flint and chert, and no agreement among geologists about the definitions of the two terms. For example, some investigators would classify small nodules of microcrystalline quartz embedded in limestone as flint, and massive, bedded deposits of microcrystalline quartz as chert (Frondel, 1962). In Ohio, however, geologists have classically differentiated flint from chert by its chemical purity, recognizing high-purity material as flint and impure material as chert (Stout and Schoenlaub, 1945). According to the latter definition, flint also can be distinguished from chert on the basis of its luster—high-purity material is lustrous and impure material looks dull. Because

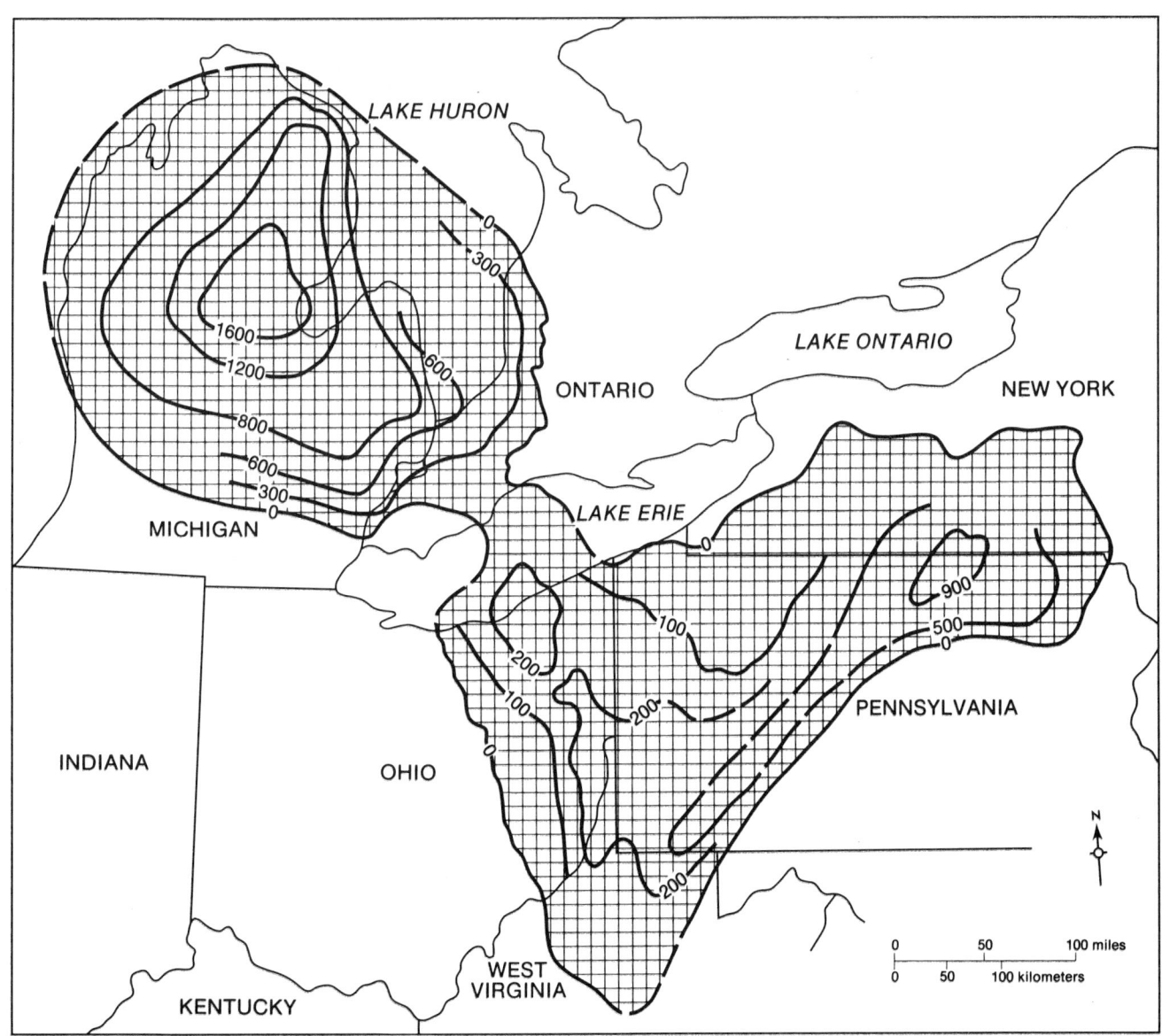

FIGURE 6.—Generalized distribution and thickness of Salina salt beds in Ohio and adjacent states; contour interval irregular (modified from Clifford, 1973, fig. 1).

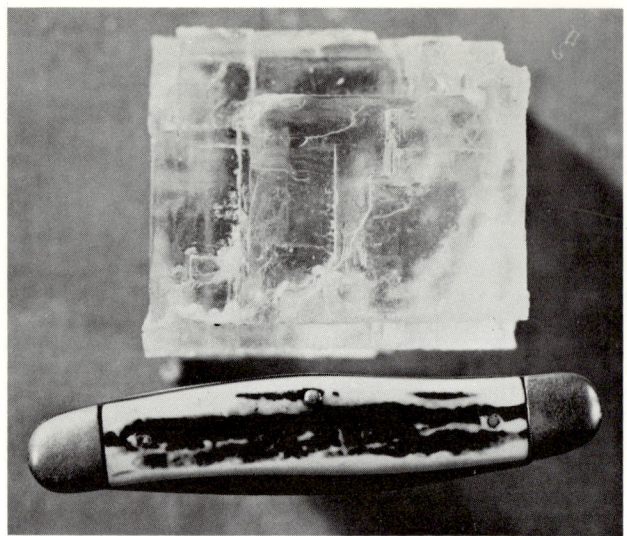

FIGURE 7.—Coarsely crystalline halite showing perfect cubic cleavage; from the International Salt Co. mine, Cuyahoga County. Knife is 3½ inches long.

the terminology of Stout and Schoenlaub (1945) has been used widely by other investigators in the state, it is adopted in this work as well. Therefore, in the subsequent discussions, impure flint and chert are considered to be identical materials and the two terms are used interchangeably.

The name chalcedony is restricted here to the microcrystalline variety of quartz that is found lining or filling cavities in the flint beds, following long-established usage (Frondel, 1962). The chalcedony was deposited from aqueous solutions sometime after the cavities in the flint beds were formed, and ordinarily is distinguished from the flint by its higher translucency and luster (waxy) and its milky-white to gray color.

Several flint beds of archaeological and mineralogical significance occur in the state (Fowke, 1902; Stout, 1927; Morgan, R., 1929; Stout and Schoenlaub, 1945; Murphy and Blank, 1970; Converse, 1972; Morton and Carskadden, 1972; Carskadden and Donaldson, 1973; Murphy, 1976). Table 2 gives some specifics for the localities that were discovered and quarried by prehistoric Indians, who used the flint as a raw material for making tools and weapons. Because the Indians only worked deposits of high quality, these sites are a good source of lapidary material today. The importance of flint as a semiprecious gem mineral was underscored in 1965 when it was selected by the Ohio legislature to be the official gemstone for the state.

A flint bed is recognized by its relationship to other strata at a site and its characteristic fossils. The field relationships are well summarized by Stout and Schoenlaub (1945), who give the sequences of strata for a large number of flint sites. With respect to fossils, Smyth (1957) has shown that fusulinids are particularly valuable in identifying the Pennsylvanian flint horizons. Other features, such as color or texture, are not as useful in identifying a flint bed because these properties can differ from site to site. In this regard, the flint beds have yet to be positively identified at several old Indian quarries, such as near Somerset, in Perry County, and in northern Erie County (Morton and Carskadden, 1972; Stothers and Rutter, 1978).

Many of the flint beds exhibit similar geological characteristics (table 2). For instance, flint generally occurs with a limestone or occupies the position normally held by a limestone, except for the Zaleski unit, which is always a flint (Stout and Schoenlaub, 1945; Cavaroc and Ferm, 1968). Most of the flint beds contain marine fossils except for the Fishpot flint, which bears a freshwater fauna (Murphy, 1976). Although flint beds range from Silurian to Pennsylvanian in age, the most important flint occurrences, both in number and size, originated during the Pennsylvanian Period in a relatively narrow interval of geologic time. The Pennsylvanian flints are restricted to eastern Ohio and lie within the Appalachian Basin. The Pennsylvanian flints and their associated marine limestones as a rule rest on continental beds, generally coal seams or underclays (Stout and Schoenlaub, 1945). Therefore, the flint beds record the change from continental to marine conditions when the Pennsylvanian coal swamps were flooded by the sea.

There are three main forms of occurrence of flint in eastern Ohio: (1) sheetlike bodies, (2) lenses and nodules, and (3) interlayers or interbeds. The sheets are continuous or nearly continuous bodies typically several miles long and several feet thick that taper toward their edges. Lenticular and nodular flint consists of numerous small masses of flint of varying shape, such as nodules, lenses, and stringers, that are enclosed in a limestone or dolostone bed. Interlayered or interbedded flint consists of several continuous layers of flint a few inches thick that are interstratified with layers of limestone, dolostone, or shale.

Quarrying activity by prehistoric Indians was greatest in the Vanport, Upper Mercer, and Zaleski units, in order of decreasing archaeological significance (Moorehead, 1892; Stout and Schoenlaub, 1945; Converse, 1972). Each of these flints occurs in one or more geographically separate districts; sheets are the most important type by far because of the greater volume of high-quality material they could supply. The Upper Mercer flint (Pottsville Group) is the oldest of the three units and the Vanport flint (Allegheny Group) is the youngest. These three beds are described individually below.

Vanport flint

Geologic setting.—The Vanport flint, a local phase of the Vanport limestone, reaches its maximum development in isolated sections of east-central and southern Ohio (Hildreth, 1838; Stout and Schoenlaub, 1945; Lamborn, 1951; Cavaroc and Ferm, 1968; DeLong, 1972). The east-central district includes southeastern Licking and western Muskingum Counties and is appropriately called Flint Ridge; the southern district encompasses western Lawrence, eastern Scioto, eastern Jackson, western Gallia, and central Vinton Counties. In addition, a small area of possible Vanport equivalent, the Plum Run flint, is present in northeastern Ohio in southwestern Mahoning and northeastern Stark Counties (Murphy and Blank, 1970). Together, the three districts form a northeasterly trending arcuate belt nearly 200 miles long. In adjoining areas, however, the Vanport unit consists of calcareous shales, shaly limestones, and limestones with very little flint.

The important flint bodies characteristically occur in the upper part of the Vanport and rest on the gray limestones at the base of the unit. As a general rule, the shale is highly fossiliferous and the limestone and flint are only sparingly so; however, in the Flint Ridge district, impure phases of the flint are particularly rich in fusulinids (Smyth, 1957).

The form of occurrence of the Vanport flint is varied in the three districts. In the Flint Ridge area it appears as a nearly continuous sheet (fig. 8), the largest and purest of its kind in the state (Stout and Schoenlaub, 1945; DeLong, 1972). In southern Ohio, where the flint is closely associated with a large body of limestone, the flint is mostly composed of lenticular and nodular bodies of lower quality; small

TABLE 2.—*Aboriginal flint quarries in Ohio and characteristics of quarried flint*

System	Group	Formation or bed	Flint unit	Typical occurrence and characteristics of flint	Quarry location
Pennsylvanian	Monongahela	Fishpot limestone	Fishpot flint	Nodular flint; light to dark brown, gray, with lighter colored streaks	Jefferson Co., Smithfield Twp. Jefferson Co., Mount Pleasant Twp.
Pennsylvanian	Conemaugh	Brush Creek limestone	Brush Creek flint	Sheets, interbedded with shale; dark gray to black with light-gray patches and streaks, also light gray	Morgan Co., York Twp. Perry Co., Bearfield Twp. Vinton Co., Madison Twp. Athens Co. Gallia Co. Lawrence Co.
Pennsylvanian	Allegheny	Vanport limestone	Vanport flint, including Plum Run flint	Sheets, lenticular and nodular flint; light colored, mottled grayish white or tan, may be brightly colored	Licking Co., Hopewell Twp. Muskingum Co., Hopewell Twp. Muskingum Co., Licking Twp. Jackson Co., Milton Twp. Vinton Co., Elk Twp. Mahoning Co., Smith Twp. Stark Co., Lexington Twp.
Pennsylvanian	Allegheny	Zaleski flint	Zaleski flint	Sheets; jet black to brownish black; lacks mottling and banding	Vinton Co., Elk Twp. Vinton Co., Jackson Twp. Vinton Co., Madison Twp. Vinton Co., Richland Twp. Jackson Co.
Pennsylvanian	Pottsville	Upper Mercer limestone	Upper Mercer flint	Sheets, nodular flint; black or dark gray with light-gray patches or streaks	Coshocton Co., Jefferson Twp. Coshocton Co., Newcastle Twp. Hocking Co., Green Twp. Muskingum Co., Falls Twp. Muskingum Co., Madison Twp. Muskingum Co., Hopewell Twp. Muskingum Co., Muskingum Twp. Perry Co., Clayton Twp. Perry Co., Pike Twp.
Pennsylvanian	Pottsville	Boggs limestone	Boggs flint	Sheets; bluish black to black or dark gray with buff-colored streaks	Muskingum Co., Falls Twp.
Devonian		Delaware Limestone	Delaware chert	Lenticular and nodular chert; tan to dark brown, black; lacks banding	Western Delaware Co. Western Franklin Co. Eastern Marion Co.
Silurian		Bisher Dolomite	Bisher flint	Interbedded flint and dolostone, nodular flint; dark gray with lighter gray bands	Highland Co., Liberty Twp. Northern Adams Co.
Silurian		Brassfield Formation	Brassfield chert	Lenticular and nodular chert; white, grayish white, or yellowish white, with light-colored streaks and patches	South-central Adams Co.

discontinuous sheets of impure porous flint also are present (Stout and Schoenlaub, 1945). The Plum Run flint in Mahoning and Stark Counties appears to be a local, 1-foot-thick sheet of high-grade material (Murphy and Blank, 1970). Indian quarries existed at several sites in the three districts where high-quality flint could be obtained, but most of the workings were located in the huge sheet at Flint Ridge (table 2). Because of the importance of the latter district, its geology is described in greater detail in Chapter 6. Quarries also were operated in the impure, porous phases of the flint by early settlers, who fashioned the rock into millstones (Hildreth, 1838; Stout and Schoenlaub, 1945). Centers of millstone production in the southern district were located near Jackson in Jackson County and near McArthur in Vinton County, and in the east-central district in the southeastern and western sections of Flint Ridge.

Mineralogy.—The typical light color of the Vanport flint, together with the bright hues that may be present, serves to distinguish Vanport material from many other Ohio flints (Hildreth, 1838; Morgan, R., 1929; Stout and Schoenlaub, 1945; Murphy and Blank, 1970; Converse, 1972; Morton and Carskadden, 1972). Good-quality flint is dense, translucent to semi-opaque, and lustrous, with a conchoidal fracture. (See Chapter 4 for explanation of fracture.) The most common Flint Ridge material is milky white or bluish white with light-gray patches and streaks, but the most distinctive and prized material is the highly colored variety with its intricate combinations of red, yellow, brown, blue, and green. The less abundant dark-gray to black varieties are easily confused with typical Upper Mercer and Zaleski materials; however, the ribbon flint from the northeastern

FIGURE 8.—Vanport flint (Pennsylvanian, Allegheny Group) at a road cut just north of Flint Ridge State Memorial, Licking County.

section of Flint Ridge, with its alternating dark- and light-gray bands, is unique (fig. 9). The Vanport flint in the southern district is slightly darker and more drab than typical Flint Ridge material and is commonly gray, tan, or brown. Fresh Plum Run flint is mottled blue and gray, but turns brown after prolonged weathering.

Crystal-filled pockets and fractures are abundant in Flint Ridge flint. Because secondary minerals have not been reported from the other Vanport districts and are comparatively uncommon in the other flints, with the exception of the Upper Mercer flint, they help distinguish Flint Ridge material. Quartz crystals are most common, especially at the old Indian quarries in the vicinity of Flint Ridge State Memorial (Hildreth, 1829; Smith, C. M., 1885; Mills, 1921). These crystals are generally colorless, but may be brown, purple, or black. Singly terminated individual crystals up to 5 inches long and 3½ inches across have been observed. In addition, the pockets and fractures commonly are lined with a thin band of translucent, bluish-white chalcedony that occurs between the flint and the quartz crystals (see fig. 9).

Cavity fillings of barite and calcite crystals are more rare at Flint Ridge (Foster, J. W., 1838; Smith, C. M., 1885). Mills (1921) has recorded the most spectacular find of barite—a yellow to light-blue barite crystal more than 4 feet long, 2 feet wide, and 15 inches thick was removed from a large pocket.

Upper Mercer flint

Geologic setting.—The Upper Mercer flint is a locally developed phase of the widespread Upper Mercer limestone and occurs in a number of isolated districts in east-central Ohio (Morgan, R., 1929; Stout and Schoenlaub, 1945; Lamborn, 1951, 1954; Morton and Carskadden, 1972). These districts are in east-central Hocking County, northeastern Perry County, north-central Muskingum County, and west-central Coshocton County; collectively, they form a north-northeasterly trending belt about 70 miles long. Between these districts the flint is either absent or appears as scattered nodules and lenses in the Upper Mercer limestone. The main masses of flint in the four districts occur in the upper part of the unit and rest on the dark-gray to black siliceous limestones at the base of the unit. The Upper Mercer flint and limestone contain a normal marine fauna particularly rich in brachiopods and distinguished by a type of fusulinid that otherwise occurs only in the Boggs and Lower Mercer limestones (Morningstar, 1922; Smyth, 1957).

The Upper Mercer flint occurs mostly in sheetlike bodies, either as a single large sheet or as a series of smaller, discontinuous sheets in the same bed. Lenticular and nodular flint also is present locally in the associated limestones below the sheets. Although prehistoric Indians utilized flint from all of the Upper Mercer districts (table 2), quarry operations were concentrated in the Coshocton County district, where the quality and thickness of the flint were exceptionally good. The features of the latter deposit are described in greater detail in the discussion of the Nellie-Warsaw area in Chapter 6.

FIGURE 9.—Slabbed specimen of ribbon flint; from the John Nethers property, Flint Ridge, Muskingum County. Some pockets in the flint are filled completely with chalcedony (gray); others exhibit a lining of chalcedony upon which drusy quartz crystals are perched. Specimen is 6 inches long.

Mineralogy.—The Upper Mercer flint is typically black or dark gray with characteristic light-gray or tan patches and streaks (Stout and Schoenlaub, 1945; Converse, 1972; Morton and Carskadden, 1972). Mottled light-gray or light-brown flint is present at some sites, although bright hues and sharp color banding are generally absent. Flint of good quality is dense and opaque appearing and has a conchoidal fracture and waxy luster. Chalcedony and drusy quartz occupy small vugs and fractures in the flint in Coshocton, Muskingum, and Perry Counties (Fowke, 1902, 1928; Stout, 1918; Morningstar, 1922; Morgan, R., 1929; Stout and Schoenlaub, 1945; Flint, 1951). Thin bands of milky-white, translucent chalcedony were deposited in the openings first and were subsequently coated with a layer of tiny, colorless quartz crystals.

Zaleski flint

Geologic setting.—The Zaleski flint or "Black Flint" has the narrowest geographic distribution of the important flint beds—its occurrence is limited to Vinton and northern Jackson Counties in southern Ohio (Stout, 1916, 1927; Stout and Schoenlaub, 1945; Cavaroc and Ferm, 1968). This unit is further distinguished by the absence of a widespread laterally equivalent limestone; for this reason the term Zaleski is restricted to the flint that lies above the Ogan coal and below the Winters coal. It is named for Zaleski, Vinton County, where the flint is well exposed. A normal marine fauna unusually rich in bryozoans characterizes the Zaleski and the adjacent rocks, especially the siliceous limestones and shales (Morningstar, 1922). Sponge spicules are locally abundant in the flint (Cavaroc and Ferm, 1968; Morton and Carskadden, 1972). These siliceous spinelike structures were probably an important source of the silica of the deposit.

The flint occurs in a nearly continuous sheet that attains a maximum thickness of about 5 feet in Elk Township, central Vinton County. This high-quality material was an important source of raw flint to prehistoric Indians, who quarried it across the entire area of Zaleski outcrop (Stout, 1927; table 2).

Mineralogy.—Good-quality Zaleski flint is characteristically jet black to brownish black, seemingly opaque, and dense and has a waxy luster and conchoidal fracture. In contrast to most other Ohio flints, the color of the Zaleski is quite uniform; mottling or banding are notably absent, although some white and gray Zaleski material has been reported (Converse, 1972; Morton and Carskadden, 1972). The black color of the Zaleski material is believed to originate from tiny particles of carbonaceous matter that are disseminated through the rock (Stout and Schoenlaub, 1945). Small, secondary quartz crystals, so common in the Upper Mercer and Vanport flints, are relatively rare in the Zaleski because of the general absence of cavities (Morgan, R., 1929; Stout and Schoenlaub, 1945).

PETRIFIED WOOD

Geologic setting

Petrified wood is fossil wood in which the original organic material is replaced by mineral matter contained in waters that infiltrate the wood. Replacement by silica (generally in the form of chalcedony) and calcium carbonate (calcite) are most common, producing silicified wood and calcified wood, respectively. For wood to be preserved by petrifaction the following conditions must be met: (1) the wood must be covered quickly by sediments, and (2) the woody tissue must be replaced by mineral matter before decomposition takes place. A water-soaked log in a lake or river, for example, might sink and become covered with sediment. A chemical reaction between the water in the sediment and the decaying wood might then initiate replacement of the organic material with dissolved mineral matter in the water.

Most petrified wood originates from trees on land that become buried and preserved in continental beds of sandstone or shale. For this reason, fossil wood is found chiefly in nonmarine strata and only rarely in marine strata. Petrified wood is generally more resistant to erosion than the sandstones and shales in which it is embedded and commonly weathers free of these rocks. The cylindrically shaped fragments of weathered-out wood are strewn loose along hillsides, at the base of rock cliffs, or along stream beds. These fragments are valued for the well-preserved tissue structure of the wood, which, in cross section, forms intricate concentric patterns. Sometimes the sections of fossil logs are so large and heavy that they can be moved only with the aid of a winch.

Much of Ohio was part of an ancient landmass during the Pennsylvanian and Permian Periods and fossil trees are especially abundant in rocks of these ages. Silicified wood occurs in the Pennsylvanian (and possibly lower Permian) rocks of the following counties: Athens, Belmont, Coshocton, Gallia, Guernsey, Jackson, Lawrence, Meigs, Monroe, Morgan, and Muskingum (Hildreth, 1827, 1838; Andrews, 1873, 1874a; Herzer, 1893; Condit, 1912; Stout, 1916, 1945, 1946; Mitchell, 1951; Berryhill, 1963; Collins, H. R., 1979). These sites are concentrated in southeastern Ohio; their distribution is shown in figure 5. The best quality material comes from beds in the upper Conemaugh and Monongahela Groups. Fossil logs several feet long and up to 2 feet in diameter have been reported from these rocks in the Shade River area of southern Athens County, a classic locality that has yielded many prize specimens. The petrified wood of this area consists of trunk sections of *Psaronius*, a giant tree fern which is extinct, and of disk-shaped masses of flattened rootlets (Hildreth, 1838; Andrews, 1873; Lesquereux, 1880). Large fossil logs of high quality have been obtained at scattered sites along Captina Creek and Sunfish Creek and their tributaries in Belmont and northern Monroe Counties (Andrews, 1874a; Stout, 1946; Mitchell, 1951; Berryhill, 1963). In productive areas such as these, some local residents decorate their yards with large trunk sections of this wood. A more detailed discussion of the Shade River area is provided in Chapter 6.

Petrified wood has been found embedded at the centers of large limestone concretions of the upper Devonian Ohio Shale. Calcified and silicified wood in concretions have been reported from the Huron River in Erie County, the Olentangy River in Delaware County, and the Beaver Pond site in Adams County (Newberry, 1870, 1889; Dawson, 1871; Orton, 1878; Rogers, M., 1935; Hoskins and Blickle, 1940). The petrified wood in concretions consists of large trunk segments of *Callixylon*, an ancestor of modern conifers.

The silica and calcium carbonate of silicified and calcified wood probably originated from the weathering of silicate and carbonate minerals in the ancient Pennsylvanian landmass. These weathering products were then transported to the depositional site, where replacement occurred. Volcanic ash, an alternative source of silica proposed by Murata (1940), seems less plausible for the Ohio occurrences because of the lack of evidence supporting volcanism.

Mineralogy

Chalcedony and calcite are the most common replacement minerals in petrified wood. In silicified wood the organic matter has been replaced by chalcedony, a variety of microcrystalline quartz displaying a fine banding and a fibrous structure under high magnification (Frondel, 1962). The localities in southeastern Ohio are especially noted for material of this type, which is prized for its hardness, its toughness, and its ability to take a high polish. Silicified wood is typically brown, black, or gray and lacks the bright hues characteristic of similar material from the western United States. Although silicified wood is ordinarily quite dense, cross sections of some logs display fractures and small pockets that are lined with tiny, colorless crystals of quartz. Calcified wood is softer and less durable than silicified wood.

CONCRETIONS

A concretion or nodule is a solid, spheroidal to irregularly shaped mass of mineral matter formed about a nucleus and enclosed in a sedimentary rock of different composition. The main mass or matrix of a concretionary body consists of a fine-grained aggregate of chiefly one or two minerals which give the concretion its name, for example, ironstone (chiefly siderite) or limestone (chiefly calcite and dolomite).

FIGURE 10.—Interior of an ironstone septarium with a nucleus of petrified wood and a granular mass of white barite; from Silver Creek, West Branch State Park, Portage County. Specimen is 7 inches long.

The nucleus commonly is a fragment of a fossil such as a shell, bone, or plant (fig. 10). Concretions typically are concentrated in beds several feet thick that can be traced laterally for distances ranging from hundreds of feet to hundreds of miles. Most concretions and nodules are resistant to weathering and commonly stand out prominently in a rock exposure or accumulate in piles of loose rock at the base of a cliff. Because they are heavy and resistant, ironstone concretions or nodules may become concentrated in stream beds, forming small "placer" deposits (Stout, 1944; Flint, 1951).

A concretion can be distinguished from a nodule by the roughness of its surface and its general shape. The outer surface of a concretion is typically smooth; that of a nodule is characteristically rough. A concretion is spherical to lenticular in shape and is commonly flattened in the plane of bedding. A nodule, on the other hand, is highly irregular in shape and may have large protuberances. Although the size of concretions and nodules can range from a fraction of an inch to several feet in length, concretions tend to be larger than nodules; concretions are commonly 2 to 3 inches in diameter, and nodules are typically 1 to 2 inches across. Some compositional types, such as ironstone, generally occur as concretions; others, such as iron sulfide, invariably occur as nodules.

Most investigators (for example, Seyfried, 1953; Clifton, 1957; Barth, 1975; Orr and others, 1982; Criss and others, 1988) believe that concretions and nodules originate shortly after deposition of the enclosing sediment. The layers of enclosing rock, which is commonly shale, wrap around the concretionary mass, indicating that the concretion had hardened into solid rock while the clays of the shale were still soft. Apparently, a nucleus settled into soft sediment, initiating the deposition of mineral matter around it and resulting in the formation of a tightly cemented spherical mass. Later, the clays enclosing the concretion were compacted into shale. The mechanism that triggers mineral precipitation is not known.

A septarium is a type of concretion or nodule displaying an internal network of crystal-lined cracks. Septaria occur in beds which typically exhibit a narrower vertical range than those of nonseptarian concretions; for example, of several concretionary layers exposed at a site only one may contain septaria. Because the cracks are rarely observed on its outer surface, a concretion ordinarily must be broken open to determine if it is a septarium. These cracks may form radiating patterns like bent or broken spokes in a wheel, with openings that taper outward. The cracks result from the internal shrinkage of the soft concretionary sediment, in a manner somewhat analogous to shrinkage cracks that form in dried mud. The cracks may be preserved as internal voids, but more commonly are filled with veins of coarsely crystallized minerals that were precipitated after the septarium formed (fig. 11).

These vein minerals were precipitated from water solutions which were derived in part from the sediment of the concretion at the time it shrank and in part from the sediment enclosing the concretion at the time the sediment was compacted into solid rock.

Several types of concretions and nodules are recognized on the basis of the composition of the matrix and include: ironstone, limestone, iron sulfide, hematite, barite, and flint. The term limestone concretion is used broadly here to include both calcite- and dolomite-rich matrix types, which tend to originate in similar sedimentary environments. These matrix types are described individually below except for flint, which was covered briefly earlier in this chapter. They are discussed in order of their estimated abundance in Ohio, starting with ironstone, which is the most plentiful. Because of the rarity and perfection of some of the vein minerals, the septaria of these compositional groups are of particular interest to mineralogists and are given special attention.

Ironstone septaria

Geologic setting.—Geologically significant occurrences of ironstone in Ohio are restricted to the Pennsylvanian Pottsville, Allegheny, and lower Conemaugh Groups in the eastern part of the state. The ironstone occurs both as continuous beds and in concretion-rich layers, which commonly contain one or more beds of septaria. The Ferriferous ore, which overlies the Vanport limestone (Allegheny Group), is a formerly economically important example of a continuous bed; it averages about a foot in thickness over an area of 1,300 square miles in the old Hanging Rock iron district of Gallia, Hocking, Jackson, Lawrence, Scioto, and Vinton Counties (Orton, 1884b; Stout, 1944). Noteworthy examples of strata rich in ironstone septaria include: (1) shales of the lower Pottsville Group, (2) shales enclosing the Lower Mercer limestone (Pottsville Group), (3) shales overlying the Lower Kittanning (No. 5) coal (Allegheny Group), (4) shales resting on the Middle Kittanning (No. 6) coal (Allegheny Group), and (5) shales overlying the Brush

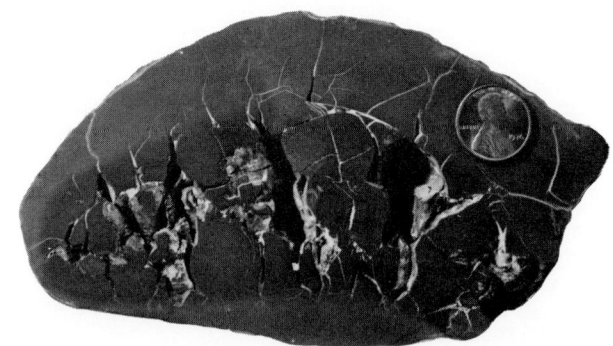

FIGURE 11.—Interior of an ironstone septarium; from a railroad cut near Marshallville, Wayne County. Coin indicates scale.

Creek limestone (Conemaugh Group) (Foster, J. W., 1838; Stevenson, 1878; Greene, 1935; Ver Steeg, 1942; Seaman and Hamilton, 1950; Hollenbaugh and Carlson, 1983). The septaria can be found in strip mines, road cuts, or hillside exposures in eastern Ohio, wherever ironstone-bearing shales are exposed (see fig. 5). However, large numbers of concretions must be broken open and examined at these sites in order to pinpoint the beds of septaria.

Ironstone septaria are typically massive, dark brown to black, ellipsoidal to disk shaped, and have smooth surfaces. They are flattened parallel to the layering of the rock and are much more resistant to weathering than the enclosing shales. The size of the septaria is fairly uniform in a given bed, but differs greatly from one bed to another. The persistence of individual beds of septaria is also quite different. For example, large septaria up to 2 feet long are locally developed in the black shales of the Pottsville Group at West Branch State Park in Portage County (fig. 10) and near Marshallville in Wayne County (fig. 11); 3- to 10-inch-long septaria in shales above the Lower Kittanning (No. 5) and Middle Kittanning (No. 6) coals (Allegheny Group) are more widespread, occurring in Tuscarawas, Carroll, and Columbiana Counties; and septaria 2 to 3 inches long in the Brush Creek shale (Conemaugh Group) have the greatest lateral distribution, extending for over 100 miles from near Glouster in Athens County to Steubenville in Jefferson County (fig. 12) and into western Pennsylvania (Seaman and Hamilton, 1950). The geology of the West Branch State Park and Steubenville (Alikanna) sites are described in Chapter 6.

The ironstone septaria typically occur with dark-colored marine shales (Lamborn and others, 1938; Stout, 1944; Stout and Schoenlaub, 1945; Weber and others, 1964; Collins, H. R., 1979; Orr and others, 1982). The mineralogical data given below indicate the siderite-rich matrix is devoid of pyrite, although later veins of pyrite may be present. These and other characteristics suggest the ironstone was deposited in brackish, nearshore waters rich in iron and poor in oxygen and sulfur. Marine fossils such as brachiopods and gastropods and, more rarely, fragments of petrified wood occur in the centers of some septaria and apparently served as nuclei for concretionary growth. The shale beds hosting the ironstone rest on marine limestone (and flint) or coal.

Black shales of the Meadville and Wooster Members of

FIGURE 13.—Scanning-electron photomicrograph of radiating group of wurtzite (6H) crystals; from Negley, Columbiana County. Axis of longest crystal is about 0.03 inch long.

the Mississippian Cuyahoga Formation also contain minor occurrences of ironstone septaria (Ver Steeg, 1940; Carlson, 1977).

Mineralogy.—The main body of an ironstone concretion or septarium typically consists of a fine-grained aggregate of siderite, calcite, clay, quartz, and carbonaceous matter (Seaman and Hamilton, 1950; Orr and others, 1982; Hollenbaugh and Carlson, 1983). Siderite, an iron carbonate and an ore of iron, is the predominant constituent. However, at a few localities the concretions display a pronounced compositional zoning, with calcite-rich cores and siderite-rich shells. After long exposure the siderite at the surface of a concretion is replaced by a weathering rind of goethite, a yellowish-brown iron hydroxide.

Barite, sphalerite, and calcite are the most abundant constituents of the veins; the association of barite and dark-colored sphalerite is particularly characteristic of the ironstone septaria. These minerals range from a fraction of an inch to over an inch in length, and their coarse-grained texture contrasts sharply with that of the matrix. The barite and calcite are white or colorless. The barite occurs in coarse, tabular aggregates, and the calcite occurs in granular aggregates. Dark-brown to black sphalerite, which obtains its color from an enrichment in iron, occurs in lustrous, coarsely granular masses and aggregates of bladed crystals.

Pyrite, kaolinite, chalcopyrite, galena, and wurtzite are less common vein minerals (Hollenbaugh and Carlson, 1983). Iridescent pyrite is found in veins, lenticular masses, or coatings of tiny cubic or octahedral crystals. Kaolinite, a type of clay, appears in fine-grained chalky-white masses and veins. Chalcopyrite is rare, occurring in small crystals and granular masses in association with the kaolinite (Carlson, 1978). Galena, which is also rare, appears as aggregates of cubic crystals in veins. Wurtzite, an unusual

FIGURE 12.—Interior of an ironstone septarium; from a road cut near Alikanna, Jefferson County. The core contains veins of coarsely granular white barite and dark-brown sphalerite. Specimen is 2 inches long.

hexagonal form of zinc sulfide, occurs in radial aggregates of small, reddish-brown, well-formed pyramidal crystals (fig. 13).

Limestone septaria

Geologic setting.—A unique layer of limestone concretions, renowned for their large size, occurs in the upper Devonian black shales of Ohio and surrounding states. Commonly septarian, these concretions form a conspicuous layer 40 to 50 feet thick that marks the lower part of the Huron Shale Member of the Ohio Shale. The concretions, first described from river-bank exposures in Adams and Pickaway Counties by Hildreth (1834), can be traced north-south across the state from Lake Erie to the Ohio River (Prosser, 1913; Lamborn, 1929). The concretion-bearing strata are exposed locally along the gorges of the following creeks and rivers: Scioto Brush Creek in Adams County, Paint Creek in Ross County, Deer Creek in Pickaway County, Olentangy River in Delaware and Franklin Counties, and Huron River in Erie and Huron Counties (Hildreth, 1834; Briggs, 1838; Foster, J. W., 1838; Locke, 1838; Newberry, 1870, 1873a, 1874b; Andrews, 1874b; Orton, 1874, 1878; Read, 1878a; Stauffer and others, 1911; Westgate, 1926; Wuestner, 1938; Seyfried, 1953; Hoover, 1960; Explorer, 1961). The concretions can be examined easily at all of these localities, where they weather out of the shale banks and roll to the beds of the rivers. The Paint Creek (Copperas Mountain) locality in Ross County and the Huron River locality in Huron County are described in more detail in Chapter 6.

The concretions are medium- to dark-gray or dark-brown, dense spheroids with smooth surfaces that exhibit a faint ribbing. They typically range from 1 to 8 feet in diameter, although Read (1878a) reported a 15-foot concretion in Huron County. The smaller ones range from nearly perfect spheres to markedly flattened spheroids; the larger ones generally exhibit a slight flattening. The ribs on the surfaces are bedding planes, which were aligned with those of the enclosing shales when they were still soft, prior to compaction. The concretions are popularly known as fossil cannonballs or iron kettles (Foster, J. W., 1838; Cole, 1968; Barth, 1975), but chemical analyses reveal little iron (Westgate, 1926; Criss and others, 1988). Limestone concretions exceeding a foot or so in diameter are commonly septarian; the smaller ones generally lack the vein-filled cracks. The larger concretions may display a well-cemented, resistant rim that is free of cracks and a less resistant septarian core that is removed after prolonged weathering, leaving a hollow shell (Andrews, 1874b; Rogers, M., 1935; Knille and Gibbs, 1942; Seyfried, 1953) (fig. 14). Fragments of fossil shark bones or trunk sections of petrified wood form the centers of many of the septaria, and their surface structures may be imprinted on minerals of the veins (Newberry, 1868, 1874b, 1889; Orton, 1878; Rogers, M., 1935; Hoskins and Blickle, 1940; Hoover, 1960; Hansen, 1986; Criss and others, 1988).

Limestone concretions also occur in beds of Pennsylvanian shale in widely scattered areas of eastern Ohio (Lamborn, 1951; Berryhill, 1963; DeLong and White, 1963). These concretions, many of which are septaria, are typically gray, flattened spheroids 1 to 12 inches in diameter.

The large limestone septaria occur in pyritiferous, carbonaceous marine shales (Westgate, 1926; Lamborn and others, 1938; Hoover, 1960). The mineralogical data given below indicate the matrices of the concretions also contain small amounts of pyrite and carbonaceous matter. These features suggest that the oxygen-deficient, iron- and sulfur-bearing waters of a stagnant sea were favorable for the

FIGURE 14.—Large limestone septarium at Copperas Mountain, Ross County. Note the resistant shell of the concretion and the compaction of the shale around it.

formation of the septaria.

Mineralogy.—The matrices of the large limestone concretions consist chiefly of a fine-grained aggregate of dolomite—the predominant mineral—calcite, and quartz (Westgate, 1926; Hoover, 1960). The chemical data of Westgate (1926) and Criss and others (1988) indicate that the dolomite is iron bearing and is probably ferroan dolomite; however, some workers have reported siderite (Reidel, 1972; Reidel and Koucky, 1981; Reidel and others, 1982). Small amounts of clay, pyrite, and carbonaceous matter also are present. The carbonaceous matter imparts a dark color and fetid odor to the concretions (Briggs, 1838). At some localities, the concretions, especially the smaller ones, exhibit a thin shell of finely crystalline or radiating pyrite surrounding the main mass of limestone (Orton, 1878; Rogers, M., 1935; Seyfried, 1953; Clifton, 1957; Barth, 1975; Criss and others, 1988).

The most abundant vein-type minerals of the large septaria are calcite, dolomite, ferroan dolomite, and barite (Hyde, C., and Landy, 1966; Leavens, 1968), an assemblage which is characteristic of the limestone concretions. The calcite, dolomite, and ferroan dolomite typically occur as coarsely granular masses and less commonly as clusters of rhombohedral crystals in pockets of the veins. Brown, yellow, or white calcite and brown ferroan dolomite commonly display a strong, yellow fluorescence; yellow to tan dolomite is generally nonfluorescent. Larger crystals of colorless calcite with complex terminations may occur in the pockets. The barite is colorless and occurs in the veins as large, lustrous plates that commonly exceed 4 inches in length (fig. 15).

Quartz, aragonite, pyrite, sphalerite, marcasite, and whewellite are less common. The colorless, transparent quartz typically occurs in granular masses, although perfect, doubly terminated crystals up to ⅝ inch in length have been observed (fig. 16). Small crystals of cream-colored aragonite and brassy pyrite and granular masses of yellowish-brown sphalerite also have been noted. Tiny crystals of pyrite and marcasite may be present as inclusions in the barite and quartz (Richards, 1985). Whewellite, an extremely rare mineral, occurs in coarsely granular, milky-white masses (fig. 17) associated with fossil shark remains (Hyde, C.,

FIGURE 15.—Vein of tabular barite in a fragment of a large limestone septarium; from the West Branch Huron River at Lamereaux Road, Huron County. Coin indicates scale.

FIGURE 17.—Vein of white whewellite in a fragment of a large limestone septarium; from the Huron River west of Milan, Erie County. Coin indicates scale.

and Landy, 1966; Leavens, 1968; Hoefs, 1969). Coatings and globules of black asphaltic material occur in the veins at some localities (Andrews, 1874b; Wuestner, 1938). Celestite, fluorite, and selenite (gypsum) reportedly also occur in the veins (Read, 1878a; Stauffer and others, 1911; Goodwin, 1940; Clifton, 1957; Hoover, 1960; Bingaman and others, 1978), but the presence of these minerals has not been confirmed.

Iron sulfide nodules and septaria

Geologic setting.—Nodules and clusters of crystals of nearly pure iron sulfide (pyrite, marcasite) commonly occur in rocks ranging in age from middle Devonian to Pennsylvanian. They are found in beds of black shale, coal, and, more rarely, carbonate rock. These iron sulfide masses are concentrated in beds ranging from 1 to 40 feet in thickness that can be traced laterally for distances of over a hundred miles in some cases. The iron sulfide nodules weather free from the shale and coal and accumulate in scree rock, where they are easily recognized by their heaviness, even when covered by rock matrix. In addition to the nodules, pyritized fossils, such as brachiopods and fragments of wood, occur in the beds at several localities; these organisms were pyritized when the original organic matter, probably still enclosed in soft sediment, was replaced with iron sulfide. Strata in Ohio that are especially noted for occurrences of nodular iron sulfide and/or pyritized fossils include: (1) the middle Devonian Olentangy Shale and rocks of the Traverse Group; (2) the upper Devonian Ohio Shale; and (3) Pennsylvanian coal beds.

The Olentangy Shale and the shales and dolostones of the Traverse Group, equivalent rock units in central and northwestern Ohio, respectively, contain iron sulfide nodules in noteworthy amounts. The Olentangy Shale is a productive unit for small, disk-shaped nodules that weather free of the rock at widely scattered sites (Stauffer, 1916; Westgate, 1926; Lamborn, 1927, 1929; Van Horn and Van Horn, 1933; Hoover, 1960). Clusters of cubic crystals of pyrite, with individual crystals up to 1¼ inches across (fig. 18), also have been reported from the Olentangy Shale east of Bellevue in Erie County (Green, R., 1970a). Attractive, cylindrical nodules about an inch long weather out of the Tenmile Creek Dolomite along Tenmile Creek and at a quarry near Silica, Lucas County (Ehlers, G. M., and others, 1951). Pyritized marine fossils and nodules of iron sulfide are quite common as well in the black shales of the underlying Silica Formation at the Silica quarry (Stewart, 1927; Nussman, 1961; Carman and others, 1962).

Iron sulfide nodules are very abundant in the Huron and Cleveland Shale Members of the Ohio Shale. Good collecting is found in the cliffs along the following streams: Scioto Brush Creek in Adams County, Paint Creek in Ross County, Deer Creek in Pickaway County, Olentangy River in Delaware and Franklin Counties, Huron River in Erie and Huron Counties, Vermilion River in Erie and Lorain Counties, and Rocky River in Cuyahoga County (Hildreth, 1834; Briggs,

FIGURE 16.—Quartz crystals with a combination of two rhombohedrons resting on small rhombohedral crystals of ferroan dolomite; from the West Branch Huron River at Lamereaux Road, Huron County. The prominent quartz crystal is ⅝ inch long.

FIGURE 18.—Pyrite crystals showing a combination of a cube and an octahedron; from a railroad yard near the intersection of Ohio Routes 4 and 113, Erie County. Specimen is 2 inches across.

1838; Foster, J. W., 1838; Locke, 1838; Andrews, 1874b; Orton, 1874, 1878; Stauffer and others, 1911; Prosser, 1912, 1913; Westgate, 1926; Cushing and others, 1931; Van Horn and Van Horn, 1933; McAllister, 1941; Knille and Gibbs, 1942; Seyfried, 1953; Hoover, 1960; Holden and Carlson, 1979). The nodules generally are shaped like rough or knobby disks and range from 1 to 4 inches in diameter. In the Huron and Vermilion River areas septaria with radial patterns of openings that taper outward are commonly present (fig. 19). Ohio Shale exposures west of Chillicothe in the valley of Paint Creek are noted for nodules of exceptional size; an irregularly shaped body nearly 4 feet long has been reported there (McAllister, 1941). Prehistoric Indians found the pyrite nodules of Ross County attractive and worked some of them into ornaments that were discovered in an Indian mound north of Chillicothe at Mound City Group National Monument (Shetrone, 1926; Morgan, R., 1929).

Most of the coals in the Pennsylvanian rocks of eastern Ohio, especially those in the Allegheny and Monongahela Groups, are high-sulfur coals characterized by high amounts of iron sulfide. Nodules in assorted sizes and shapes, lenticular bodies, beds up to an inch or so thick, clusters of crystals, and fragments of pyritized wood are quite common in the coals (Bownocker and others, 1908; Tucker, 1919; Bownocker and Dean, 1929; Stout, 1946; Wiese and Fyfe, 1986). Formerly economically important deposits of iron sulfide were obtained from the Middle Kittanning (No. 6) coal (Allegheny Group) in the Tuscarawas Valley field in Tuscarawas County (Tucker, 1919; Stout, 1946). Significant production also came from the Lower Kittanning (No. 5) coal in the Tuscarawas Valley field, the Pittsburgh (No. 8) coal in the Belmont field in Belmont County, and the Pomeroy-Redstone (No. 8A) coal in the Pomeroy field in Meigs County. The iron sulfide from these coals and others was obtained by sorting material from the spoil banks of coal-mining operations. The iron sulfide was used chiefly in the manufacture of sulfuric acid, and production was greatest around the period of World War I (Tucker, 1919; Espenshade and Broedel, 1952). In the late 1800's, pyrite from the Pennsylvanian coal fields was roasted at plants in Steubenville, Jefferson County, and in Cleveland, Cuyahoga County, to produce copperas for the clothes-dyeing industry (Brown, 1888; Stout, 1946). In comparison, the Pennsylvanian marine shales are not particularly noted for the occurrence of nodular iron sulfide, although pyritized brachiopods and other marine fossils may be found (Condit, 1912; Lamborn and others, 1938).

The occurrence of iron sulfide nodules in black carbonaceous marine shales and swamp coals (Tucker, 1919; Van Horn and Van Horn, 1933; Lamborn and others, 1938) indicates that the oxygen-deficient, sulfur- and iron-rich waters of a stagnant sea or coastal swamp, in which partially decayed organic matter could accumulate, were particularly favorable for iron sulfide formation.

Mineralogy.—Pyrite and marcasite, which are both iron sulfide but have different crystal structures, are the dominant constituents of the nodules. As determined in unpublished x-ray diffraction studies by the writer, the majority of the nodules and crystals are composed of pyrite. X-ray determinations recorded for specific sites are given in the catalog portion of this report under the entries for pyrite and marcasite. Although the predominance of pyrite is not unexpected, many of the nodules examined, such as those from the Ohio Shale in Ross County and elsewhere, are widely believed to consist of marcasite rather than pyrite. However, marcasite does occur in the Pennsylvanian coals, generally in complex intergrowths with the predominant pyrite (Wiese and Fyfe, 1986), and nodular masses of spear-shaped marcasite crystals occur in the Olentangy Shale near Delaware in Delaware County (Van Horn and Van Horn, 1933). Nodular marcasite undoubtedly occurs elsewhere in the state as well. The Devonian-age pyrite is quite pure and forms massive aggregates or radiating aggregates of fibrous to acicular crystals, commonly with a thin surface layer that is coarsely granular (fig. 19). Clay is the major impurity in the Pennsylvanian-age nodules, and small amounts of sphalerite and organic matter occur as well (Zubovic and others, 1966; Wiese and Fyfe, 1986). Because of the included clays and its porous or spongy

FIGURE 19.—Internal structure of pyrite nodules. Septarium on the left has veins of white barite, is 4 inches long, and is from the West Branch Huron River at Lamereaux Road, Huron County. Nodule on the right displays a radial habit, is 2 inches across, and is from the Paint Creek area, western Ross County.

texture, coal-bed pyrite has a strong tendency to decompose on storage and does not make good specimen material (Wiese and others, 1987). The pyrite septaria from the Ohio Shale typically contain veins of coarsely crystallized minerals such as barite, calcite, dolomite, and sphalerite (fig. 19). Tabular white barite is the dominant vein mineral and is characteristic of the septaria. More rarely the cracks are unfilled or lined with tiny cubes of pyrite.

Hematite nodules

Geologic setting.—Hematite nodules are common in the red and green shales of southeastern Ohio. Nodule-rich beds in the Pennsylvanian Conemaugh and Monongahela Groups and the Permian Dunkard Group are present in Athens, Columbiana, Gallia, Lawrence, Meigs, Morgan, Muskingum, Noble, Perry, Scioto, and Washington Counties (Hildreth, 1838; Condit, 1912; Stauffer and Schroyer, 1920; Stout, 1944, 1945; Flint, 1951; Sturgeon and associates, 1958). Small "placer" deposits have been reported from Athens, Lawrence, Morgan, and Perry Counties (Stout, 1944; Flint, 1951). Two persistent nodule-bearing red shales occur in the Conemaugh Group. The lower one, the Round Knob shale, occurs between the Cambridge and Ames limestones (Condit, 1912; Stout, 1944). This unit is well exposed in Columbiana County, where it attains a thickness of over 50 feet. The upper and more important hematite-bearing bed is known as the "Big Red" shales and occurs between the Ames limestone and the Pittsburgh (No. 8) coal at the base of the Monongahela Group; the "Big Red" averages about 200 feet in thickness (Stout, 1944). The Athens County occurrences are described more fully under the Shade River-Federal Creek site in Chapter 6.

The nodules originated in relatively quiet waters with an abundance of oxygen, possibly brackish lagoons in Pennsylvanian time and freshwater lakes in the Permian (Condit, 1912; Stauffer and Schroyer, 1920). These environmental interpretations are based on the close association of the hematite nodules with red shales, the types of fossils present, and the general absence of pyrite and organic matter in the matrix. Because red iron oxides today typically occur in regions of deeply weathered rock, deep weathering must have occurred in the source area of the red sediment during the late Pennsylvanian and early Permian.

The hematite nodules are irregular in shape, commonly knobby, and slightly flattened in the plane of bedding, and range from less than an inch to over 4 inches in length (fig. 20). They can be easily recognized in rock exposures and piles of loose rock because of their red color, heaviness, and resistance to weathering. A few nodules are septaria, displaying polygonal patterns of internal shrinkage cracks. Fossils, such as brachiopods and other marine animals or leaves and fragments of wood, form the centers of some of the nodules (Condit, 1912).

Mineralogy.—The body of a typical nodule is composed of a massive, dull, red or reddish-brown aggregate of hematite and goethite (iron hydroxide). Smaller amounts of quartz and clay generally are present also. Septaria contain veins of finely granular, colorless to white calcite or quartz. According to Stout (1944), some of the larger, more impure nodules may also be pyritic in character.

Many of the smaller nodules consist of nearly pure hematite; analyses have yielded over 80 percent ferric oxide (Stout, 1944). These high-quality nodules are hard, dense, semi-metallic, and reddish gray; they provide a valuable source of lapidary material because they take a high polish. Ornamental objects and tools made from the nodules by prehistoric Indians have been found at the Feurt Mound and Village Site in Scioto County (Mills, 1917; Morgan, R.,

FIGURE 20.—Hematite nodules; from a road cut south of Senecaville, Noble County. Coin indicates scale.

1929). Powdered hematite from the nodules also was used by the Indians as a red pigment for paint. Fine-grained hematite disseminated through the rock is the coloring agent of the red shales in the region.

Barite septaria

Geologic setting.—Barite septaria are present near the base and top of the Cleveland Shale Member of the Ohio Shale in north-central Ohio (Holden and Carlson, 1979). These unusual nodules occur in beds about 6 feet thick that can be traced along a 5-mile length of the Vermilion River in eastern Erie and western Lorain Counties. The most accessible site, Mill Hollow-Bacon Woods Park in Lorain County, is described in Chapter 6. Their association with black, carbonaceous, and pyritiferous marine shales, together with the mineralogical data given below, indicates that the barite septaria originated in oxygen-poor, iron- and sulfur-bearing stagnant marine waters.

The dark-gray septaria average about 3 inches in length and typically are shaped like rough disks. They are more resistant to weathering than the enclosing shales and accumulate along the banks and bed of the river. The surface of a weathered nodule, or turtle rock as it is popularly known, is characterized by a prominent, polygonal pattern of vein-filled cracks (fig. 21).

Mineralogy.—The main body of a weathered nodule consists of a fine-grained aggregate of barite, quartz, pyrite, clay, and bituminous matter (Holden and Carlson, 1979). Barite is the chief constituent and accounts for the heaviness of a nodule; the bituminous material is responsible for its dark color. An unweathered nodule has a thin shell of fine-grained pyrite, which is only partially penetrated by the white, vein-filled cracks of the main nodular mass. After weathering has removed the pyrite shell, the veins stand out in relief because they are more resistant than the material of the main body.

The walls of the veins commonly are composed of a thin layer of white, microcrystalline chalcedony, and their centers are composed of white, granular aggregates of coarsely crystalline barite, quartz, calcite, and pyrite. Barite, chalcedony, and quartz are abundant and form the characteristic assemblage of vein minerals for the barite

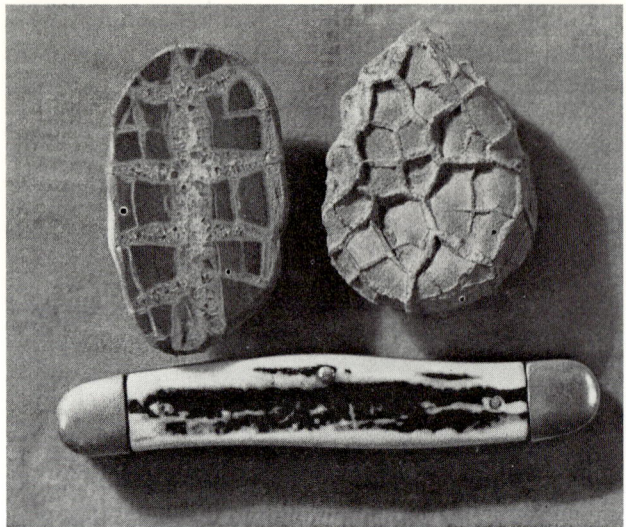

FIGURE 21.—Barite septaria; from Mill Hollow-Bacon Woods Park, Lorain County. The internal structure is shown in the specimen on the left, which contains veins of barite and quartz. Knife is 3½ inches long.

septaria. The durability of quartz and chalcedony accounts for the resistance of the veins to weathering. Rarely, tiny, well-formed crystals of colorless barite and quartz occur in small pockets within partially filled cracks.

GEODES

Geologic setting

A geode is a hollow, rounded body of rock, separable and differing in composition from the enclosing rock. The internal cavity of a geode is coated with several concentric bands of minerals, the innermost one generally consisting of inward projecting crystals. Although differing internally, a geode and a concretion may have a similar outer appearance, and a specimen ordinarily must be broken or cut open to determine whether it is hollow (geode) or solid (concretion) inside.

Most Ohio geodes consist of marine fossils whose skeletons (or shells) and internal cavities form the walls and cavities of the geodes, respectively. Subsequent to the deposition of the enclosing rocks, the skeletal parts of these fossils were replaced with silica contained in waters that infiltrated the rocks. Later, other silica-bearing waters were able to penetrate the walls, enabling quartz crystals to grow on their inner surfaces.

Siliceous geodes have been reported from Silurian rocks of the following areas in southwestern Ohio: (1) old quarries in the vicinity of Hillsboro, Highland County; (2) hilltops in western Brush Creek, eastern Jackson, and eastern Marshall Townships, Highland County; and (3) the region bordering the Serpent Mound disturbance, northern Adams County (Orton, 1871b; Rogers, J. K., 1936; Goodwin, 1940; Stout, 1941; Bowman, 1956; Bingaman and others, 1978). The geodes are confined to the Silurian-age dolostones of the Bisher Dolomite and the overlying Lilley Dolomite (Rogers, J. K., 1936); the Bisher Dolomite also contains nodules and thin layers of fossiliferous flint, as noted earlier in this chapter. The Bisher and Lilley rocks have siliceous cement and thus are resistant to weathering and cap many of the hills in southeastern Highland County where the geodes are most prevalent.

The geodes typically appear as hollow, silicified fossils, such as corals, stromatoporoids, and sponges, with rough tan to light-gray surfaces. The stromatoporoids sometimes display bulbous, globular, or domal shapes with concentric patterns of ridges and are known popularly as cabbage heads (La Rocque and Marple, 1955; Bingaman and others, 1978). According to Foerste (1919) and J. K. Rogers (1936), silicified stromatoporoids of exceptional quality, generally 2 to 4 inches long but many exceeding 6 inches in length, occur in the Lilley Dolomite. Because of their resistance, the geodes weather out of the rock and litter ridges and hillsides.

Mineralogy

The internal cavities of the geodes are lined chiefly with quartz, chalcedony, and calcite; smaller amounts of sphalerite and asphalt also are present (Orton, 1871b; Rogers, J. K., 1936; Goodwin, 1940). The prismatic quartz crystals, which are colorless or less commonly yellow, gray, or amethystine, are small but well formed (fig. 22). The chalcedony is translucent to semi-opaque and colorless to white, forming a series of thin colloform layers on the cavity walls or on quartz crystals. Calcite occurs as white or colorless rhombohedral crystals that partially fill some cavities and as coarsely granular, white aggregates that completely fill others. Coarsely crystallized, granular aggregates of lustrous, yellowish-brown sphalerite may be present, commonly in association with the calcite. Shiny black masses of bituminous matter (asphalt) may appear as a coating on the other minerals. According to Bingaman and others (1978), crystals of fluorite and goethite also occur in the geodes.

FIGURE 22.—Interior of a geode lined with tiny quartz crystals; from a hillside west of Elmville, Highland County. The specimen, which is 2¼ inches across, has the appearance of a fossil sponge.

ORE MINERAL OCCURRENCES IN CAVERNOUS AND FRACTURED DOLOSTONES

Two mineral districts in the state are renowned for minor occurrences of ore minerals: the Findlay Arch mineral district in northwestern Ohio and the Serpent Mound zinc district in southwestern Ohio (fig. 5) (Heyl, 1968; Reidel, 1975; Botoman and Stieglitz, 1978; Carlson, 1983; Clark, 1987). Mining operations have never been significant and were apparently restricted to two short-lived ventures in the Findlay Arch district, for which only minor production has been recorded (Phalen, 1914; Schreck and

Arundale, 1959). However, both districts have been an important source of mineral specimens for museums and mineralogists worldwide.

The two mineral districts have several geological characteristics in common, including: (1) mineralization that is younger than the enclosing rocks; (2) the conspicuous absence of igneous rocks related to the mineralization; (3) layers of porous dolostones that preferentially host the mineralization; and (4) a simple suite of ore metals. Although the mineral occurrences are not economically valuable, it is interesting to note that a number of important lead-zinc ore bodies in the midwestern United States have similar geological characteristics (Ohle, 1959; Anderson, G. M., and MacQueen, 1982).

The occurrence of ore minerals in the rocks exposed at the surface may be indicators of economically important ore bodies hidden at depth. Reasons supporting this view are the similarities of the Ohio occurrences to ore deposits elsewhere, as noted above, and the presence of favorable beds beneath the land surface of Ohio that host ore elsewhere in the Midwest (Stieglitz, 1975; Botoman and Stieglitz, 1978; Carlson, 1986). In this regard, some exploratory drilling was done in both Ohio districts in the 1960's and 1970's by mining companies such as Cominco, Marathon Resources, and the St. Joseph Lead Company, but no significant ore bodies appear to have been discovered (Reidel, 1972, 1975; S. P. Reidel, 1981, oral communication; P. E. Price, 1982, oral communication).

There is little agreement today among researchers about the origin of the mineralization. Even though studies (Roedder, 1969, 1979) of microscopic inclusions of fluid in the ore minerals have demonstrated convincingly that the metals were precipitated from warm, saline waters, the ore metals could have been derived from a number of sources. The different origins of the metals that have been suggested include: (1) metal-bearing basinal brines were generated in the sedimentary rocks of the adjoining Appalachian and Michigan Basins and moved up the flanks of the Cincinnati and Findlay Arches; (2) hot, metal-rich solutions, of deep-seated origin, rose upward along fractures in the underlying Precambrian basement rocks; and (3) trace metals contained in the rocks enclosing the mineralization were liberated by the partial dissolution of these strata (Reidel, 1972; Botoman and Faure, 1976; Botoman and Stieglitz, 1978; Kessen and others, 1981; Hansen, 1984; Carlson, 1986, 1987c). A detailed discussion of the origin of the ore mineral occurrences is beyond the scope of this work, and the interested reader should consult the papers noted above.

Findlay Arch mineral district

Geologic setting.—The Findlay Arch district is marked by a suite of ore minerals of strontium (celestite), fluorine (fluorite), zinc (sphalerite), and lead (galena). Nearly 100 minor occurrences of these minerals have been reported in a northeast-southwest-trending area about 60 miles wide and 120 miles long (fig. 5). The district is bordered by Parkertown in Erie County on the east, Huntsville in Logan County on the south, Van Wert in Van Wert County on the west, and West Sister Island in Lucas County on the north and extends into northeastern Indiana and southeastern Michigan (Carlson, 1983). Natural rock exposures are uncommon because the terrain is generally flat; most mineral occurrences are in the numerous quarries of the region. Unfortunately, most of these quarries are closed to collecting at present.

The restriction of the mineralization to carbonate rocks, chiefly dolostones and more rarely limestones, of middle Silurian to middle Devonian age (fig. 23) is an important

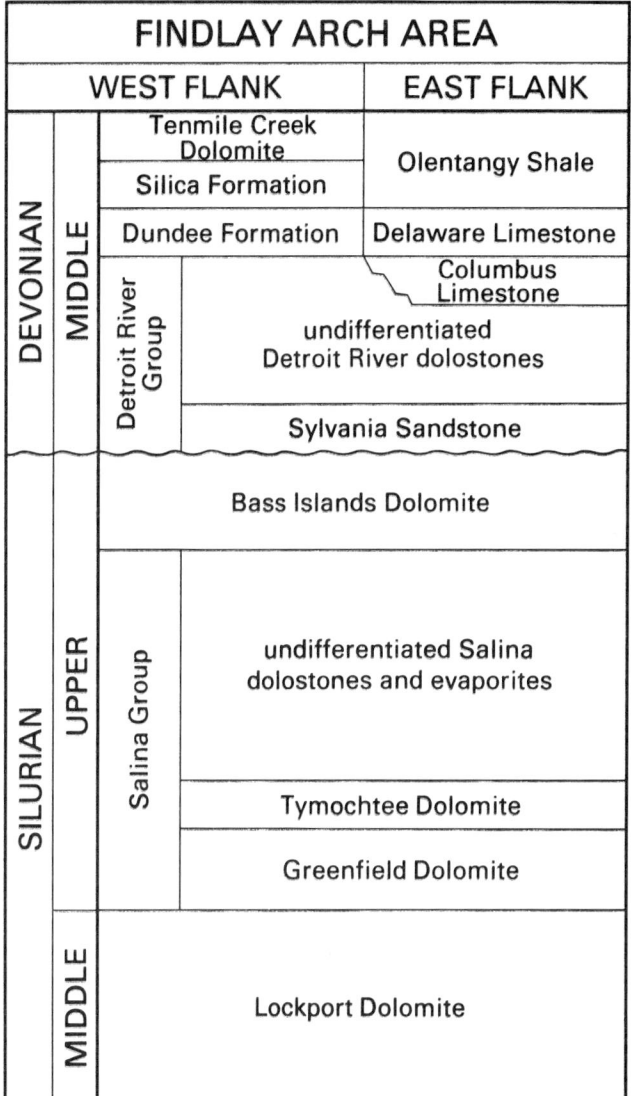

FIGURE 23.—Stratigraphic section of the Silurian and Devonian rocks of the Findlay Arch area, northwestern Ohio (after Janssens, 1970b, 1977).

characteristic of the district. The Lockport Dolomite is the oldest exposed formation and the most prominent one because of its resistant, reeflike character. It is overlain successively by the upper Silurian Salina Group and Bass Islands Dolomite; the Salina Group is subdivided into the Greenfield Dolomite, Tymochtee Dolomite, and undifferentiated Salina dolostones and evaporites. The middle Devonian Detroit River Group, consisting of a basal sandstone (Sylvania Sandstone) and an undifferentiated sequence of dolostones, rests unconformably on the Silurian beds. The Detroit River dolostones are overlain successively by the Dundee Formation, Silica Formation, and Tenmile Creek Dolomite in the western part of the district and the Columbus Limestone and Delaware Limestone in the eastern part. Exposures of the Lockport and Greenfield Dolomites at the center of the district in western Ottawa, western Sandusky, and eastern Wood Counties exhibit the most intense mineralization in the district. The ore minerals postdate the youngest of the host beds and were introduced sometime after the middle Devonian.

Regional controls on mineralization appear to be provided by the Findlay Arch and the Bowling Green Fault Zone, two major structures that run through the central part of the district. The arch is now beveled by erosion, exposing an elliptical mass of Lockport Dolomite and horseshoe-shaped bands of younger formations that bend around the crest of the structure (Janssens, 1977). The center of the district is located on this elliptical mass of Lockport Dolomite; the margins of the district are situated on the east and west flanks of the Findlay Arch. Several important ore districts in the Midwest are similarly positioned on large dome or arch structures, for example, the Wisconsin-Illinois-Iowa zinc district near the crest of the Wisconsin Dome (Ohle, 1959; Anderson, G. M., and MacQueen, 1982). The north-south-trending Bowling Green Fault Zone is parallel to and about 15 miles west of the crest of the arch. Both the Tymochtee Dolomite at the surface and the Ordovician Trenton Limestone in the subsurface are strongly mineralized along this fault zone (Stieglitz, 1975; Carlson, 1983; Coogan and Parker, 1984).

The mineralization at specific sites was controlled by the availability of open spaces in the rocks at the time the ore minerals were introduced. The high porosity of the carbonate-rock strata is one of the main reasons they are important hosts for the mineralization. Most of the open spaces postdate the rock, originating from the selective dissolution of more soluble phases, such as evaporites, and/or the enlargement of pre-existing rock openings, such as fractures, by dissolution.

The most important types of rock cavities that were subsequently mineralized include: caves; open spaces in sedimentary breccias; irregularly shaped vugs; molds of crystals, fossils, and nodules; and openings between joint and fault planes. Caves, the largest and most productive cavities, in terms of minerals, are mineral bearing in the following strata: (1) the uppermost beds of the Lockport Dolomite near Maumee in Lucas County, Clay Center and Genoa in Ottawa County, Woodville in Sandusky County, and Portage in Wood County; (2) the base of the Greenfield Dolomite near Lime City in Wood County; (3) the Bass Islands Dolomite on South Bass Island in Ottawa County; and (4) the dolostones of the Detroit River Group near Custar in Wood County and Silica in Lucas County (Kraus, 1905a; Carman, 1922; White, G. W., 1926; Gettings, 1952a; Stansbery, 1965; Strogonoff, 1966; Janssens, 1970a; Sparling, 1970; Kahle and Floyd, 1972; Kahle, 1974; Fisher, H. H., 1977; Carlson, 1986; Wilson, W. E., 1986). Sedimentary breccias cemented with secondary crystals are locally present in several formations in the district, most notably in dolostones of the Detroit River Group near Custar in Wood County (Janssens, 1970a). Small, irregularly shaped vugs, filled with various late-stage minerals, are particularly characteristic of the upper beds of the Lockport Dolomite. Mineralized molds of evaporite crystals and nodules occur in the Greenfield and Tymochtee Dolomites and dolostones of the undifferentiated Salina Group throughout much of the district (Kahle and Floyd, 1972; Carlson, 1987c; Richards and Chamberlain, 1987). With the exception of the Salina Group and the Bass Islands Dolomite, the rocks are highly fossiliferous and molds of these fossils are commonly filled with crystals. The Bowling Green Fault Zone is exposed at Waterville, Lucas County, where it is filled with a thick vein of calcite.

Mineralogy.—Mineralogical interest in northwestern Ohio dates back to the discovery by Douglass (1820, 1821) of large, well-formed celestite crystals on Green Island (Ottawa County), which was known for many years after the initial find as Strontian Island. Subsequently, new finds of celestite, brown fluorite, golden calcite, ruby sphalerite, and other minerals have enhanced the reputation of the district. Because most cavities in the carbonate rocks are only partially filled with these later minerals, crystal development is commonly good. Pockets commonly are lined with crystals of a single mineral species; less commonly, different minerals may be found together either as intergrowths or as encrustations.

Celestite is present in the eastern part of the district, chiefly in Lucas, Ottawa, Sandusky, Seneca, Wood, and Wyandot Counties. This ore of strontium is the most abundant vug-filling mineral in that part of the region and occurs in quantities large enough to be mined. Celestite was once produced at two sites in Ottawa County—Crystal Cave on South Bass Island in the 1890's and the United States Gypsum Company quarry at Genoa in 1940—for use in the manufacture of fireworks and tracer bullets (Phalen, 1914; Schreck and Arundale, 1959). The geological and mineralogical features of the spectacular Crystal Cave occurrence are described in Chapter 6. The crystals are found in two contrasting habits—tabular to bladed and columnar. The bladed and tabular celestite, one of the first minerals to be deposited, generally occurs alone in reticulated groups of crystals, but later minerals such as calcite, fluorite, and sphalerite may occupy the voids in the celestite networks. The columnar celestite, on the other hand, commonly is perched on the calcite and postdates it. Large tabular and bladed crystals of white, colorless, and pale-blue celestite have been obtained near Clay Center and Genoa in Ottawa County (fig. 24), Woodville in Sandusky County, and Portage in Wood County; slender, columnar blue crystals have been collected from near Custar and stout white ones from Lime City, both in Wood County (Gettings, 1952a; Strogonoff, 1966; White, J. S., 1975; Fisher, H. H., 1977; Parr and Chang, 1980; Wilson, W. E., 1986). Unusual crystals of celestite are found at Waterville, Lucas County. The crystals are embedded in nodules of massive gypsum and originated by replacing some of the gypsum.

Fluorite, the ore of fluorine, is common throughout the district. The typical brown to brownish-yellow fluorite occurs in translucent to transparent cubic crystals and coarsely granular aggregates characterized by an intense yellow fluorescence and phosphorescence (see Chapter 4). Crystals of brown fluorite are commonly hopper shaped, exhibiting cube faces whose centers are slightly depressed (see fig. 40B). Colorless, pale-yellow, purple, and pale-green nonfluorescent crystals are less common and formed later

FIGURE 24.—Bladed celestite; from Clay Center, Ottawa County. Specimen is 4½ inches long.

than the brown fluorite. Color-zoned phantom crystals, with brown cores and colorless rims, occur at several sites. Fluorite was first reported from the eastern side of the district in the Erie County area (Silliman, 1822b; Porter, 1823). Attractive specimens of dark-brown fluorite surrounding netlike clusters of bladed, white celestite are found at several quarries in Ottawa, Sandusky, and Seneca Counties. In the early 1900's Tiffin, a classic locality in Seneca County, produced many superb clusters of iridescent brown crystals with celestite (Dana and Ford, 1932; Palache and others, 1951). Some of the largest crystals, groups of brown cubes with individuals up to 3 inches across, are present at a quarry near Gibsonburg in Sandusky County (fig. 25). Clusters of iridescent dark-brown fluorite crystals have been obtained in recent years from quarries near Bellevue in Sandusky County, Bluffton in Allen County, Junction in Paulding County, and Maple Grove in Seneca County.

FIGURE 26.—Scalenohedral calcite crystals on dolostone matrix; from Custar, Wood County. Specimen is 3 inches long.

FIGURE 25.—Cubic fluorite crystals on dolostone matrix; from Gibsonburg, Sandusky County. Coin indicates scale.

Vug-type calcite occurs throughout the region but is best developed in the cavernous middle Devonian dolostones and limestones. Early interest in calcite centered on crystals with rare forms, such as the dipyramid-pinacoid combinations (see fig. 40L), that were found in pockets of the Detroit River Group and Columbus Limestone at Bellevue in Sandusky County and Kelleys Island in Erie County (Farrington and Tillotson, 1908; Ford and Pogue, 1909; Whitlock, 1910). Caves in the Detroit River Group in Lucas and Wood Counties are especially renowned for large crystals of golden calcite (Carman, 1922; Gettings, 1950; Nelson, 1967; Parr and Chang, 1979). A partial scalenohedron over 18 inches long and 12 inches wide has been reported (Nelson, 1967) from a quarry near Custar, Wood County, which in the recent past has been an important source of this material (fig. 26). Scalenohedral crystals and coarsely granular aggregates are most abundant in the district; rhombohedrally modified scalenohedrons and prisms are more rare (fig. 27). The calcite commonly is golden, colorless, or white, transparent to translucent, and generally nonfluorescent. However, a 2-foot-thick vein of coarsely granular tan calcite with an intense yellow fluorescence occurs along the Bowling Green Fault Zone at a quarry near Waterville in Lucas County. Other minerals, such as celestite, fluorite, and sulfides, are conspicuously absent from this vein.

Sulfide minerals in the Findlay Arch mineral district include pyrite, marcasite, sphalerite, and galena. Pyrite is more common than marcasite and was one of the first minerals deposited in the cavernous rocks. It typically occurs in thin mats of tiny iridescent crystals upon which celestite, calcite, and other minerals are perched; the bright hues of this pyrite commonly result in its misidentification as a copper mineral. Vug-type pyrite is most common in the Tymochtee Dolomite and dolostones of the undifferentiated Salina Group in the southern part of the district in Auglaize, Allen, Hancock, Hardin, Logan, and Putnam Counties. Comparatively large, well-formed crystals, chiefly diploids and trapezohedra in combination with other forms (see figs. 40I and 40F), were first recorded at the Huntsville site in Logan County (Fisher, H. H., 1976; Anderson, V., 1979a; Gait, 1980; Richards and Chamberlain, 1987). Marcasite is particularly abundant at a quarry near Custar in Wood County, where a thick mass of radiating crystals occurs as a

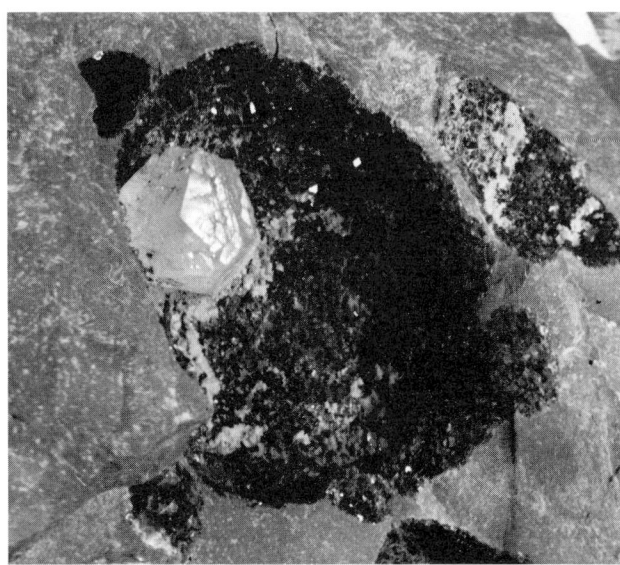

FIGURE 27.—Hexagonal prism of calcite with rhombohedral termination on dolostone matrix; from Lima, Allen County. Pocket, which is lined with asphalt (black), is 1¾ inches long.

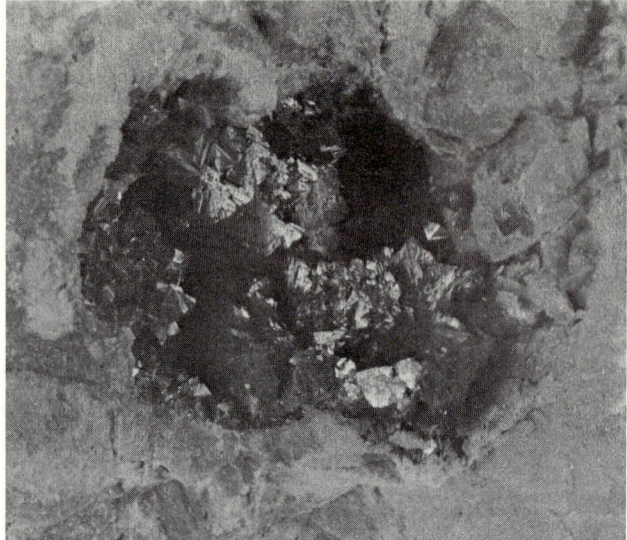

FIGURE 28.—Tetrahedral crystals of ruby sphalerite (dark) on dolostone matrix; from Buckland, Auglaize County. Pocket is 1½ inches across.

cement in sedimentary breccias of the Detroit River Group (Parr and Chang, 1977). Sphalerite, the main ore mineral of zinc, is common throughout the district and occurs as ruby-red tetrahedral crystals with curved faces as large as ½ inch in diameter, subspherical clusters of tiny orange crystals, and coarsely granular, yellowish-brown aggregates (fig. 28). Pockets lined with striking ruby-red crystals have been observed near Findlay (Hancock County), Maumee (Lucas County), Celina (Mercer County), Clay Center, Genoa, and Rocky Ridge (Ottawa County), Woodville (Sandusky County), Van Wert (Van Wert County), and West Millgrove (Wood County). Galena, the least common of the sulfides, occurs in small groups of well-formed cubic crystals; individual crystals range from a fraction to ¾ of an inch in diameter. This ore of lead is restricted to the center of the district and occurs chiefly in the Lockport Dolomite in the western parts of Ottawa, Sandusky, and Seneca Counties and eastern Wood County.

Vug-type dolomite, quartz, barite, strontianite, sulfur, and gypsum also have been reported from the Findlay Arch district. Dolomite is quite common, and generally occurs alone as early-formed, tiny, gray to tan rhombohedral crystals lining the walls of cavities. However, crystals of white saddle dolomite, with curved rhombohedral faces that average slightly less than ¼ inch in length (fig. 29), are abundant at quarries near Bluffton and Lima in Allen County, Huntsville and Northwood in Logan County, Custar in Wood County, and at several other sites. Tiny crystals of colorless quartz appear chiefly in the pockets of cherty dolostones at a few widely scattered localities. Barite, a late-formed mineral that is rare in the district, is relatively common at a quarry near Custar in Wood County, where it occurs as small, tabular, white or pale-blue crystals perched on calcite or rock matrix (Parr and Chang, 1980). Barite also forms brown rims on colorless scalenohedrons of calcite at Lime City in Wood County. Masses of fibrous, white to yellow strontianite crystals with a bluish-white fluorescence have formed from the alteration of celestite and occur either as encrustations on celestite or as solitary, spherical groups of radiating fibers (fig. 30). Rarely, small crystals of late-formed bright-yellow sulfur are found resting on calcite crystals or bedded gypsum. Cavities filled with groups of small gypsum crystals have been reported near Clay Center, Ottawa County (Morrison, 1935). Thin layers of black, lustrous asphaltic material occur in places as coatings on the walls of pockets or on crystals of calcite and other minerals; such coatings have been found near Lima in Allen County, Maumee in Lucas County, and Junction in Paulding County.

Serpent Mound zinc district

Geologic setting.—The Serpent Mound zinc district, as defined in this report, is a broad region in southwestern Ohio that is distinguished by minor occurrences of zinc ore (fig. 5). Vein-type occurrences are characteristic of the

FIGURE 29.—Rhombohedral crystals of saddle dolomite on dolostone matrix; from Custar, Wood County. Pocket is 1 inch long.

FIGURE 30.—Acicular crystals of white strontianite on dolostone matrix; from Silica, Lucas County. Strontianite mass is ¼ inch across.

center of the district, and mineralized vugs are typical of the peripheral zone. Here, the general absence of associated minerals, such as the fluorite and celestite that accompany the zinc minerals in the Findlay Arch district, is quite conspicuous. The district is particularly noted for the vein-type zinc found within a circular area of strongly deformed strata known as the Serpent Mound disturbance (Reidel and others, 1982). Over 50 closely spaced zinc sites have been located within this structure, which covers an area 5 miles in diameter at the junction of northern Adams, southeastern Highland, and southwestern Pike Counties (Heyl and Brock, 1962; Reidel, 1975). In contrast, persistent but widely spaced vug-type occurrences of zinc minerals are characteristic of the undeformed rocks in the bordering region of Adams, Highland, southern Fayette, and western Ross Counties (Orton, 1871b; Rogers, J. K., 1936; Stout, 1941; Botoman and Stieglitz, 1978; Rexroad and Kleffner, 1984). On the basis of the distribution of the sites listed in the catalog (Chapter 7), the district is about 40 miles long and 20 miles wide, and has a long axis that runs north-south. The mineralized rock within the disturbance is poorly exposed; it can be observed at a few road cuts and small abandoned quarries and along several hillsides where the rocks are deeply weathered. Active rock quarries provide better exposures of the more sparsely distributed vug-type occurrences bordering the disturbance. That the zinc minerals in the disturbance were not discovered sooner (Heyl and Brock, 1962) is undoubtedly due to the highly fractured nature and poor exposures of these rocks.

The ore minerals of the district are preferentially localized in carbonate-rock strata of middle and late Silurian age. This association is particularly striking in a region where a thick and varied sequence of upper Ordovician to lower Mississippian sedimentary rocks is exposed (fig. 31). Outside the disturbance, where the undeformed strata can be examined, the mineralization is confined to the following formations: Brassfield Formation, Bisher Dolomite, Lilley Dolomite, Peebles Dolomite, Greenfield Dolomite, and Tymochtee Dolomite. Unconformities separate the Peebles Dolomite from the younger Greenfield rocks, and the Tymochtee Dolomite from the overlying upper Devonian Ohio Shale. Inside the disturbance the mineralization is restricted to the Peebles-Greenfield-Tymochtee dolostones. Exposures of these rocks and the associated zinc occurrences are mainly confined to a ring-shaped belt along the inner boundary of the disturbance (Reidel, 1975). However, the rocks are commonly shattered beyond recognition and individual formations of this group cannot be readily distinguished.

The Serpent Mound zinc district is on the east flank of the northerly trending Cincinnati Arch; the center of the district lies approximately 50 miles east of the crest of the arch. The strata in the outer zone of the mineral district, which are tilted slightly eastward, are only slightly deformed. However, this gentle structure contrasts markedly with that of the disturbance.

The mineralization inside the Serpent Mound disturbance is controlled by fault systems. The zinc minerals mainly occupy open spaces related to the fracturing, including openings between fault planes, open spaces in shatter breccias, and vugs in the brecciated rock. Some of the zinc ore in the veins is slightly brecciated, indicating that a second, milder stage of deformation occurred along the mineralized fractures (Heyl and Brock, 1962; Reidel and others, 1982). Because the ore minerals postdate the main episode of faulting that produced the disturbance, the mineralization is later than early Mississippian, the youngest of the faulted beds. The origin of the disturbance is discussed in Chapter 6.

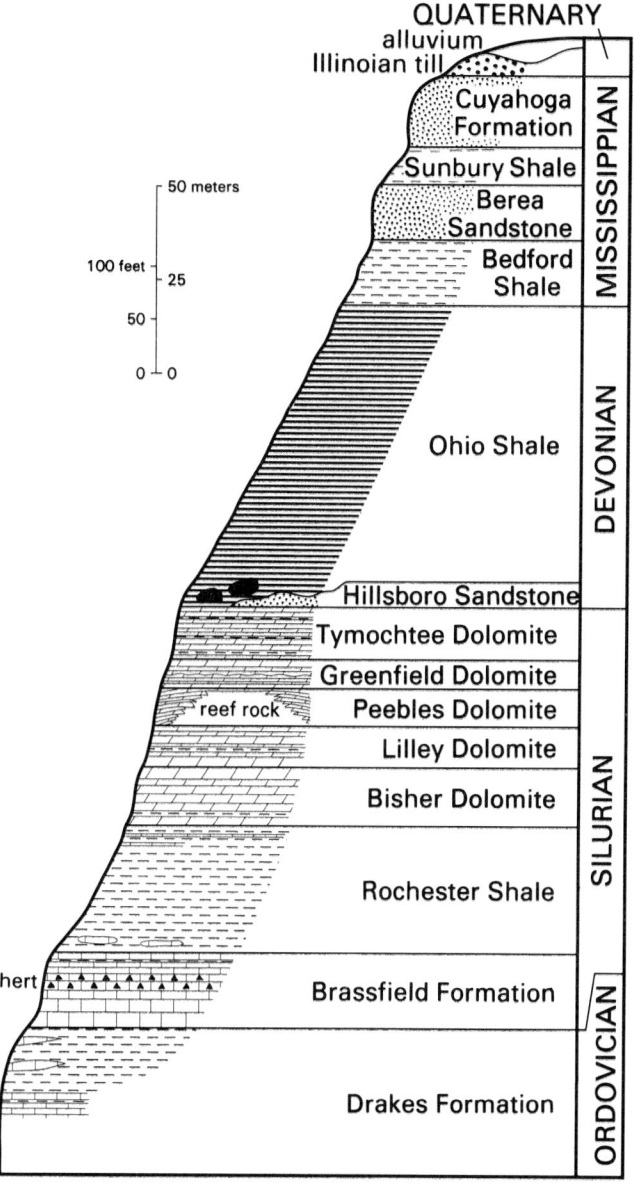

FIGURE 31.—Stratigraphic section of the Paleozoic rocks of the Serpent Mound area, southwestern Ohio (modified from Reidel and Koucky, 1981, fig. 3; used with permission of American Geological Institute, Alexandria, Virginia).

In the strata outside the disturbance the zinc minerals occur in rock cavities, such as small caves, open spaces in sedimentary breccias, irregularly shaped vugs, fossil molds, and openings between joint surfaces (Napper, 1917; Rexroad and others, 1965; Reidel and others, 1982; Rexroad and Kleffner, 1984). The Peebles and Greenfield Dolomites are particularly favorable hosts because both formations exhibit porous, reeflike buildups of carbonate rock. The Bisher, Lilley, and Peebles Dolomites are quite fossiliferous and mineralized fossil molds are common, especially in the Peebles.

Mineralogy.—Sphalerite, smithsonite, hydrozincite, and hemimorphite are the ore minerals of zinc that occur in the faulted rocks of the Serpent Mound disturbance. The latter three are secondary minerals that originate from the prolonged weathering of sphalerite and are unknown in Ohio outside the Serpent Mound disturbance. This unique occurrence is apparently due to the position of the area at the southern edge of the glacial boundary, where the deeply weathered rock was not scoured away by Pleistocene ice, as it was farther north. The sphalerite, smithsonite, and hydrozincite were originally discovered by Heyl and Brock (1962); hemimorphite is reported here for the first time. These minerals are quite concentrated in the veins and pockets of the breccia; analyses of zinc run as high as 20 percent locally in loose chunks of rock (Heyl and Brock, 1962). Sphalerite, the original vein mineral, is adamantine to resinous, reddish brown, brown, or orange, and coarse grained, and most commonly occurs in irregularly shaped granular masses in the dolostone breccia (fig. 32); well-formed crystals are rare. Brown cellular boxworks and gray colloform crusts of fine-grained smithsonite and powdery to silky masses of white hydrozincite are abundant. The smithsonite boxworks commonly are encrusted with tiny crystals of tan or brownish-yellow smithsonite, and, more rarely, the hydrozincite is spotted with small, isolated crystals of bright-yellow sulfur. Tiny, delicate, white crystals of hemimorphite, the rarest of the zinc minerals, occur together with smithsonite in thin, porous, yellowish-white crusts. These weathering products typically surround remnants of the sphalerite and embellish the walls of vugs.

Dolomite, calcite, and asphaltic material also are common vein constituents of the disturbance (Heyl and Brock, 1962; Reidel, 1972; Koucky, 1975; Reidel and Koucky, 1981). Finely granular tan dolomite is typically associated with and formed earlier than the sphalerite; the dolomite occurs as veinlets that cement breccia. Veins up to 2 inches wide composed of coarsely granular, milky-white, fluorescent calcite occur in the fractured rock at some sites. Black asphaltic material occurs in veinlets with and formed later than the sphalerite and dolomite. Pyrite, observed by Galbraith (1968), Reidel (1972), and Botoman and Stieglitz (1978), is apparently less abundant than sphalerite because the weathered vein rocks are not significantly enriched in secondary iron minerals such as goethite. Vein-type barite and fluorite also reportedly occur in the disturbance (Worl and others, 1974; Heyl and Van Alstine, 1976; Botoman and Stieglitz, 1978; Clark, 1987), but their occurrence has not been substantiated.

Vug-type sphalerite is the most abundant and characteristic ore mineral in the undeformed dolostones bordering the disturbance (Orton, 1871b; Hawes, 1884; Bownocker, 1915; Rogers, J. K., 1936; Stout, 1941; Bowman, 1956; Schmidt and others, 1961; Reidel, 1972; Botoman and Stieglitz, 1978). Coarsely granular masses of red to yellowish-brown sphalerite weighing up to 30 pounds have been reported from the Greenfield Dolomite at the old Rucker quarry in Ross County just east of Greenfield in Highland County (Napper, 1917). Small, well-formed crystals and coarse-grained granular aggregates of colorless to white calcite are common, either alone or in association with sphalerite (Rogers, J. K., 1936; Goodwin, 1940; Reidel, 1972). Tiny quartz crystals are particularly abundant in fossil cavities of the siliceous Bisher and Lilley Dolomites (see discussion of geodes earlier in this chapter). Minor amounts of vug-type pyrite have been reported at a few Highland County sites (Rogers, J. K., 1936; Bowman, 1956; Botoman and Stieglitz, 1978). More rarely, groups of small crystals and granular aggregates of barite, celestite, and fluorite are encountered in the region (Reidel, 1972; Koucky, 1975). Pockets with coatings of black, asphaltic material are extremely abundant throughout the region (Napper, 1916; Rogers, J. K., 1936; Stout, 1941; Reidel and others, 1982; Rexroad and Kleffner, 1984).

MINERALS IN GLACIAL SEDIMENTS

Gypsum crystals

Geologic setting.—Superb gypsum (selenite) crystals of worldwide renown are found in the Pleistocene glacial lake deposits of northeastern Ohio. The host beds consist of unconsolidated bluish-gray to brown silt and clay that were deposited in meltwater lakes marginal to the Wisconsinan ice sheet. Many large lakes of this type were present in lowland areas; one such lake occupied the present valley of the Cuyahoga River in Summit and Cuyahoga Counties when the ice front dammed the mouth of the river at Cleveland (White, G. W., 1953; Miller, 1970). Occurrences of gypsum have been reported in the glacial silts and clays exposed along the banks of the following drainage systems: Cuyahoga River in Cuyahoga and Summit Counties; Lake Milton-Meander Creek-Mahoning River in Mahoning County; and West Branch Mahoning River in Portage County (Cleaveland, 1816, 1822; Silliman, 1821; Hildreth, 1837; Whittlesey, 1838; Greene, 1937; Birkheimer, 1938). Of the above sites, the finest crystals came from the banks of Meander Creek near Ellsworth, a classic locality in the past, and more recently from the north bank of West Branch Mahoning River in West Branch State Park. The geology of the West Branch site is described in greater detail in Chapter 6. As a general rule, loose crystals can be collected at the surface of gypsum-bearing silt and clay banks. The glitter of crystal faces is striking on a sunny day. These crystals, which appear when the enclosing silt and clay beds begin to erode away, commonly are corroded because of the high solubility of gypsum (fig. 33). The best crystals are obtained by digging into the banks and carefully working through the clay or silt by hand. Unfortunately, the crystals are easily damaged because of their softness and perfect cleavage.

The origin of the gypsum crystals is poorly understood. They are embedded in the silt and clay in a zone that extends from the surface to depths of several inches. The crystals originated when the beds were saturated with water; precipitation of gypsum apparently occurred when the ground waters were drawn to the surface by evaporation, causing the concentrations of calcium and sulfate ions to increase. The crystals grew larger by pushing aside the

FIGURE 32.—Coarse-grained granular masses of yellowish-brown sphalerite (light) in brecciated dolostone matrix (dark); from the Serpent Mound area, Adams County. Specimen is 4 inches long.

FIGURE 33.—Prismatic gypsum (selenite) crystals; from Meander Creek south of Ellsworth, Mahoning County. Lower crystal is corroded; upper one is uncorroded and exhibits an hourglass pattern of inclusions. Upper crystal is 1¾ inches long and is from the collection of Andy Love.

enclosing soft sediment, incorporating tiny particles of the sediment as impurities along earlier formed crystal faces. Crystals can be found attached to the roots of growing vegetation, indicating that some crystals are forming today.

Mineralogy.—Noted for their exceptional quality, these crystals consist of the colorless, transparent variety of gypsum known commonly as selenite. The selenite occurs as: (1) isolated crystals, typically exhibiting a combination of monoclinic prisms and a side pinacoid (see fig. 40U); (2) clusters of interpenetrating prisms; and (3) long, lath-shaped blades. The prisms are elongate, averaging about 1 inch in length and ½ inch in width, although perfect individuals up to 4 inches long have been recorded; the lath-shaped blades range from 2 to 8 inches in length. Inclusions of silt, clay, or organic matter, which give the material a slightly cloudy appearance, may be arranged in concentric bands (phantom crystals) or hourglass structures (fig. 33) in the isolated crystals and in herringbone patterns in the lath-shaped blades. The isolated selenite crystals display a characteristic bluish-white fluorescence and phosphorescence of low intensity (Birkheimer, 1938; Gleason, 1960).

Vivianite

Geologic setting.—Vivianite, a colorful iron phosphate, is found in Pleistocene glacial deposits at several widely separated localities. It has been observed in exposures of Illinoian and Wisconsinan drift at gravel pits and along stream banks in Brown, Hamilton, Medina, Montgomery, and Warren Counties (Orton, 1870, 1871a; Orton and Peppel, 1906; Wuestner, 1938; Sarles, 1951). The vivianite is always associated with fossil plant debris, particularly wood, that was buried in the glacial drift. Small masses of vivianite perched on fossil twigs and branches have been obtained from a deposit thought to represent an ancient beaver pond at a gravel pit near Lodi in Medina County (Totten, 1976). The wood, which has been partially compacted into peat, is believed to be the source of the phosphate in the vivianite; the association of vivianite and decayed wood also is common elsewhere (Palache and others, 1951).

Mineralogy.—The vivianite is deep blue in color and typically occurs alone as dull, fine-grained encrustations on dark, organic-rich rock or plant debris. Crystals of vivianite up to ¼ inch in length have been reported from stream banks in Brown and Warren Counties (Wuestner, 1938; Sarles, 1951). The crystals are colorless in freshly broken rock but change to deep blue on continued exposure to air.

Diamonds and gold

Geologic setting.—Diamonds and gold are the most intriguing minerals reported from the Pleistocene glacial drift of Ohio and adjoining parts of the Great Lakes region (Newberry, 1874a; Hobbs, 1899; Blatchley, 1902; Gunn, 1968; Hansen, 1982, 1985a, 1985b). Because no diamond- or gold-bearing source rocks have been identified in Ohio, the diamonds and gold are believed to have originated from Canadian occurrences that were situated in the path of the Pleistocene ice. Weathering of the resulting glacial drift or its erosion by streams has released some of the diamonds and gold, enabling them to be recovered by panning or other techniques.

Finds of drift diamonds in Ohio are rare; two discoveries have been reported from Clermont County, and single finds have been recorded from Cuyahoga, Hamilton, Mahoning, and Summit Counties (Gunn, 1968; Hansen, 1982, 1985a). Of the six drift diamonds discovered between 1870 and 1982, only a few of the sites are precisely located and all of the recovered stones are now lost. These diamonds, which were found in gravel pits or in the gravel beds of active streams, were apparently picked up by chance because of their striking appearance. Several similar drift diamonds in Indiana and Wisconsin, on the other hand, were first recognized and recovered by prospectors panning for gold (Blatchley, 1902). Based on directions of ice movement and presently known distribution patterns of the drift diamonds and diamond-bearing igneous rock (kimberlite) in the Great Lakes region and eastern Canada, most workers believe that the source rocks are located at a still-undiscovered site south of James Bay in northern Ontario (Brummer, 1978).

Traces of gold in glacial drift are concentrated by streams eroding through the drift, particularly in southwestern and central Ohio, and form placer deposits. Drift gold in Ohio was apparently discovered in 1853 north of Bellville in Richland County; this find was soon followed by others near Williamsburg in Clermont County and near Brownsville and Newark in Licking County (Andrews, 1871; Orton, 1873; Newberry, 1874a; Read, 1878a; Baughman, 1904; Wuestner, 1938; Caster and others, 1970; Totten, 1973). Background data for these localities and several others where small quantities of gold have been recovered were compiled by Hansen (1985b). Because gold is heavy it is concentrated preferentially at the base of the drift at the contact with the underlying bedrock; thus streams exposing the drift-bedrock contact provide the best panning opportunities. However, the value of drift gold recovered would not ordinarily exceed a few dollars a day, although gravels along Stonelick Creek in Clermont County were worked successfully during the economic depression of the 1930's. The geology of the Stonelick Creek site is described more fully in Chapter 6.

Wright (1890) and later Blatchley (1902) observed that concentrations of drift gold in Ohio, Indiana, and Pennsylvania were greatest in streams near the glacial boundary (see fig. 3). Because an arcuate belt of Illinoian drift occurs along the glacial boundary at the sites noted by those workers, the Illinoian drift is generally considered to be the most favorable glacial unit for gold. Gold in Clermont, Licking, and Richland Counties has been recovered in the hilly terrain of this belt, where exposures of Illinoian drift cap the bedrock. Elsewhere in Ohio the Illinoian drift is not exposed because it is covered by younger, Wisconsinan deposits. The apparent enrichment of gold in the Illinoian drift, relative to the Wisconsinan drift, may be related to different flow paths of the Canadian ice and the amounts of gold-bearing rock encountered, or, alternatively, to the longer period of weathering associated with the Illinoian drift, which would carry more free gold from decomposed glacial boulders. The drift gold in Ohio probably originated from one or more of the important gold-mining districts in Ontario and Quebec (Boyle, 1979).

Mineralogy.—A rough diamond is distinguished by its peculiar greasy luster, transparency, and crystal form, which is characteristically octahedral. Drift diamonds are colorless, pale bluish gray, white, or pale yellow and are mostly less than a carat in weight, although a 21¼ carat stone was recorded from Wisconsin (Gunn, 1968). The best stone from a well-documented find in Ohio was a white, octahedral diamond of 6 carats that was discovered in 1897 at Milford in Clermont County (Hobbs, 1899).

Drift gold typically occurs in tiny yellow flakes or scales a fraction of an inch across, although larger, pea-size grains have been reported (Hansen, 1985b). Its color and specific gravity are the most distinguishing features.

METEORITES

Geologic setting

A meteorite is a fragment of natural metal or rock that has fallen from outer space onto the Earth's surface. Meteorites range in dimension from dust-size particles to large masses measuring over 10 feet across (Mason, 1962). They are irregular in shape and generally have a dull surface with shallow pits resembling thumbprints in clay. Most meteorites are believed to have originated in our solar system from fragments of asteroids that first become visible as meteors or shooting stars while falling through the Earth's atmosphere. Because of the frictional heat generated when a meteor passes through the atmosphere, a thin, black fusion crust forms on the surface of a meteorite. After prolonged exposure this fusion crust weathers to a brown rind of iron oxide. Therefore, the degree of weathering of the fusion crust can help establish whether a meteorite fell recently or many years ago. A meteorite picked up shortly after it was observed falling to Earth is designated as a fall, whereas a meteorite discovered by chance after an unobserved landing is called a find.

Meteorites are classified by the relative amounts of silicate minerals and native iron that they contain (Mason, 1962). The three main compositional types recognized are (1) stony meteorites, or stones, which are rich in silicate minerals, (2) iron meteorites, or irons, which are enriched in native iron, and (3) stony-iron meteorites, or stony-irons, which are mixtures of the other two. Stones are the most abundant of the three compositional types, accounting for well over 90 percent of the falls. Conversely, irons greatly exceed stones among the finds, probably because of the striking appearance of an iron, with its black color, great weight, and strong magnetism. In contrast, a stony meteorite resembles a common igneous rock. Interestingly, radiometric determinations of the ages of stones and irons give a time of formation of about 4.5 billion years before the present, making them older than any known rocks on Earth.

Because of their great rarity and scientific value, most meteorites are housed in special meteorite collections, such as those in the U.S. National Museum in Washington, D.C., or the American Museum of Natural History in New York City. Therefore, any specimen that is suspected of being a meteorite should not be broken or cut open; a small specimen or chip from a large one, together with a description and the location and date of the find, should be submitted to the Ohio Division of Geological Survey in Columbus for evaluation.

Meteorites may be found anywhere in Ohio. They can be hunted most easily in rock-free flat ground, such as freshly plowed fields, because they stand out in such terrain. Because meteorites originating from a meteor shower would be confined to a restricted area, successful hunts can sometimes be made at sites of previous falls or finds. Iron-rich meteorites that are buried at shallow depth can be located with a metal detector.

Nine meteorites have been recorded in Ohio, including two falls, five finds, and two discoveries in prehistoric Indian burial mounds (table 3). The New Concord fall of May 1, 1860, is the most noteworthy occurrence by far (Andrews, 1860; Shepard, 1860; Smith, J. L., 1861; Hansen, 1983). About 30 stones from this spectacular meteor shower were recovered along a northwest-southeast-trending belt 10 miles long and 3 miles wide in western Guernsey and eastern Muskingum Counties. The largest stone retrieved from the New Concord area weighed 103 pounds (47 kilograms) and is currently housed at Marietta College in Washington County (fig. 34). Another fall was observed on February 13, 1893, near Pricetown, Highland County, but only one stone weighing 2 pounds (0.9 kilogram) was recovered from that locality. The five finds are the Cincinnati, Dayton, Enon, New Westville, and Wooster meteorites, which include four irons and one stony-iron; the largest were the Dayton and Wooster irons, which weighed 58 and 50 pounds (26 and 23 kilograms), respectively. Because of discrepancies in reports about the Dayton meteorite, some doubt exists about the exact location of that find (Buchwald, 1975). The stony-irons discovered in the Anderson and Hopewell Mounds are similar to meteorites from the Brenham locality in Kiowa County, Kansas, and are believed to have been brought into Ohio by Indian traders (Wasson and Sedwick, 1969; Buchwald, 1975).

Mineralogy

Nineteen minerals have been reported in Ohio meteorites (table 4). These include four native elements, three sulfides, one phosphide, three oxides, four phosphates, and four silicates. The distribution of these minerals in specific meteorites is given in table 3. With the exception of the Pricetown stone and the Enon stony-iron, the mineralogy of Ohio meteorites is fairly well known.

The New Concord and Pricetown stones are composed chiefly of olivine and hypersthene; notable amounts of sodium plagioclase (albite) also occur in the New Concord meteorite (Mason and Wiik, 1961). Both stones are classified as chondrites because they contain tiny spherical grains (chondrules) of olivine and hypersthene embedded in the other minerals.

The Dayton, New Westville, and Wooster irons contain notable amounts of nickel. These meteorites are composed dominantly of kamacite and taenite, two strongly magnetic minerals, the former being nickel poor and the latter nickel rich. When these irons are cut and polished they display a distinctive cross-hatched intergrowth of kamacite and taenite that is known as Widmanstatten structure. The Cincinnati iron is nickel poor and contains only kamacite. A small amount of troilite, a weakly magnetic iron sulfide, also is present in these four irons.

TABLE 3.—Ohio meteorites

Name	County	7.5-minute quadrangle(s)	Latitude, longitude	Number of specimens	Date	Weight (kg)	Classification	Mineralogy	Present location of specimen	References
Anderson (Turner Mounds)	Hamilton	Madeira	39°10'N, 84°18'W	several masses and worked objects	prehistoric	0.85	stony-iron	bronzite, kamacite, olivine, taenite	Harvard University	Farrington (1915), Hey (1966), Wasson and Sedwick (1969), Buchwald (1975)
Cincinnati	Hamilton	Covington, Newport	39°07'N, 84°30'W	single mass	1870	1-2	iron	kamacite, schreibersite, troilite	Naturhistorisches Museum (Vienna)	Cohen, E. W. (1898), Farrington (1915), Hey (1966), Buchwald (1975)
Dayton	Montgomery	Dayton North, Dayton South	39°45'N, 84°10'W (approx.)	single mass	1892	26.3	iron	albite, brianite, bronzite, graphite, kamacite, magnetite, panethite, schreibersite, sphalerite, taenite, troilite, whitlockite	U.S. National Museum	Fuchs and others (1967), Buchwald (1975)
Enon	Clark	Yellow Springs	39°52'N, 83°57'W	single mass	about 1883	0.76	stony-iron	alabandite, chromite, kamacite, schreibersite, silicates (unspecified), taenite, troilite	Arizona State University	Nininger (1942), Hey (1966), Ramdohr (1973)
Hopewell Mounds	Ross	Andersonville	39°23'N, 83°02'W	single mass and several worked objects	prehistoric	0.130	stony-iron	kamacite, olivine, schreibersite, taenite, troilite	Field Museum of Natural History	Farrington (1915), Wasson and Sedwick (1969), Buchwald (1975)
New Concord	Muskingum-Guernsey	New Concord, Byesville	39°54'N-40°00'N, 81°34'W-81°45'W	about 30 stones	May 1, 1860 (fall)	227	stony	albite, chlorapatite, chromite, copper, hypersthene, ilmenite, kamacite, magnetite, olivine, taenite, troilite, whitlockite	Marietta College	Andrews (1860), Shepard (1860), Smith, J. L. (1861), Farrington (1915), Mason and Wiik (1961), Mason (1963), Fuchs (1969), Ramdohr (1973)
New Westville	Preble	New Paris	39°50'N, 84°47'W	single mass	1941	4.8	iron	chromite, kamacite, schreibersite, taenite, troilite	U.S. National Museum	Henderson and Perry (1946), Buchwald (1975)
Pricetown	Highland	Sardinia	39°07'N, 83°51'W	single mass	February 13, 1893 (fall)	0.9	stony	hypersthene, olivine	American Museum of Natural History	Farrington (1915), Mason (1963), Hey (1966)
Wooster	Wayne	Wooster	40°46'N, 81°57'W	single mass	1858	22.5	iron	kamacite, schreibersite, taenite, troilite	main mass is lost, 14 g at Philadelphia Academy of Natural Sciences	Smith, J. L. (1864), Farrington (1915), Buchwald (1975)

FIGURE 34.—Fragment of the New Concord stony meteorite; from the Guernsey-Muskingum County area. Specimen, from the collection of Marietta College, Washington County, is approximately 13¾ inches high.

The other minerals in the meteorites (table 4) are either relatively rare or occur in grains that are microscopic. Two of the phosphates, brianite and panethite, were unknown prior to their discovery in the Dayton meteorite (Fuchs and others, 1967).

TABLE 4.—*Minerals in Ohio meteorites*

Native elements:	copper (Cu), graphite (C), kamacite (Fe,Ni), taenite (Fe,Ni)
Sulfides:	alabandite (MnS), sphalerite (ZnS), troilite (FeS)
Phosphides:	schreibersite ((Fe,Ni)$_3$P)
Oxides:	chromite (FeCr$_2$O$_4$), ilmenite (FeTiO$_3$), magnetite (Fe$_3$O$_4$)
Phosphates:	brianite (Na$_2$CaMg(PO$_4$)$_2$), chlorapatite (Ca$_5$(PO$_4$)$_3$Cl), panethite ((Na,Ca)$_2$-(Mg,Fe)$_2$(PO$_4$)$_2$), whitlockite (Ca$_3$(PO$_4$)$_2$)
Silicates:	albite (NaAlSi$_3$O$_8$), bronzite ((Mg,Fe)SiO$_3$), hypersthene ((Mg,Fe)SiO$_3$), olivine ((Mg,Fe)$_2$SiO$_4$)

EFFLORESCENCES

Geologic setting

An efflorescence is a crusty coating of mineral salts that forms on a rock by the evaporation of water drawn to the surface through capillary-size openings. These minerals accumulate on the protected undersides of rock ledges. Particularly large buildups occur after long periods of hot, dry weather. Conversely, the efflorescences may entirely disappear after heavy rains because of their high solubility. The best collecting is obtained on sheltered exposures of black shale and coal. Cliffs of Ohio Shale along the following streams are especially noted for the occurrence of efflorescences: Alum Creek in Delaware County, Black River in Lorain County, Deer Creek in Pickaway County, Euclid Creek in Cuyahoga County, Huron River in Erie and Huron Counties, Olentangy River in Delaware and Franklin Counties, Paint Creek in Ross County, Rocky River in Cuyahoga County, Scioto Brush Creek in Adams County, Tinkers Creek in Cuyahoga County, and Vermilion River in Erie and Lorain Counties (Hildreth, 1834; Briggs, 1838; Locke, 1838; Read, 1878a; Collins, R. F., 1924; Westgate, 1926; Knille and Gibbs, 1942; Seyfried, 1953; Carlson, 1987b). Weathered exposures of coal and shale in road cuts and abandoned strip mines of eastern Ohio also yield good specimens (McCaughey, 1918; Brant and Foster, 1959; Ehlers, E. G., and Stiles, 1965; Nuhfer, 1972; Fisher, H. H., 1975).

Most efflorescences are closely associated with weathered pyrite in the host rock; the thickest efflorescence crusts develop on rocks having a high pyrite content. Pyrite weathers rapidly when it is exposed to oxygen and water vapor in the air, leaving behind a rust-colored residue of hydrated iron oxide and liberating sulfuric acid, which attacks the enclosing rocks. The evaporation of this acidic water rich in sulfate and metals, particularly aluminum, iron, and magnesium dissolved from the rock, enables the efflorescence to form.

Accumulations of melanterite, an efflorescence formerly known as copperas, were collected and used to dye clothes by early settlers in Ohio (Hildreth, 1834). These settlers also named prominent landmarks after the extensive occurrences they found—Copperas Mountain and Alum Cliffs in Ross County, and Alum Creek in Delaware and Franklin Counties.

Mineralogy

An efflorescence typically consists of a delicate, fine-grained, fibrous white aggregate of one or more hydrous sulfate minerals. The encrustation may also be pale green, light blue, orange, yellow, or cream colored. The bright hues contrast with those of the dark-colored host rock and give rise to the terms bloom and blossom that are applied to the efflorescence (Nuhfer, 1972). The efflorescences occur in powdery coatings ranging from a fraction of an inch to several inches in thickness or in fluffy, porous balls up to several inches in diameter (figs. 35 and 36). They are characteristically astringent and sour tasting. Because individual crystals are too small to test easily, microscopic or x-ray diffraction techniques and, in some cases, chemical analyses may be required for positive identification. Some efflorescent minerals are unstable when changes in humidity or temperature occur and may alter to other minerals. These new minerals are generally distinguished by a gain or loss of combined water originating from the hydration or dehydration, respectively, of the original mineral. Specimens may be preserved in their original state by storage in a refrigerator or in sealed containers immediately after collection (Nuhfer, 1967).

Ohio efflorescences are fascinating because of the diverse mineral assemblages that can be present at a site. The following sulfates have been identified: alunogen, botryogen, copiapite, epsomite, gypsum, halotrichite, hexahydrite, melanterite, pickeringite, potash alum, rozenite, szomolnokite, and thenardite. In addition, aragonite and calcite, both carbonates, may occur as efflorescences. Other interesting minerals will undoubtedly be added to this list as Ohio efflorescences are investigated in the future.

Gypsum, halotrichite, and pickeringite, which are typical

FIGURE 35.—Efflorescence of white halotrichite-pickeringite; from Copperas Mountain, Ross County. Horizontal field of view is approximately 2 feet.

of shale exposures, are the most common efflorescences. Gypsum characteristically appears as vitreous, fibrous and foliated, colorless to white aggregates. Because gypsum is the least soluble and most persistent of the sulfates, it is the dominant efflorescence during wet weather. Halotrichite and pickeringite have identical habits, occurring in distinctive masses of silky, fibrous, white crystals (figs. 35, 36). These minerals constitute the halotrichite-pickeringite chemical series and differ only in their respective ratios of iron to magnesium; halotrichite has a higher iron content and pickeringite has a higher magnesium content. Because a chemical analysis is necessary for a specific identification, the term halotrichite-pickeringite should be used if chemical data have not been obtained. Only a few chemical determinations in Ohio have been recorded, two of pickeringite from the Cleveland Shale Member of the Ohio Shale and one of halotrichite in shales of the Allegheny Group (Collins, R. F., 1924; Brant and Foster, 1959). Most of the Ohio material known as alum, a term broadly used in older geologic reports to designate any white efflorescence, is really halotrichite-pickeringite.

Copiapite, melanterite, rozenite, szomolnokite, botryogen, and alunogen are generally associated with pyrite-rich sequences of coal and shale. As a group, these minerals are generally unstable and decompose corrosively into a pile of white powder after long periods of storage. Lemon-yellow copiapite commonly occurs in finely granular crusts and globular masses that have mistakenly been described as sulfur in many geologic reports (McCaughey, 1918). Melanterite, rozenite, and szomolnokite are hydrous iron sulfates that are related chemically, and readily alter to one another when changes in humidity occur (Ehlers E. G., and Stiles, 1965; Nuhfer, 1972). Melanterite, by far, is the most abundant of the three and commonly occurs as crusts of fibrous to acicular light-green to light-blue crystals. More rarely, small, globular masses of orange-brown botryogen and tiny, bladed crystals of white alunogen occur on shale (Fisher, H. H., 1975).

Hexahydrite commonly forms fibrous, powdery, white crusts on weathered exposures of dolostone, such as the abandoned faces of quarries or rock cliffs, in western Ohio (Foster, W. R., and Hoover, 1963). Efflorescences of aragonite, calcite, epsomite, potash alum, and thenardite are relatively uncommon and have a spotty distribution in the state (Connors, 1974).

FIGURE 36.—Efflorescence of white halotrichite-pickeringite; from the banks of the West Branch Huron River at Lamereaux Road, Huron County. Specimen is 3½ inches long.

Chapter 4

HOW TO IDENTIFY MINERALS

A mineral is a naturally occurring solid substance that has specific physical properties and in most cases a definite chemical composition. On an atomic scale, the arrangement of atoms or ions within a specific mineral always forms a fixed pattern. A snow flake, which invariably has a six-sided pattern and contains one atom of oxygen (O) for every two of hydrogen (H), is a mineral. Its chemical composition is written H_2O. Although more than 3,000 mineral species are known, only a fraction of these are native to Ohio.

A mineral is identified by comparing its diagnostic physical and chemical properties with the properties of minerals whose identities are known. Physical properties include: crystal habit, cleavage, fracture, luster, color, streak, hardness, specific gravity, magnetism, luminescence, radioactivity, and taste. Chemical properties on the other hand, refer to characteristics such as the behavior of a specimen in acid or the color its powder imparts to a flame. This section outlines several properties and tests that are used to identify minerals and includes tables for the systematic identification of minerals of Ohio. Palache and others (1944, 1951), Frondel (1962), and Roberts and others (1974) provide excellent general descriptions of minerals. Fleischer (1987) gives an up-to-date list of mineral species and their chemical compositions. An extensively modified form of these descriptions has been used in this report. Additional information on testing minerals may be found in works by O. C. Smith (1953), Mason and Berry (1968), and Klein and Hurlbut (1985). The techniques of mineral identification are learned only by repeated practice, and expertise in mineral recognition can be gained only after frequent observation of specimens. As an aid, Appendix B lists public museums in Ohio that house important mineral collections.

Most minerals can be identified at a field site with the aid of suitable tools. Two essential tools are illustrated in figure 37. Some suggested testing items and possible supply sources are given in table 5. In addition, basic kits for mineral testing can be purchased at many universities that offer beginning courses in geology. The most important tool in mineral recognition is a pocket magnifier or hand lens that provides a magnification of about 10 times (10X). A careful examination with a hand lens will quickly establish if a specimen is an aggregate of minerals or a single mineral, and, once isolated under a lens, many minerals will be recognized immediately by their distinctive features. The hand lens is particularly useful for observing crystal habit and breakage (cleavage and fracture). The lens should be held fairly close to the eye in one hand while the specimen, which is held in the other hand under a good source of light, is brought into focus. For use in the field, it is recommended that a cord be tied to the lens and looped around one's neck.

CRYSTAL HABIT

Habit refers to the characteristic shape of isolated crystals or groups of crystals of a mineral. A mineral species generally displays a characteristic habit that serves to distinguish it from other minerals. This characteristic crystal shape corresponds to the pattern formed on an atomic scale by the internal arrangement of ions or atoms. Galena crystals, for example, almost always exhibit a cubic habit owing to the cubic arrangement of lead and sulfur atoms that they contain. In practice, the determination of crystal habit can be difficult because crystal shapes may be incomplete. For instance, crystals may be broken or attached to the surface of a rock or another mineral so that only the free ends are terminated by crystal faces. Measurements of crystal size should always accompany descriptions of crystal habit. In this report the terms well crystallized or coarse grained and poorly crystallized or fine grained are used, respectively, for individual crystals that are easily visible to the unaided eye and for crystal outlines that require magnification to discern.

For specimens that contain several well-formed crystals,

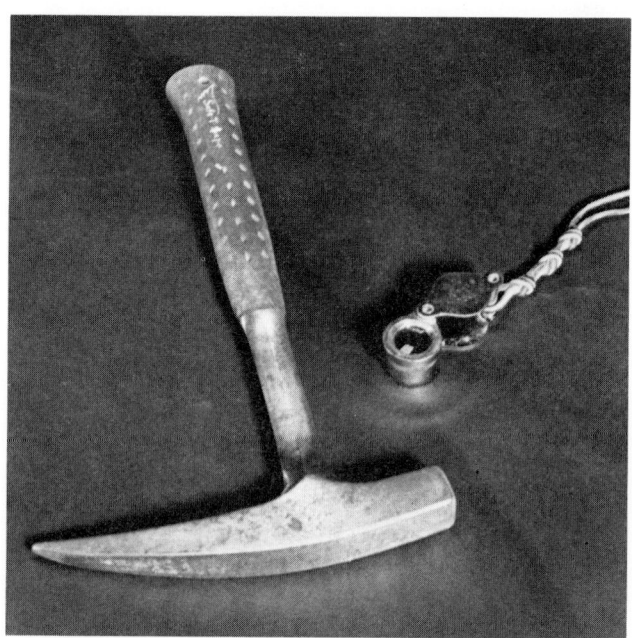

FIGURE 37.—Rock hammer (left) and hand lens (right), two essential tools for geologic field trips.

TABLE 5.—*Testing items for mineral identification and possible sources of supply*[1]

rock hammer—H,R,W,M
hand lens—R,E,W,M,G
pocket knife—H
streak plate—W,M
hand magnet—H,R,E,W,M
dilute hydrochloric (muriatic) acid—H,P
small (about 2 oz) plastic dropper bottle for dilute acid—P,M
Bunsen burner or microflame propane torch kit (optional)—H,E,W
mineral set for hardness determination or hardness pencils (optional)—R,W,G
flame test kit (optional)—W,M
pan balance (optional)—W
portable ultraviolet light (optional)—R,E,W,M,G
small Pyrex beakers or test tubes (optional)—E,W
tweezers or forceps (optional)—P,W,M,G
gold pan (optional)—H,W,M
compass (optional)—H,E,W,M

---

[1]Possible sources of supply:

H hardware store	M Miners, Incorporated P.O. Box 1301 Riggins, ID 83549
P pharmacy	
R rock shop or lapidary supply	W Wards Natural Science Establishment, Inc. P.O. Box 92912 5100 West Henrietta Road Rochester, NY 14692-9012
E Edmund Scientific Company 101 E. Gloucester Pike Barrington, NJ 08007	
G GEM Instruments Corporation 1735 Stewart Street P.O. Box 2147 Santa Monica, CA 90406	

the habits of both the aggregate and the isolated crystals should be noted. Because of the nature of geological environments, mineral aggregates are more common than single crystals; therefore, in the discussion below, the habits of mineral aggregates are treated before the habits of single crystals.

Habits of mineral aggregates

Mineral aggregates contain groups of imperfectly formed crystals, and descriptive terms such as columnar characterize the shapes of individual crystals in the group. In rocks where distinct crystal faces are generally absent, the shape of an individual grain is estimated by observing its boundaries with other grains. The following terms are used to describe aggregate habits and are based on the shape of individual crystals or grains:

fibrous, individual grains are long and thin, like a fiber of hair (fig. 38A).
acicular, individual grains are long and needlelike (fig. 38B).
columnar, individual grains are long, parallel or subparallel, and stout like a pencil (fig. 38C).
bladed, individual grains are thin, much longer than wide, and flattened like the blade of a table knife (fig. 38D).
tabular, individual grains are flat and platy like the top of a table or the cover of a book (fig. 38E).
granular, individual grains are equant (about equal in length, breadth, and height), like grains of salt or sand (fig. 38F).
oolitic, individual grains are small and rounded, and look like fish eggs that are cemented together (fig. 38G).
massive, mineral is poorly crystallized and dense, and without apparent internal structure; compact, individual grains are microscopic, as in flint.
powdery, mineral is poorly crystallized and porous; may appear as a dusting of tiny delicate and matted crystals, as in an efflorescence of hexahydrite.

Some mineral aggregates are characterized by the distinctive appearance of the aggregate as a whole. The following terms describe this overall appearance and are used to supplement the descriptions of crystal shapes given above:

banded, parallel bands of different color, such as in agate (fig. 38H).
radiating, elongate grains that radiate from a common center, like spokes in a wheel (fig. 38I).
rosette, tabular grains that are arranged like petals in a rose (fig. 38J).
dendritic, tiny grains or slender, skeletal crystals that form a branchlike aggregate resembling the veins of a leaf (fig. 38K).
colloform, groups of radiating hemispherical or globular masses that form a knobby surface; individual masses may consist of radiating fibers (fig. 38L).
drusy, a layer of small projecting crystals that line a pocket or outer surface, as in a geode (fig. 38M).
cellular or *boxwork*, a porous, honeycomblike arrangement of thin plates or fine scales (fig. 38N).

Habits of single crystals

A perfect crystal has faces with definite geometric shapes (fig. 39). If the faces are identical in size and shape, the crystal is said to display a single form, and the number and shapes of the faces determine the name of the form. For example, a pyrite crystal that displays a cubic habit or form (fig. 40A) has six identical square faces, and a pyrite crystal with an octahedral habit has eight faces in the shape of equilateral triangles (fig. 40C). A crystal with faces of different shapes displays a combination of forms, each form distinguished from the others by the unique shape and size of its faces. For example, a pyrite crystal may have a combination of a cube and an octahedron, as shown in fig. 40D. In this combination, the cubic and the octahedral forms are recognized by sets of six and eight identical faces, respectively, although the specific shapes of the faces in each form have changed. The habit of a complex crystal is described as combinations of single forms, with each form referring to the shape that the entire crystal would take if the others were missing. Crystal faces are generally flat, but appear curved in some specimens of dolomite (fig. 40P) and sphalerite. Examples of simple and complex crystal habits in Ohio minerals are given below.

cube, six square faces (figs. 40A, 40B, and 40D).
octahedron, eight equilateral triangular faces (figs. 40C and 40D).
dodecahedron, 12 rhombus-shaped faces (fig. 40E).
trapezohedron (isometric), 24 trapezium-shaped faces, each face having two sets of equal adjoining sides (fig. 40F).
tetrahedron, four equilateral triangular faces (fig. 40G).
pyritohedron, 12 pentagonal faces (fig. 40H).
diploid, 24 trapezium-shaped faces, each face having no equal sides (fig. 40I).
trigonal pyramid, three isosceles triangular faces that meet at a common point (fig. 40J).
pedion, a single face unrelated to any others; this face generally is aligned with the base of a crystal (figs. 40J and 40K).
hexagonal pyramid, six isosceles triangular faces that meet at a common point (fig. 40K).
hexagonal dipyramid, 12 identical faces that are formed by joining two equal hexagonal pyramids across a horizontal plane (fig. 40L).
pinacoid, two identical parallel faces; these faces generally are aligned with the front, side, or base of a crystal (figs.

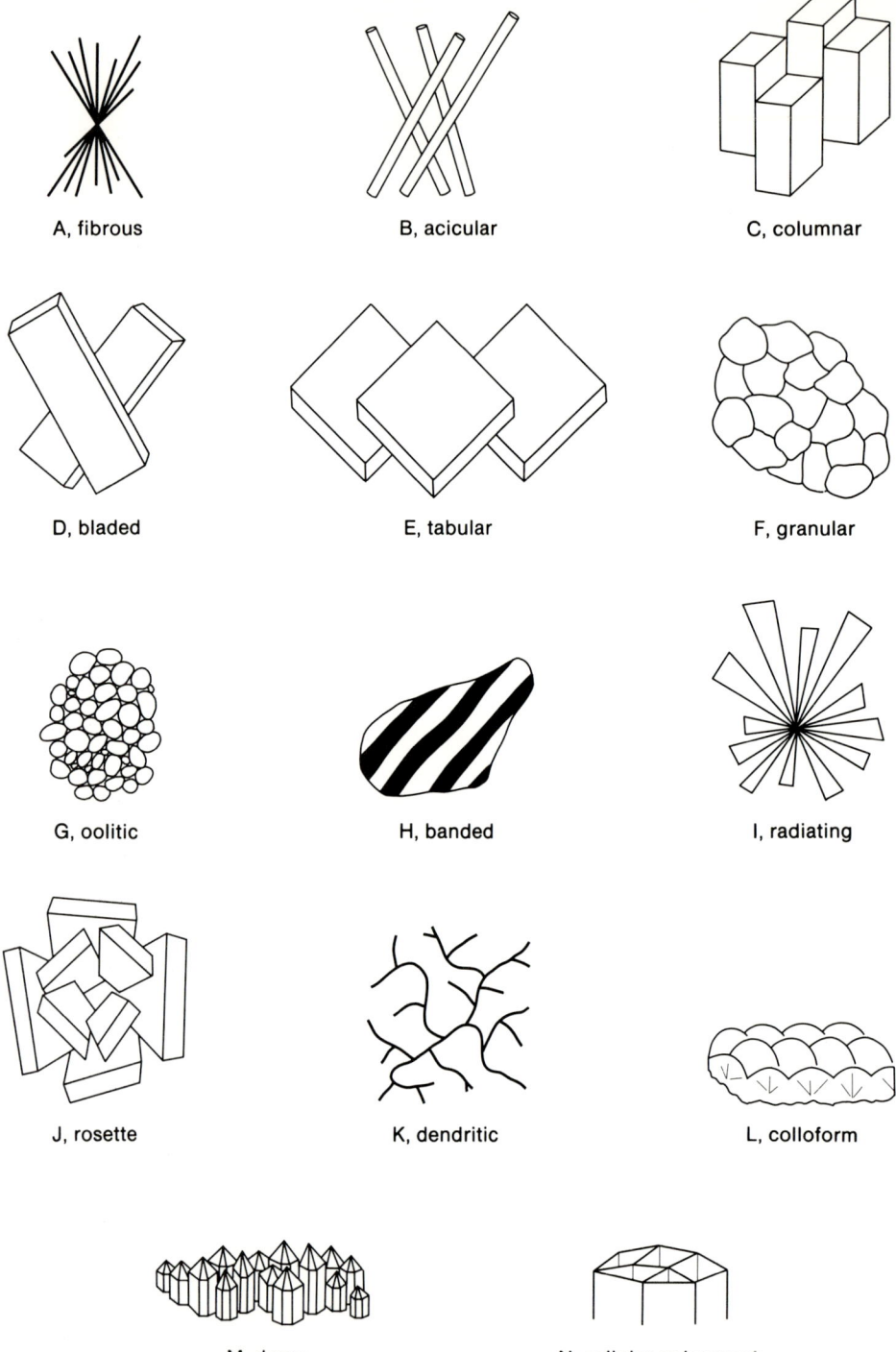

FIGURE 38.—Crystal habits of mineral aggregates. Minerals represented: A, pickeringite from Mill Hollow-Bacon Woods Park, Lorain County; B, strontianite from Lime City, Wood County; C, celestite from Lime City, Wood County; D, celestite from Clay Center, Ottawa County; E, barite from Custar, Wood County; F, halite from International Salt Co. mine, Cuyahoga County; G, hematite from Jacksonville area, Adams County; H, flint from John Nethers property, Flint Ridge, Muskingum County; I, wurtzite from Alikanna area, Jefferson County; J, barite from Custar, Wood County; K, manganese oxides from Flint Ridge State Memorial area, Licking County; L, smithsonite from Serpent Mound disturbance, Adams County; M, quartz from Flint Ridge State Memorial area, Licking County; N, smithsonite from Serpent Mound disturbance, Adams County.

40L, 40Q, 40R, 40S, 40T, and 40U).

hexagonal scalenohedron, 12 scalene triangular faces that are arranged in symmetrical pairs with three pairs meeting at a common point above and three pairs meeting below (fig. 40M).

rhombohedron, six rhombus-shaped faces (figs. 40N, 40O, and 40P).

prism, three or more identical faces whose lines of intersection are mutually parallel (figs. 40O, 40Q, 40R, 40S, 40T, and 40U).

The habit of a single crystal is difficult to recognize when the crystal is malformed. For example, the faces of a malformed octahedron are shaped differently than those of a perfect octahedron (compare figs. 40C and 40V). In such cases the measurement of crystal angles would prove useful, as the angles between similar faces on crystals of the same mineral never vary. The adjacent faces on a pyrite octahedron, for instance, always form angles of 70°32' even when the crystal is malformed (fig. 40V). Unfortunately, malformed crystals are common because crystal growth is seldom perfect. Professional mineralogists can measure crystal angles routinely with a specially designed instrument known as an optical goniometer.

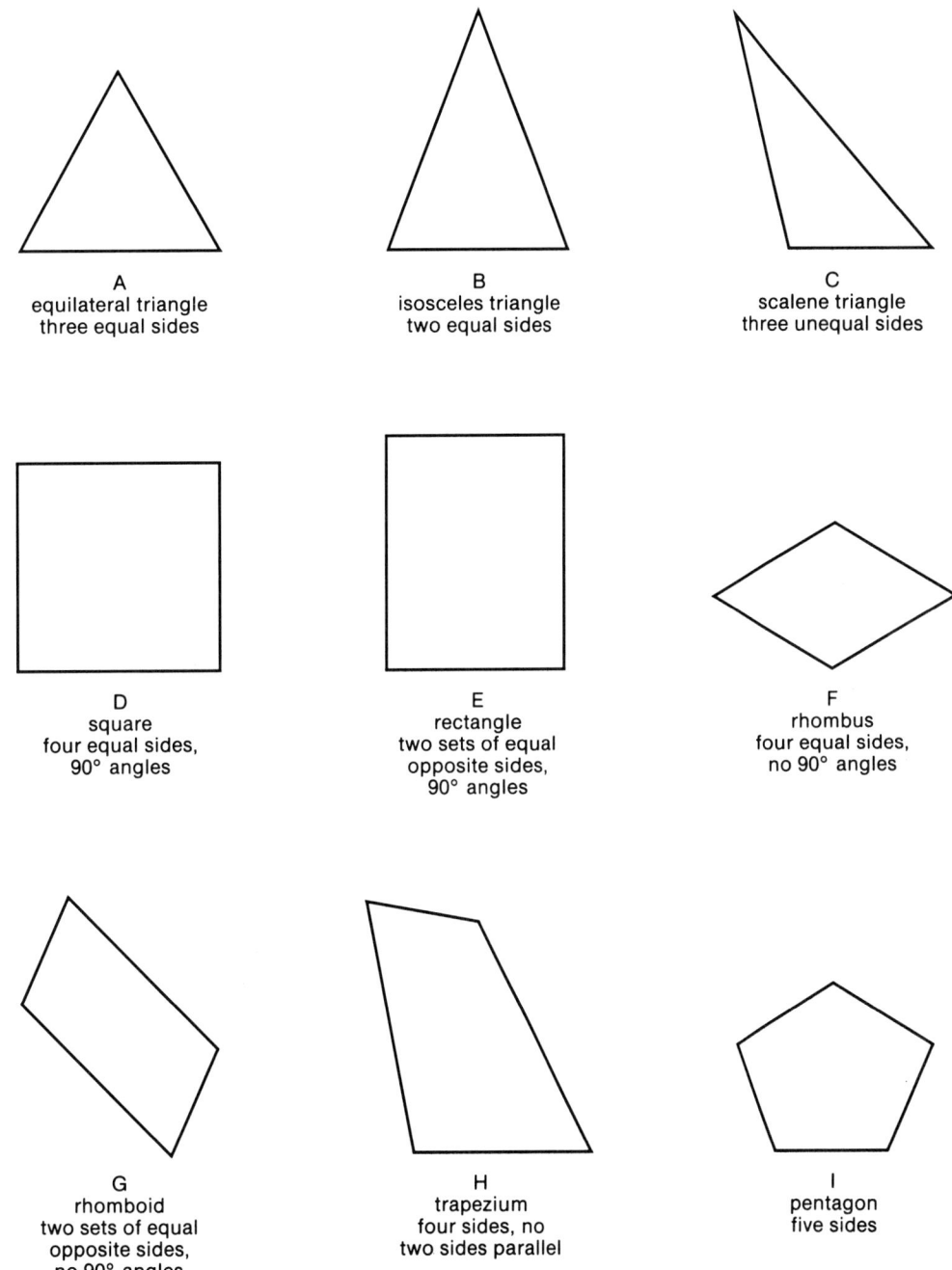

FIGURE 39.—Geometric shapes of crystal faces.

40 MINERALS OF OHIO

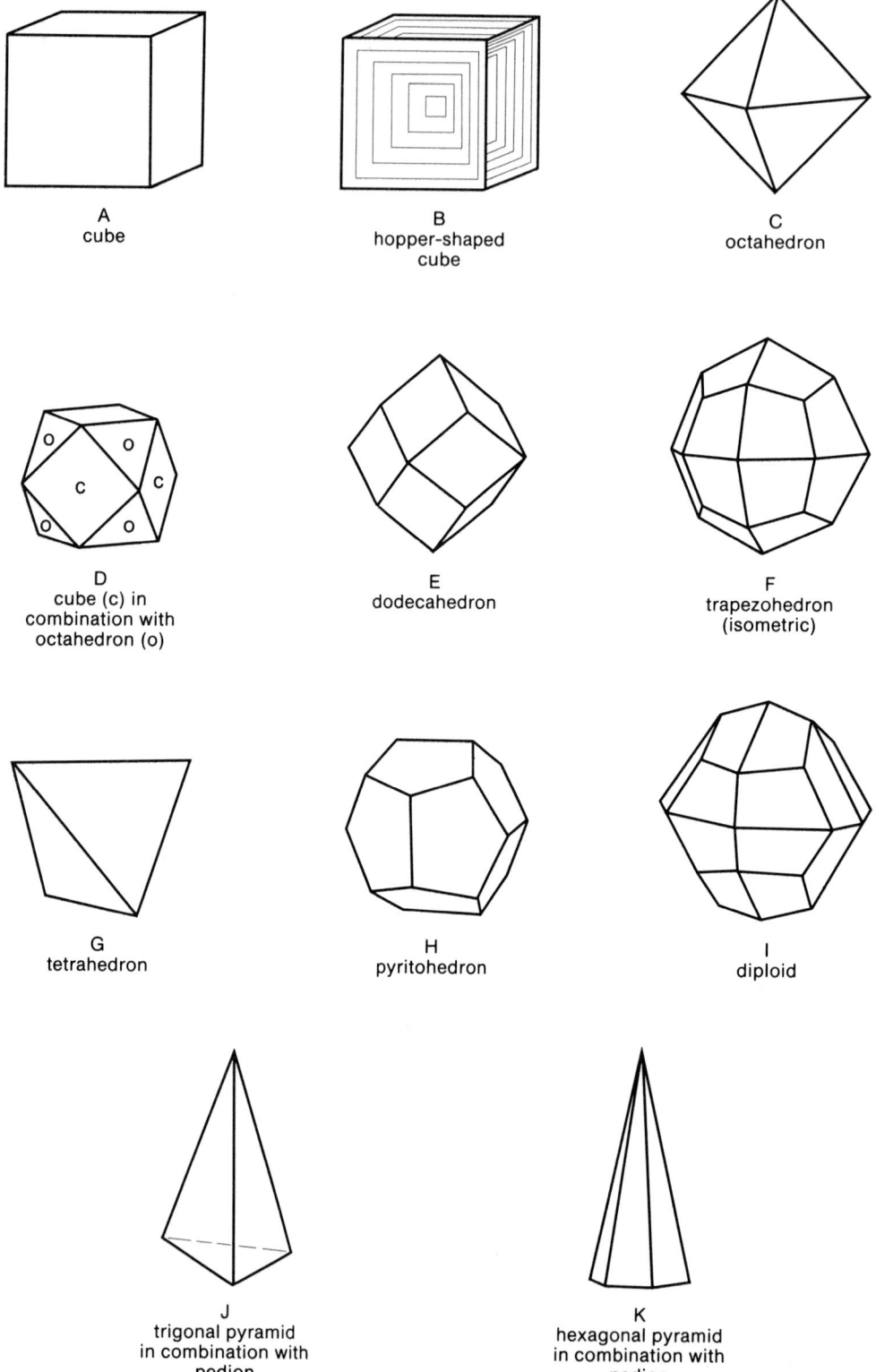

FIGURE 40.—Habits of single crystals. Minerals represented: A, fluorite from Clay Center, Ottawa County; B, halite mold from Tymochtee Creek, Wyandot County; C, pyrite from Findlay, Hancock County; D, pyrite from railroad yard near Bellevue, Erie County; E, F, pyrite from Huntsville, Logan County; G, sphalerite from Clay Center, Ottawa County; H, I, pyrite from Huntsville, Logan County; J, wurtzite (15R) from Alikanna area, Jefferson County; K, wurtzite (6H) from Alikanna area, Jefferson County;

CRYSTAL HABIT

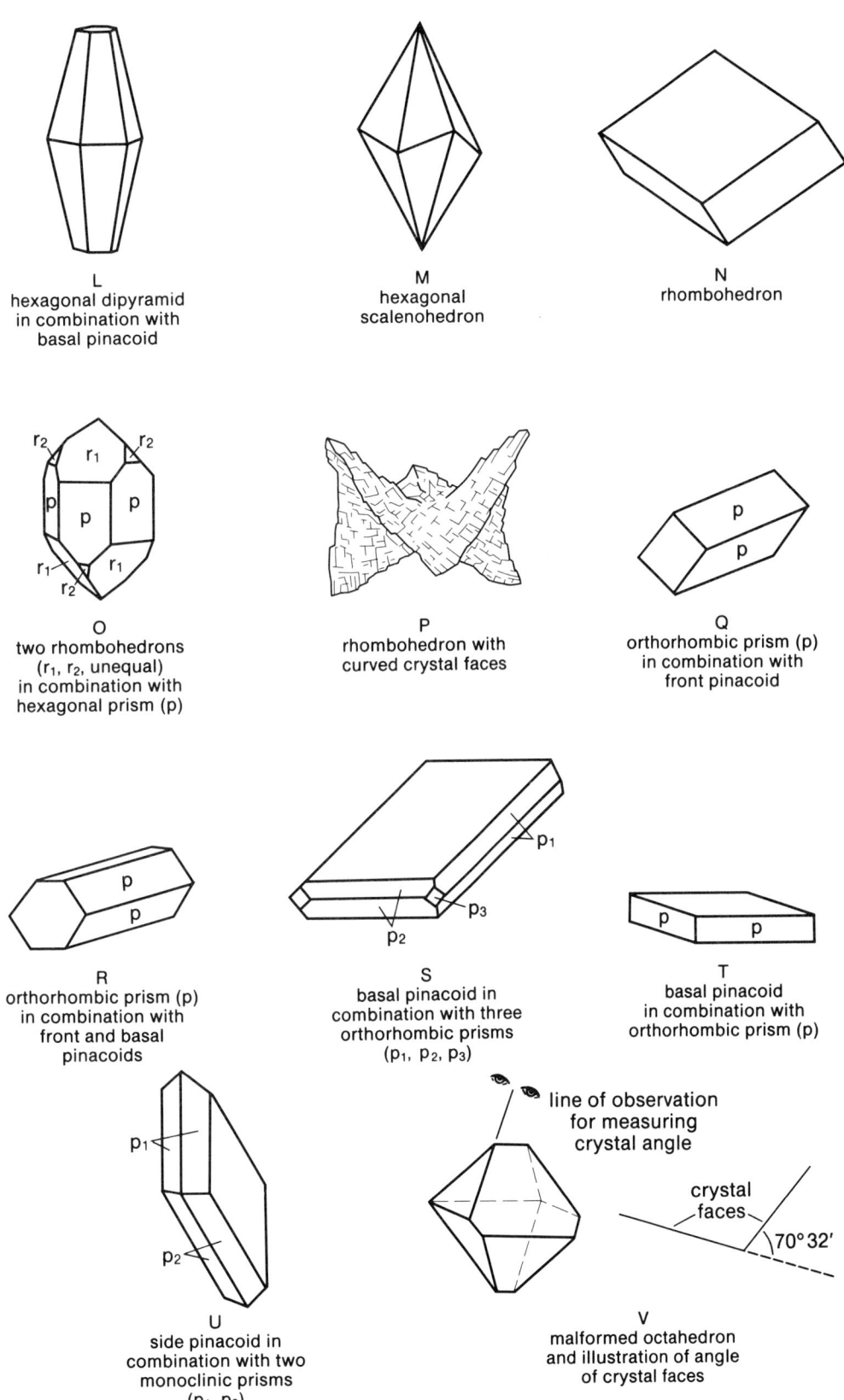

L, calcite from Kelleys Island, Erie County; M, calcite from Custar, Wood County; N, ferroan dolomite from the West Branch Huron River near Monroeville, Huron County; O, quartz from Flint Ridge State Memorial area, Licking County; P, saddle dolomite from Huntsville, Logan County; Q, celestite from Custar, Wood County; R, celestite from Lime City, Wood County; S, celestite from Clay Center, Ottawa County; T, barite from Custar, Wood County; U, gypsum from West Branch State Park, Portage County; V, pyrite from Findlay, Hancock County.

CLEAVAGE AND FRACTURE

A mineral breaks with cleavage or fracture, and the particular type of breakage it displays is an important identifying characteristic. If a mineral splits along one or more sets of parallel plane surfaces (see fig. 41), it shows cleavage, and if it breaks along an irregular surface, it shows fracture. The type of breakage that a mineral displays depends on the arrangement of atoms or ions within the mineral. All specimens of a specific mineral, therefore, break with the same kind of cleavage or fracture.

In practice, cleavage (or fracture) must be observed on a fragment of a single grain. To obtain a suitable fragment, a specimen should be placed on a hard surface such as a metal plate and struck with a rock hammer (see fig. 37). If a broken piece is rotated slowly under a good source of illumination and a sudden flash of light is observed reflecting off a flat surface, cleavage is indicated. The quality of cleavage development, which is unique for each mineral species, is described by the terms perfect, good, or poor. If cleavage is perfect, light will reflect across a single, flat, shiny surface (fig. 41A). In good cleavage, the mineral does not split cleanly and a stair-step surface develops in which the tops of the steps are flat, shiny, and parallel to one another (fig. 41B). Poorly developed cleavage is difficult to recognize without careful study because the stair-step effect is less distinct. If a fragment lacks cleavage entirely and breaks with a fracture, light will be scattered in all directions as the specimen is rotated; therefore, as a general rule, a fracture surface is not as shiny as a cleavage surface. In a specimen that displays perfect or good cleavage, each cleavage direction is represented by parallel surfaces on opposite sides of the fragment, and traces of internal cleavage planes appear on the edges as a pattern of straight cracks aligned in the cleavage direction (figs. 41, 42A).

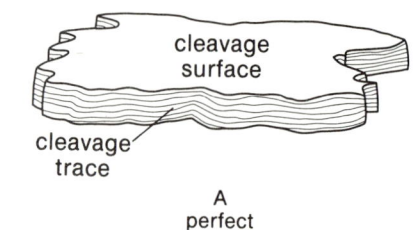

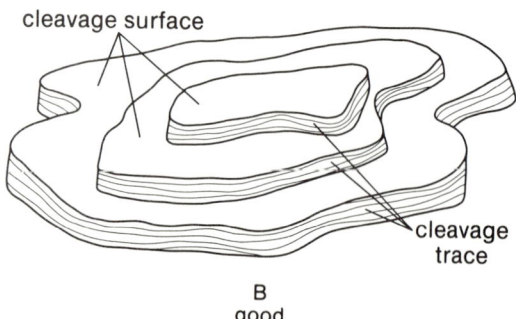

FIGURE 41.—Quality of cleavage development.

If a fragment displays two directions of cleavage, each direction will reflect light, and the intersection of the two cleavage surfaces will be marked by a straight edge. The cleavage angle is determined by looking down this edge and measuring or visually estimating the included angle; two different cleavage angles will be formed depending on which line of intersection is observed, but the sum of the two angles will always equal 180° (fig. 42B).

Ohio minerals display six types of cleavage: pinacoidal, prismatic, cubic, rhombohedral, octahedral, and dodecahedral. Each type is distinguished by a specific number of cleavage directions and corresponding cleavage angles, and each type is recognized by the distinctive shapes of cleaved fragments. The pattern of cracks on the edges of fragments, because of internal cleavage planes, also is distinctive for most types of cleavage.

pinacoidal cleavage, one direction of cleavage. Barite, celestite, and gypsum exhibit perfect pinacoidal cleavage. Cleaved fragments are shaped like plates or sheets if cleavage is perfect. The trace of pinacoidal cleavage on the surface of a cleaved fragment forms a pattern of straight parallel lines when viewed along an edge (fig. 42A).

prismatic cleavage, two equally developed directions of cleavage. The cleavage angles are unique for each mineral species. Barite, celestite, and strontianite show good prismatic cleavage at angles of 78° and 102° (fig. 42G), 76° and 104°, and 63° and 117° (fig 42B), respectively. Cleaved fragments are shaped like prisms if cleavage is perfect. The trace of prismatic cleavage on the surface of a cleaved prism when viewed end-on forms a pattern of rhombuses and rhomboids if the cleavage angle is not 90°; if the cleavage angle is 90° a pattern of squares and rectangles is formed.

cubic cleavage, three equally developed directions of cleavage that meet at 90° angles. Halite and galena display perfect cubic cleavage. Cleaved fragments are shaped like cubes or bricks if cleavage is perfect. The trace of cubic cleavage on the cleaved surface of a fragment forms a pattern of squares and rectangles (fig. 42C).

rhombohedral cleavage, three equally developed directions of cleavage parallel to the opposite faces of a rhombohedron. Calcite and dolomite exhibit perfect rhombohedral cleavage; the cleavage angles in calcite are 75° and 105° and in dolomite are 73° and 107°. Cleaved fragments are shaped like rhombohedrons if cleavage is perfect. The trace of rhombohedral cleavage on the cleaved surface of a fragment forms a pattern of rhombuses and rhomboids (fig. 42D).

octahedral cleavage, four equally developed directions of cleavage parallel to the opposite faces of an octahedron. Fluorite shows perfect octahedral cleavage. Cleaved fragments display complex shapes and rarely form octahedrons. The trace of octahedral cleavage on the cleaved surface of a fragment forms a pattern of equilateral triangles (fig. 42E).

dodecahedral cleavage, six equally developed directions of cleavage parallel to the opposite faces of a dodecahedron. Sphalerite displays perfect dodecahedral cleavage (fig. 42F). Cleaved fragments display complex shapes and the trace of the cleavage on a cleaved surface of a fragment forms complex patterns.

Complications in recognizing cleavage type arise when a mineral exhibits two types of cleavage. The individual cleavage types can still be distinguished, however, if they display different degrees of perfection. For example barite shows two types of cleavage with different quality: perfect pinacoidal cleavage and good prismatic cleavage. Therefore, a fragment of barite displays large faces paralleling the direction of the more prominent pinacoidal cleavage and smaller faces aligned with the directions of the less pronounced prismatic cleavage (fig. 42G).

Two types of fracture can be seen in Ohio minerals: conchoidal and uneven.

conchoidal fracture, smooth, curved surface with sharp edges similar to a piece of broken glass. Quartz and flint exhibit conchoidal fracture (fig. 42H).

uneven fracture, rough, irregular surface like that of a rock. Pyrite, marcasite, and sulfur display uneven fracture.

When examining a mineral aggregate for cleavage and fracture, observations must be restricted to individual grains. Minerals that have a massive habit, for instance, may appear to break with a fracture because the cleavage can only be observed under high magnification. Ordinarily a few grains of a mineral aggregate can be dislodged with the tip of a knife blade and then carefully observed for type of cleavage with a hand lens. Even though the kind of cleavage cannot be determined in every case, establishing the presence or absence of cleavage can aid in identification. For example, the presence or absence of cleavage can be used to distinguish barite (perfect cleavage) from quartz (no

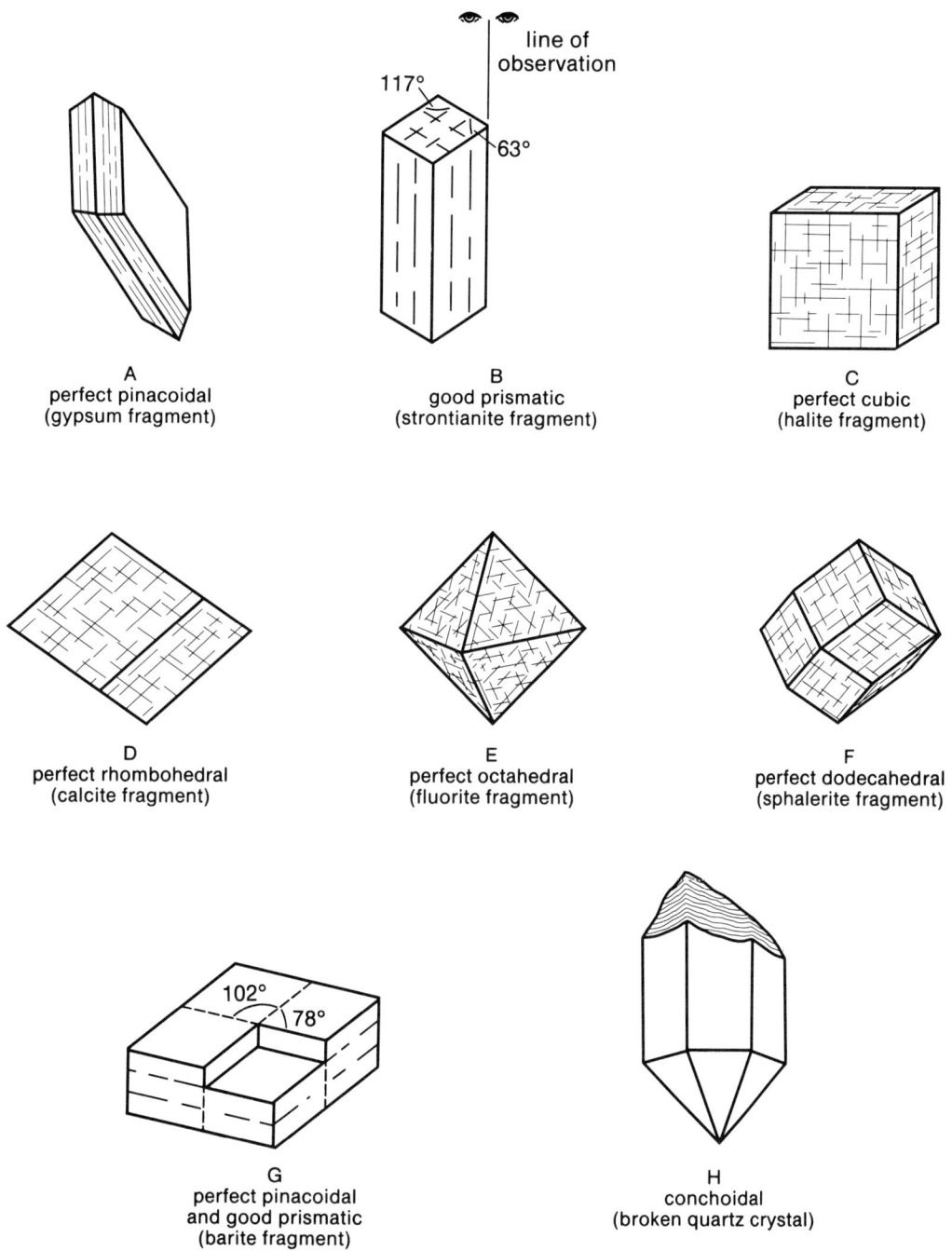

FIGURE 42.—Types of cleavage (A-G) and fracture (H). Figure 42B illustrates the line of observation for estimating cleavage angle.

cleavage), both of which appear as colorless, transparent, glassy grains in veins of large limestone concretions in central Ohio.

LUSTER

Luster denotes the appearance and intensity of light that is reflected from the surface of a mineral. When determining luster, an unweathered surface of a mineral should be examined under a good light source. Two major types of luster (defined below) are recognized—metallic and nonmetallic. No precise boundary exists between the two divisions; minerals that are intermediate are said to have a submetallic luster. Nonmetallic lusters are most common, and several kinds are recognized based on the intensity of the reflected light, although, again, there are no sharp boundaries between the different kinds of nonmetallic luster. Generally, nonmetallic minerals that are fine grained, such as flint or clay, have a low (greasy or dull) luster, and well-crystallized minerals have a high (vitreous) luster. The types of luster that can be observed are:

metallic, looks like a piece of broken or polished metal; examples: pyrite, galena.
submetallic, has a high luster that is transitional between that of broken metal and that of broken glass; example: black sphalerite.
nonmetallic, does not look like metal; several types of nonmetallic luster have been defined:
  adamantine, has extreme brilliance like a faceted diamond; examples: diamond, red sphalerite.
  vitreous, has a high luster like the surface of glass; example: quartz.
  resinous, has a lustrous yellow or brown appearance like resin or tree pitch; examples: yellow or brown sphalerite, sulfur.
  silky, has the sheen of an aggregate of fibrous grains that have a parallel arrangement; example: pickeringite.
  greasy or waxy, has a faint gloss like a coating of oil; examples: whewellite, flint.
  dull, lacks glossiness; appears earthy like soil or clay; examples: oolitic hematite, impure flint.

COLOR AND STREAK

Color, the hue reaching the eye from the surface of a mineral, is a helpful identification aid. However, in many minerals, such as calcite or quartz, colors are somewhat variable, and only rarely, as in gold and sulfur, is color unique. Color variations in a mineral generally are due to chemical impurities. The yellowish-brown or reddish-brown sphalerite of western Ohio contains very little iron, for instance, while the black sphalerite of eastern Ohio contains significant amounts of iron. Iron clearly is an important coloring agent in sphalerite. Color should always be observed on an unweathered surface, as color may change because of tarnishing. For example, a yellow tarnish that develops on pyrite and marcasite results in the confusion of those minerals with chalcopyrite or gold. Some minerals may display a variety of colorful, prismatic hues known as iridescence. Well-known examples include iridescent varieties of pyrite and marcasite, which exhibit bright blue, green, purple, red, and yellow colors, and brown fluorite, which may exhibit purple and red colors.

Streak refers to the color of the powder that is left when a mineral is rubbed across a plate of unglazed white porcelain (streak plate) (fig. 43A). The color of a mineral and the color of its streak are not necessarily the same. Pyrite, for example, has a pale brass-yellow color but has a greenish-black streak. For some minerals, the color of the streak is more diagnostic than the color of the mineral itself. Hematite may be red, brown, or steel gray but always leaves a unique brownish-red streak. Most minerals that have a nonmetallic luster have a light-colored streak, and minerals that have a metallic luster tend to leave a dark-colored streak. Minerals with a hardness of 7 or higher (see section below) will not leave a streak, but instead will scratch the streak plate.

HARDNESS

Hardness is the resistance that a mineral offers to being scratched and is one of the most distinguishing properties of a mineral. The hardness of a mineral, which is dependent on its crystal structure, is measured on a scale of 1 to 10 that is known as Mohs scale of hardness (table 6). A given mineral will scratch another mineral that has a lower

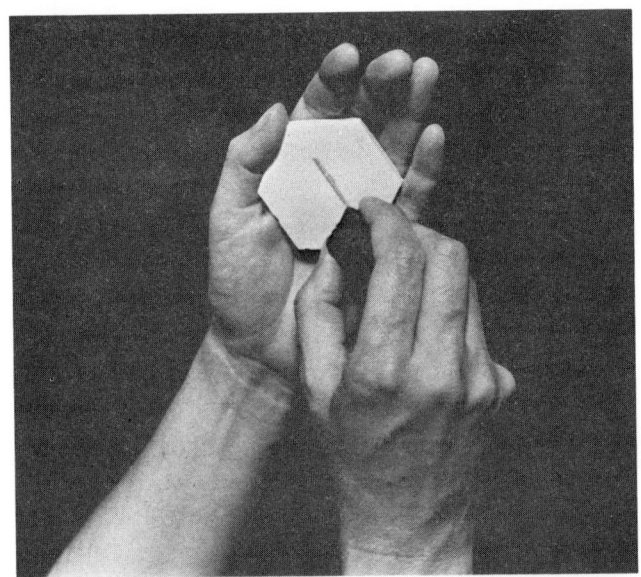

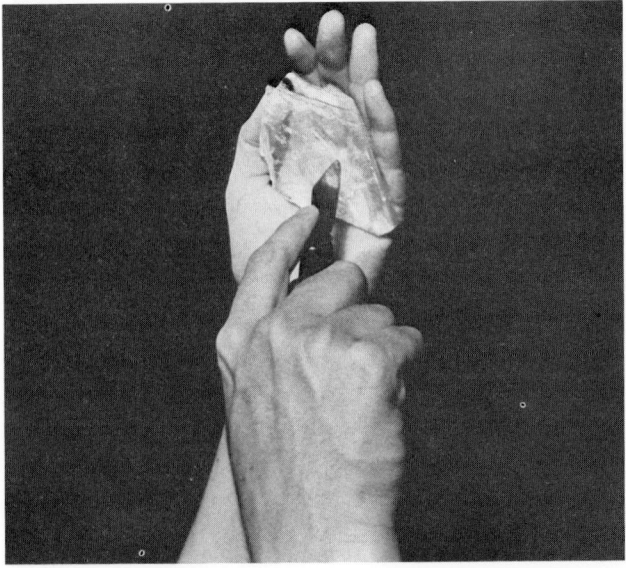

FIGURE 43.—Upper photo, using a streak plate to test for streak; lower photo, using a pocket knife to test for hardness.

TABLE 6.—*Mohs scale of hardness*

Hardness	Mineral	Hardness of common materials	
1	talc		
2	gypsum	2½	fingernail
3	calcite	3	copper penny
4	fluorite		
5	apatite	5-5½	steel knife blade or window glass
6	orthoclase		
7	quartz		
8	topaz		
9	corundum		
10	diamond		

hardness number, but will be scratched by a mineral with a higher number on the scale. In practice, hardness is measured by comparison with minerals or tools of known hardness, such as the blade of a pocket knife (fig. 43B), which provides both an edge for scratching and a flat surface for receiving scratches. Mineral kits for determining hardness and sets of hardness pencils also can be obtained commercially (see table 5). To insure that a correct determination is made, an attempt should be made to scratch the unknown mineral with the testing tool and the testing tool with the unknown mineral. A copper penny will not scratch sphalerite, for example, but sphalerite will scratch a copper penny. Therefore, sphalerite has a hardness greater than 3. By testing the sphalerite specimen with a knife blade, which will scratch sphalerite but will not be scratched in return, the hardness of sphalerite can be bracketed between 3 and 5. To determine hardness more precisely, comparisons are made with minerals on Mohs scale. Hardness should be determined on an unaltered mineral grain that is large enough to be scratched. A hard mineral, such as quartz, is difficult to scratch, and a firm pressure must be applied when attempting to test it. A soft mineral, on the other hand, may leave a streak on the surface of a harder mineral that superficially looks like a scratch. A streak, however, can be rubbed off a surface, but a scratch cannot. Minerals that have the same hardness will appear to scratch each other.

SPECIFIC GRAVITY

Specific gravity is defined as the ratio of the weight of a mineral to the weight of an equal volume of water. For example, aragonite, which weighs 2.9 times as much as an equivalent volume of water, has a specific gravity of 2.9. The specific gravity of a mineral, which depends on its chemical makeup, may differ slightly from specimen to specimen because of impurities. Therefore, specific gravity determinations should always be made on pure minerals and on specimens that are not porous. Table 7 gives specific gravities of Ohio minerals in their purest form. As a general rule, minerals with a metallic luster are quite heavy. Because the common nonmetallic minerals such as calcite, dolomite, and quartz have relatively low specific gravities (less than 3), heavy nonmetallic minerals such as barite, celestite, and strontianite are unusual and can be recognized easily.

Specific gravity can be determined on a Jolly specific gravity balance (fig. 44). The instrument is used as follows: (1) place the specimen on the upper pan and, with the lower, glass pan submerged in water, record the specimen's weight in air (W_a); (2) place the specimen on the glass pan so that it is completely submerged in water and record its weight in water (W_w). The specific gravity (G) can then be determined from the formula:

$$G = \frac{W_a}{W_a - W_w}$$

A pan-type chemical balance can be modified for a simple method of specific gravity measurement. A weighing basket can be made from a piece of galvanized wire screen that is suspended by fine wire from the rod under the balance pan. A plastic jug from which the top has been cut away can serve as a water container. The specific gravity is then determined using the balance pan and basket as described for the Jolly balance. The accuracy of the balance should be checked against samples of known specific gravity, and, except for small specimens, good results generally will be obtained.

A useful method of estimating specific gravity involves hefting (testing the weight by lifting) a specimen in one's hand. By this method, which requires practice to be effective, the heaviness of a sample of an unknown mineral is compared with one of known specific gravity that is about the same size.

MAGNETISM

Magnetism is a property that describes the behavior of a

TABLE 7.—*Specific gravities of Ohio minerals*

Less than 3.0

1.7	epsomite	2.1	botryogen	2.65	chalcedony-flint
1.7	hexahydrite	2.1	copiapite	2.65	quartz
1.8	alunogen	2.1	sulfur	2.7	calcite
1.8	potash alum	2.2	halite	2.7	thenardite
1.9	halotrichite-pickeringite	2.2	rozenite	2.7	vivianite
1.9	melanterite	2.2	whewellite	2.8	dolomite
2.0-2.2	opal	2.3	gypsum	2.9	aragonite
2.0-2.4	diadochite	2.6	kaolinite	2.9	glauconite

3.0 or greater

3.0	anhydrite	4.0	celestite	4.5	barite
3.1	szomolnokite	4.0	hydrozincite	4.7	ilmenite*
3.2	fluorite	4.0-5.1	manganese oxides*	4.9	marcasite
3.4	hemimorphite	4.1	sphalerite	5.0	hematite*
3.5	diamond*	4.1	wurtzite	5.0	pyrite
3.6-4.3	garnet*	4.3	chalcopyrite	5.2	magnetite*
3.8	siderite	4.3	goethite*	7.5	galena
3.8	strontianite	4.4	smithsonite	19.3	gold*

*Resistant to weathering and may be found in panned concentrates.

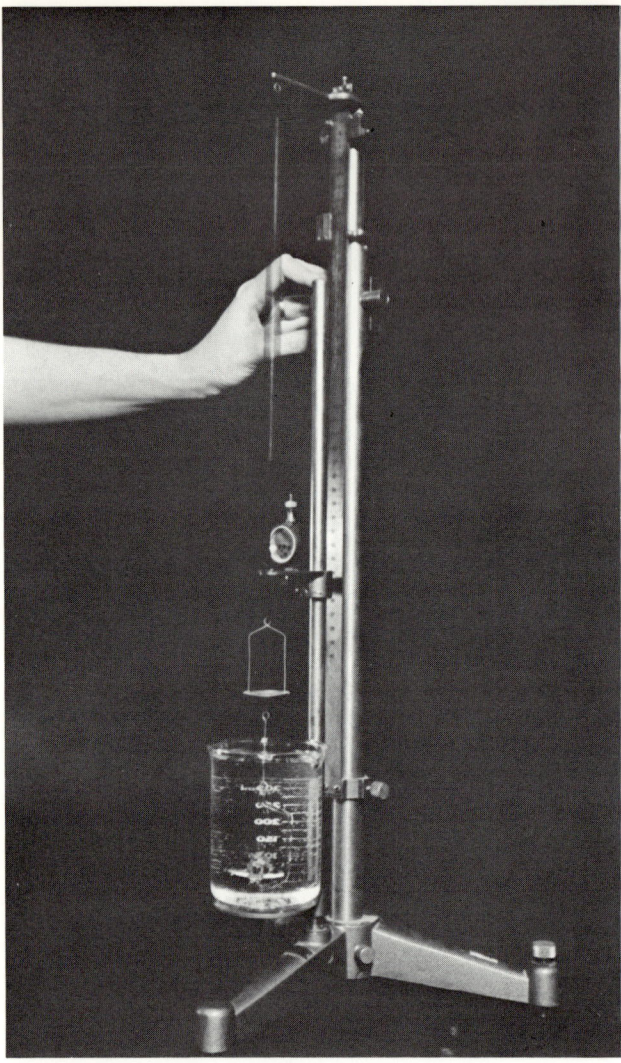

FIGURE 44.—Using a Jolly balance to determine specific gravity. In this photograph, the mineral specimen is suspended on a glass pan in a beaker of water to measure the specimen's weight in water.

substance in a magnetic field. Minerals that are attracted to a hand magnet contain a high percentage of iron; depending upon the iron content some minerals are more strongly magnetic than others. Strong magnetism can be discerned easily with a hand magnet, and weak magnetism can be detected with a magnet suspended on a string.

Magnetite and native iron are strongly magnetic, a property exhibited by just a few minerals. Magnetite-rich sand can be collected easily in the glaciated parts of Ohio (see fig. 3) and along many beaches of the Lake Erie shore by panning stream and beach gravels. The magnetite can be separated from the other heavy minerals in the sand by placing the dried concentrate on a piece of paper and running a magnet underneath the paper. Of the minerals found in iron meteorites, native iron, the chief constituent, is strongly magnetic and troilite is weakly magnetic. Magnetism thus can be used to identify these meteorites.

LUMINESCENCE

When a mineral is exposed to ultraviolet light, x-rays, or cathode rays and emits visible light, fluorescence is observed. If the mineral continues to glow after exposure has ceased, phosphorescence is observed. Luminescence is a general term that includes both fluorescence and phosphorescence. Luminescence should be observed in a dark area, and the rays from an ultraviolet lamp should never be directed towards the eyes of a viewer because serious eye injury could result. Because luminescence generally is caused by small amounts of impurities, some specimens of a mineral species will luminesce and others will not, depending on the presence or absence of an impurity. For example, brown fluorite, the most renowned luminescent mineral in Ohio, is believed to contain microscopic inclusions of hydrocarbon compounds (Gunnell, 1933; Allen, 1952); the colorless, pale-yellow, and purple nonluminescent varieties of fluorite lack these activating impurities. Both the ability of a mineral to luminesce and the intensity of its luminescence may vary with the wavelength of the ultraviolet rays. For this reason, many commercially available lamps provide for both long and short wavelength viewing in a single instrument. A portable, battery-operated lamp is particularly convenient because it can be used for prospecting at night. Table 8 gives data for several luminescent minerals of Ohio; the intensity of fluorescence in these minerals is about the same in both short- and long-wavelength ultraviolet rays.

TABLE 8.—*Fluorescent Ohio minerals*

Mineral	Fluorescent color	Locality
white barite	greenish yellow, yellowish orange, weak; also phosphorescent	Custar, Wood County
brown barite coatings of calcite	yellow, greenish yellow, intense to moderate; also phosphorescent	Lime City, Wood County
white to colorless calcite scalenohedrons	greenish yellow, moderate to weak; also phosphorescent	Clay Center and Genoa, Ottawa County; Lime City, Wood County; and other sites in northwestern Ohio
white vein calcite	yellow	Serpent Mound area, Adams County
tan vein calcite	yellowish orange, intense	Waterville, Lucas County
yellow and brown vein calcite and ferroan dolomite in large limestone concretions	yellow	central Ohio
white celestite and white rims of blue color-zoned celestite	yellowish white, moderate; also phosphorescent	Lime City, Wood County
brownish-yellow and brown fluorite	yellow, intense; also phosphorescent	many quarries in northwestern Ohio
hydrozincite	bluish white, moderate	Serpent Mound area, Adams County
selenite	greenish white, weak; also phosphorescent	northeastern Ohio
strontianite	bluish white, greenish yellow, intense to moderate; also phosphorescent	many quarries in northwestern Ohio

RADIOACTIVITY

Minerals that contain uranium or thorium emit a type of radiation known as radioactivity. This property results from the spontaneous breakdown of the uranium or thorium and the accompanying emission of three types of atomic particles. Radioactivity is detected with Geiger or scintillation counters, and portable, battery-operated instruments can be used for prospecting in the field. Although some black shales in central Ohio contain trace quantities of uranium, no commercial uranium or thorium deposits have been discovered in the state.

TASTE

Minerals that dissolve easily in water commonly have a distinctive taste, which can be a useful test for that mineral. The test is performed by touching a small surface area of the mineral with the tip of one's tongue. Halite, for example, has a salty taste, and almost all efflorescences are astringent (puckery). However, minerals should not be tasted routinely because some of them could contain toxic substances such as arsenic or mercury.

CLASSIFICATION OF MINERALS AND CHEMICAL TESTING

A mineral is classified according to its chemical composition. This important system, employed by mineralogists throughout the world, utilizes the fact that the chemistry of most minerals is exact. For example, galena always contains equal numbers of lead and sulfur atoms, the major chemical elements composing that mineral. Table 9 lists the major chemical elements and elemental groups of minerals in Ohio.

Several classes of minerals are recognized, each characterized by a specific element or group of elements for which the class is named. All minerals that belong to the sulfide class, for instance, contain elemental sulfur, and all minerals in the sulfate class contain the sulfate elemental group. In a given chemical class, each mineral contains the same specific element or group of elements but in combination with different metals. For example, galena and sphalerite are both sulfide minerals, but galena contains lead and sphalerite contains zinc.

The nine chemical classes in which the minerals of Ohio are grouped are listed in table 10. The silicate class is the most complex and consists of six subtypes. However, mineral examples of only three silicate subtypes are found in Ohio (table 9). Note that the presence or absence of water in a chemical formula is not used in determining the class for a mineral.

The identification of some minerals is greatly aided by chemical testing. Tests are particularly useful in distinguishing minerals with similar physical properties but different

TABLE 9.—*Major chemical elements and elemental groups in Ohio minerals*

Element	Chemical symbol	Elemental group	Chemical symbol
aluminum	Al	carbonate	CO_3
barium	Ba	oxalate	C_2O_4
calcium	Ca	phosphate	PO_4
carbon	C	silicate, hemimorphite type	Si_2O_7
chlorine	Cl	silicate, mica and clay type	Si_4O_{10}
chromium	Cr	silicate, quartz type	SiO_2
copper	Cu	sulfate	SO_4
fluorine	F	water	H_2O
gold	Au		
hydrogen	H		
iron	Fe		
lead	Pb		
magnesium	Mg		
manganese	Mn		
nickel	Ni		
oxygen	O		
phosphorus	P		
potassium	K		
silicon	Si		
sodium	Na		
strontium	Sr		
sulfur	S		
titanium	Ti		
zinc	Zn		

TABLE 10.—*Chemical classes of Ohio minerals*

Chemical class	Chemical character	Example of mineral species
native elements	single elements, uncombined	sulfur (S)
sulfides	elemental sulfur (S) combined with different metals	pyrite (FeS_2)
oxides	elemental oxygen (O) combined with different metals	hematite (Fe_2O_3)
halides	elemental fluorine (F) or chlorine (Cl) combined with different metals	fluorite (CaF_2); halite (NaCl)
carbonates	carbonate (CO_3) elemental group combined with different metals	calcite ($CaCO_3$)
sulfates	sulfate (SO_4) elemental group combined with different metals	barite ($BaSO_4$)
phosphates	phosphate (PO_4) elemental group combined with different metals	vivianite ($Fe_3(PO_4)_2 \cdot 8H_2O$)
oxalates	oxalate (C_2O_4) elemental group combined with different metals	whewellite ($Ca(C_2O_4) \cdot H_2O$)
silicates	silicate elemental groups, with variable silicon-oxygen (Si, O) ratios, occurring alone or combined with different metals	quartz (SiO_2); glauconite ($K(Fe, Mg, Al)_2Si_4O_{10}(OH)_2$)

chemical compositions. Calcite and dolomite are easily confused because they both display rhombohedral cleavage. Barite and celestite, which have similar habits and cleavage, also can be difficult to distinguish. Aragonite and strontianite both have fibrous or acicular habits and may be hard to tell apart. Because impurities could interfere with the test results, mineral fragments should be selected for testing only after a careful examination with a hand lens. Distinguishing chemical tests for the mineral pairs noted above and others are described below.

One of the most useful chemical tests is made with dilute hydrochloric (muriatic) acid (HCl) (see table 5). For field use, the diluted acid should be carried in a plastic dropper bottle. To make the test, a drop of acid is placed on the mineral and the point of reaction is examined with a hand lens. In this manner, activity originating in the main mass of a mineral can be distinguished from misleading effects centered along cracks. Vigorous effervescence, which is due to the release of bubbles of harmless carbon dioxide gas, occurs if the reaction is strong. If the reaction is moderate, tiny bubbles of gas can be seen to rise rapidly through the drop. No bubbles will be observed if the mineral is unreactive. If the drop is absorbed by the specimen before any reaction can be noted, a small fragment should be placed on a nonporous surface such as a streak plate before the acid is applied. To avoid staining a specimen, the drop of acid should be blotted dry immediately after the test, and any acid that is accidentally spilled on fingers or clothing must be washed off with water immediately. The acid is obtained commercially (table 5) or prepared in a well-ventilated room by carefully adding one part of concentrated acid to 10 parts of water.

All minerals in the carbonate class effervesce in dilute hydrochloric acid; effervescence, therefore, is a positive test for a carbonate mineral. The reactions of specific carbonate minerals to acid are different. Calcite, aragonite, and strontianite effervesce vigorously, but dolomite and smithsonite effervesce more slowly. Stronger effervescence can be obtained if the acid is applied to a powdered mineral fragment. Siderite, another carbonate mineral, effervesces only in warm acid. A fragment of a mineral that is suspected to be siderite should be placed in a small Pyrex beaker or test tube and just covered with dilute acid. The reaction should be observed as the acid is being warmed gently over a low flame.

Flame tests can be used to detect the presence of a specific element in a mineral. A flame, for example, burns green if the element barium is present, crimson red from elemental strontium, or orange from calcium. Thus, barite (green flame) can be distinguished easily from celestite (red flame), and strontianite (red flame) can be told readily from aragonite (orange flame). Mineral powders are prepared by placing a fragment in an envelope and crushing it with a hammer. A flame test kit (see table 5) and either a Bunsen burner or a hand propane torch are needed. A few particles of the powdered mineral are introduced into the flame by means of a platinum wire that has been first moistened with dilute hydrochloric acid (fig. 45). The critical color of the flame generally appears at the instant the wire is inserted into the flame and then burns off rapidly. For this reason, the test should be perfected on known minerals before it is applied to unknown minerals. To prevent contamination the wire must be burned clean from the previous sample before testing a new sample; for maximum effect, flame tests should be performed in a dark room.

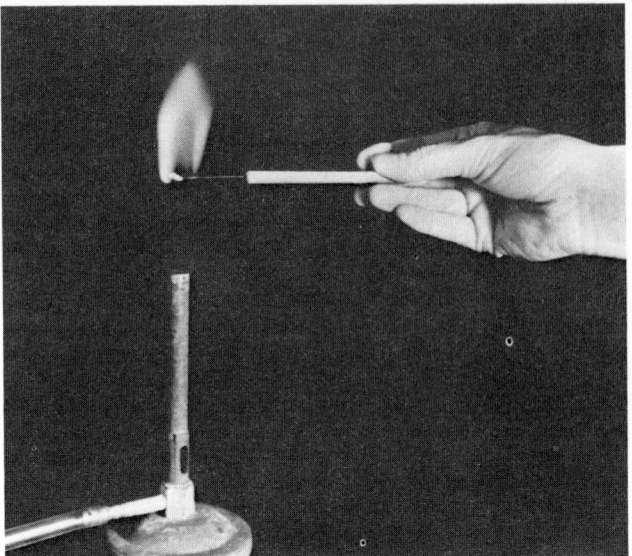

FIGURE 45.—Flame test.

SPECIAL METHODS OF MINERAL IDENTIFICATION

When minerals occur in aggregates of grains that are too small to test, as in a rock, special methods of mineral identification may be required. The most commonly used supplemental means of identification are x-ray diffraction and optical microscopy. These topics are beyond the scope of this work, but any standard text in mineralogy will provide the reader with details of these powerful mineralogical tools.

THE SYSTEMATIC IDENTIFICATION OF MINERALS

A determinative table (also termed a key) should be consulted if a mineral cannot be identified easily from its physical properties. A systematically organized set of physical properties (table 11) enables unlikely minerals to be eliminated in a series of steps, each step narrowing down the number of possible choices until a single entry remains. The determinative table of Ohio minerals is arranged as follows:

LUSTER: METALLIC or SUBMETALLIC
   I. Hardness: less than 5½
  II. Hardness: 5½ or greater

LUSTER: NONMETALLIC
   I. Colored minerals
     A. Hardness: less than 3
     B. Hardness: 3 to 5½
     C. Hardness: greater than 5½
  II. White or colorless minerals
     A. Hardness: less than 3
     B. Hardness: 3 to 5½
     C. Hardness: greater than 5½

The main division of this table is based on luster (metallic or nonmetallic); further subdivision of the nonmetallic minerals is based on color (colored or white). Additional subdivisions are based on hardness, using a copper penny (H = 3) and a knife blade (H = 5½) as testing materials. The table also contains data on specific gravity (G), crystal habit, cleavage and fracture, streak, luminescent character, behavior in acid, and geological occurrence. These latter characteristics are used to eliminate other minerals from consideration that are grouped in the same range of hardness. Information on the geological occurrence is an extremely useful identification aid, and additional data on occurrences are found in the catalog of mineral localities (Chapter 7).

The application of the determinative table can be illustrated by a soft, yellow, nonmetallic mineral with a conchoidal fracture. Because of its luster, one would locate the section: "LUSTER: NONMETALLIC"; next, because of its color and hardness, one would turn to: "Colored minerals: Hardness: less than 3." All but six minerals have been eliminated at this point and, by using other characteristics, the list can be narrowed further. The color, for example, would indicate that the mineral is either copiapite or sulfur, while the breakage would suggest that it is sulfur. Knowledge of the occurrence would be helpful, as copiapite generally occurs as an efflorescence on shale or coal, while sulfur typically occurs with celestite or bedded gypsum.

In addition to the minerals described in Chapter 7, the determinative table includes data for a few fine-grained minerals, such as kaolinite, goethite, and siderite, that are commonly encountered in Ohio. Table 11 also contains data for a few minerals that are commonly found in panned concentrates of glacial gravels, such as garnet, ilmenite, and magnetite.

TABLE 11.—*Determinative table of Ohio minerals*
H = hardness, G = specific gravity
LUSTER: METALLIC or SUBMETALLIC
I. Hardness: less than 5½

Color	H	G	Other characteristics	Name, composition
lead gray	2½	7.5	cubic crystals and cleavage; granular; lead-gray streak	galena, PbS
gold yellow	2½-3	19.3	small grains or scales; rare; found in panned concentrates	gold, Au
brass yellow	3½-4	4.3	small granular masses; uneven fracture; may be iridescent; greenish-black streak; rare; found in concretions	chalcopyrite, CuFeS$_2$
black, yellowish brown, greenish yellow, orange, red	3½-4	4.1	granular; dodecahedral cleavage; submetallic luster when black, lighter colors nonmetallic	sphalerite, (Zn,Fe)S
dark gray, brownish black	2-6	4.0-5.1	generally massive; dendritic; acicular; brown to black streak	manganese oxides (pyrolusite, etc.)

II. Hardness: 5½ or greater

Color	H	G	Other characteristics	Name, composition
black	5½-6½	5.2	generally granular; octahedral crystals; strongly magnetic; black streak; found in panned concentrates	magnetite, Fe$_3$O$_4$
black	5-6	4.8	generally granular; nonmagnetic or very slightly magnetic; black streak; found in panned concentrates	ilmenite, FeTiO$_3$
red, gray, black, dark brown	5½-6½	5.0	generally massive and red; uneven fracture; may be earthy; red streak	hematite, Fe$_2$O$_3$
pale bronze yellow	6-6½	4.9	massive; granular; radiating; tabular and equant crystals; may form spear-shaped crystal intergrowths; uneven fracture; tarnishes easily; grayish black streak	marcasite, FeS$_2$
pale brass yellow	6-6½	5.0	massive; granular; acicular; radiating; cubic and octahedral crystals; uneven to conchoidal fracture; may be iridescent; tarnishes easily; greenish-black streak	pyrite, FeS$_2$

LUSTER: NONMETALLIC
I. Colored minerals
A. Hardness: less than 3

Color	H	G	Other characteristics	Name, composition
pale to dark blue (colorless or white when fresh)	1½-2	2.7	generally massive; prismatic crystals; pinacoidal cleavage; dull to vitreous luster; color darkens on exposure to light	vivianite, Fe$_3$(PO$_4$)$_2$·8H$_2$O
lemon yellow	1½-2½	2.1	small crystals; granular; conchoidal to uneven fracture; resinous to greasy luster; burns with a blue flame	sulfur, S
pale bluish white, pale greenish white, colorless	2	1.9	generally fibrous; acicular; pinacoidal cleavage; vitreous to silky to dull luster; soluble in water; found as efflorescence	melanterite, FeSO$_4$·7H$_2$O

TABLE 11.—*Determinative table of Ohio minerals*—continued
LUSTER: NONMETALLIC
I. Colored minerals
A. Hardness: less than 3—continued

Color	H	G	Other characteristics	Name, composition
green, greenish black	2	2.9	massive; pinacoidal cleavage; dull luster	glauconite, $K(Fe,Mg,Al)_2Si_4O_{10}(OH)_2$
orange red	2-2½	2.1	small, rounded, fibrous masses; pinacoidal cleavage; vitreous to dull luster; rare; found as efflorescence	botryogen, $MgFe(SO_4)_2(OH) \cdot 7H_2O$
lemon yellow	2½-3	2.1	granular; minute scales; pinacoidal cleavage; greasy to dull luster; readily soluble in water; found as efflorescence	copiapite, $Fe^{+2}Fe_4^{+3}(SO_4)_6(OH)_2 \cdot 20H_2O$

B. Hardness: 3 to 5½

Color	H	G	Other characteristics	Name, composition
brown, yellow, white, colorless, gray, black	3	2.7	scalenohedral or rhombohedral crystals; granular; rhombohedral cleavage; vitreous luster; may fluoresce; effervesces vigorously in cold dilute HCl	calcite, $CaCO_3$
pale yellow, pale blue, white, colorless, gray, black, brown	3-3½	4.5	tabular crystals; granular; massive; pinacoidal cleavage; vitreous to dull luster; dark gray when massive; gives green color in flame test	barite, $BaSO_4$
pale greenish yellow	3-4	2.0-2.4	colloform, well crystallized; uneven fracture; waxy to dull luster; found as nodules	diadochite, $Fe_2(PO_4)(SO_4)(OH) \cdot 5H_2O$
blue, pale yellow, white, colorless	3-3½	4.0	tabular, bladed, columnar crystals; pinacoidal cleavage; vitreous luster; may fluoresce; gives crimson-red color in flame test	celestite, $SrSO_4$
blue, white, gray, colorless	3½	3.0	generally massive; pinacoidal cleavage; vitreous to greasy luster; found in evaporite beds	anhydrite, $CaSO_4$
yellow, white, colorless	3½	3.8	generally acicular or fibrous; massive; prismatic cleavage; vitreous luster; effervesces vigorously in cold dilute HCl; commonly fluoresces; gives crimson-red color in flame test	strontianite, $SrCO_3$
yellow, white, colorless	3½-4	2.9	generally massive; acicular or fibrous; pinacoidal cleavage; vitreous luster; effervesces vigorously in cold dilute HCl	aragonite, $CaCO_3$
brown, tan, pink, gray, white	3½-4	2.8	rhombohedral crystals and cleavage; curved crystal faces common; granular; vitreous luster; may fluoresce; powder effervesces slowly in cold dilute HCl	dolomite, $CaMg(CO_3)_2$
brown, gray, black	3½-4	3.8	generally massive; granular; rhombohedral crystals and cleavage; dull luster when massive; light-colored streak; effervesces in hot dilute HCl; found in concretions	siderite, $FeCO_3$
yellowish brown, greenish yellow, black, orange, red	3½-4	4.1	generally granular; tetrahedral crystals; dodecahedral cleavage; resinous to adamantine luster; brown to yellow streak	sphalerite, $(Zn,Fe)S$
red, brown	3½-4	4.1	tiny pyramidal crystals; acicular; radiating; adamantine to resinous luster; rare; found in concretions	wurtzite, ZnS
brown, yellow, purple, pale green, colorless	4	3.2	cubic crystals; granular; octahedral cleavage; vitreous luster; yellow and brown varieties fluoresce	fluorite, CaF_2
brown, white, gray	4-4½	4.4	cellular and colloform masses; rhombohedral cleavage; dull to vitreous luster; effervesces slowly in cold dilute HCl; rare; weathering product of sphalerite	smithsonite, $ZnCO_3$
brown, yellowish brown	5-5½	4.3	massive; cellular; pinacoidal cleavage; dull luster; porous varieties may appear softer; yellowish-brown streak; weathering product of hematite, pyrite, and siderite	goethite, $HFeO_2$

C. Hardness: greater than 5½

Color	H	G	Other characteristics	Name, composition
red, brown	5½-6½	5.0	generally massive; oolitic; uneven fracture; dull luster, but may be metallic; may appear softer; red streak	hematite, Fe_2O_3
gray, black, white, red, green, brown	7	2.65	massive; banded; conchoidal to uneven fracture; vitreous to dull luster, also greasy or waxy; chalcedony is translucent and white, flint is opaque appearing and white to black	chalcedony, flint, SiO_2

SYSTEMATIC IDENTIFICATION OF MINERALS

TABLE 11.—*Determinative table of Ohio minerals*—continued
LUSTER: NONMETALLIC
I. Colored minerals
C. Hardness: greater than 5½—continued

Color	H	G	Other characteristics	Name, composition
gray, brown, purple, white, colorless	7	2.65	generally white or colorless; prismatic crystals with rhombohedral terminations; granular; conchoidal fracture; vitreous luster	quartz, SiO_2
red, reddish brown	7-7½	3.6-4.3	generally granular; dodecahedral crystals; uneven fracture; vitreous luster; found in panned concentrates	garnet, complex silicate

II. White or colorless minerals
A. Hardness: less than 3

Color	H	G	Other characteristics	Name, composition
white, pale yellow, pale red	1½	1.9	fibrous; pinacoidal cleavage; vitreous to silky luster; astringent taste; soluble in water; found as efflorescence	halotrichite-pickeringite series, $(Fe,Mg)Al_2(SO_4)_4 \cdot 22H_2O$-$(Mg,Fe)Al_2(SO_4)_4 \cdot 22H_2O$
white	1½-2	1.8	fibrous; tiny scales; powdery; pinacoidal cleavage; silky luster; acid, sharp taste; soluble in water; found as efflorescence	alunogen, $Al_2(SO_4)_3 \cdot 17H_2O$
white, gray, colorless	2	2.3	prismatic or tabular crystals, commonly transparent; massive; fibrous; pinacoidal cleavage; vitreous to dull luster; selenite may fluoresce; massive variety found in evaporite beds	gypsum (selenite), $CaSO_4 \cdot 2H_2O$
white	2	1.7	fibrous or acicular; powdery; pinacoidal cleavage; silky to dull luster; bitter, salty taste; soluble in water; found as efflorescence	hexahydrite, $MgSO_4 \cdot 6H_2O$
colorless, pale bluish white, pale greenish white	2	1.9	fibrous or acicular; powdery; pinacoidal cleavage; silky to dull luster; astringent taste; soluble in water; found as efflorescence	melanterite, $FeSO_4 \cdot 7H_2O$
white, colorless	2-2½	1.7	fibrous or acicular; powdery; pinacoidal cleavage; silky to dull luster; bitter, salty taste; soluble in water; found as efflorescence	epsomite, $MgSO_4 \cdot 7H_2O$
white	2-2½	4.0	massive; pinacoidal cleavage; dull luster; fluoresces bluish white; rare; weathering product of sphalerite	hydrozincite, $Zn_5(CO_3)_2(OH)_6$
white, pale yellow, pale blue	2-2½	2.6	massive; pinacoidal cleavage; dull luster; found in concretions	kaolinite, $Al_4Si_4O_{10}(OH)_8$
white, colorless	2-2½	1.8	massive; powdery; conchoidal fracture; vitreous to dull luster; sweetish, astringent taste; soluble in water; found as efflorescence	potash alum, $KAl(SO_4)_2 \cdot 12H_2O$
white, colorless	2½	2.2	cubic crystals and cleavage; granular; vitreous luster; salty taste; soluble in water; found in evaporite beds	halite, $NaCl$
white, pale yellow	2½	3.1	fibrous; powdery; conchoidal to uneven fracture; silky to dull luster; bitter, astringent taste; dissolves slowly in water giving solution a brown color; found as efflorescence	szomolnokite, $FeSO_4 \cdot H_2O$
white, greenish white	soft	2.2	powdery; pinacoidal cleavage; dull luster; found as efflorescence	rozenite, $FeSO_4 \cdot 4H_2O$
white, grayish white, colorless	2½-3	2.7	powdery; pinacoidal cleavage; dull luster; slightly salty taste; slowly soluble in water; found as efflorescence	thenardite, Na_2SO_4
white	2½-3	2.2	coarsely granular; pinacoidal cleavage; greasy luster; found in concretions	whewellite, $Ca(C_2O_4) \cdot H_2O$

B. Hardness: 3 to 5½

Color	H	G	Other characteristics	Name, composition
white, colorless, yellow, brown, gray, black	3	2.7	scalenohedral or rhombohedral crystals; granular; rhombohedral cleavage; vitreous luster; may fluoresce; effervesces vigorously in cold dilute HCl	calcite, $CaCO_3$
white, colorless, pale green, pale blue, gray, black, brown	3-3½	4.5	tabular crystals; granular; rosettes; pinacoidal cleavage; vitreous luster; may fluoresce; gives green color in flame test	barite, $BaSO_4$
white, colorless, blue	3-3½	4.0	tabular, bladed, columnar crystals; pinacoidal cleavage; vitreous luster; may fluoresce; gives crimson-red color in flame test	celestite, $SrSO_4$
white, gray, blue, colorless	3½	3.0	generally massive; pinacoidal cleavage; vitreous to greasy luster; found in evaporite beds	anhydrite, $CaSO_4$
white, colorless, yellow	3½	3.8	generally acicular or fibrous; massive; prismatic cleavage; vitreous luster; effervesces vigorously in cold dilute HCl; commonly fluoresces; gives crimson-red color in flame test	strontianite, $SrCO_3$

TABLE 11.—*Determinative table of Ohio minerals*—continued
LUSTER: NONMETALLIC
II. White or colorless minerals
B. Hardness: 3 to 5½—continued

Color	H	G	Other characteristics	Name, composition
white, colorless, yellow	3½-4	2.9	generally massive; acicular or fibrous; pinacoidal cleavage; vitreous luster; effervesces vigorously in cold dilute HCl	aragonite, $CaCO_3$
white, brown, tan, pink, gray	3½-4	2.8	rhombohedral crystals and cleavage; curved crystal faces common; granular; vitreous luster; powder effervesces slowly in cold dilute HCl	dolomite, $CaMg(CO_3)_2$
colorless, yellow, brown, purple	4	3.2	generally colored; cubic crystals; granular; octahedral cleavage; vitreous luster; yellow and brown varieties fluoresce	fluorite, CaF_2
white, yellowish white, colorless, brown	4½-5	3.4	small, thin, tabular crystals; commonly massive; colloform; prismatic cleavage; vitreous luster; white streak; weathering product of sphalerite	hemimorphite, $Zn_4(Si_2O_7)(OH)_2 \cdot H_2O$

C. Hardness: greater than 5½

Color	H	G	Other characteristics	Name, composition
white, gray, yellow, red, blue, green	5½-6½	2.0-2.2	small masses; conchoidal fracture; vitreous to greasy luster; commonly iridescent; rare; found with fossilized bone in limestone	opal, $SiO_2 \cdot nH_2O$
colorless, white, purple, brown	7	2.65	prismatic crystals with rhombohedral terminations; granular; conchoidal fracture; vitreous luster	quartz, SiO_2
white, red, brown, green, gray, black	7	2.65	massive; banded; conchoidal to uneven fracture; vitreous to dull luster; chalcedony is translucent and white, flint is opaque appearing and white to black	chalcedony, flint, SiO_2
colorless, white, yellow	10	3.5	octahedral crystals and cleavage; adamantine luster; rare; found in glacial gravels	diamond, C

Chapter 5

COLLECTING AND PREPARING MINERALS

PLANNING THE FIELD TRIP

A field trip to collect minerals should be planned carefully. The precise location of the field-trip site should be known ahead and the best travel route determined from road maps. A county highway map is particularly useful for this purpose because of the detail it provides and is ordinarily available from the county engineer's office. Before departure, individuals who are familiar with the site should be consulted because they could offer a practical knowledge of what to look for. A nearby university geology department or a local rock and mineral club (see list on p. 57) is a good source of information. The time of year is also an important consideration for field trips. At sites along rivers and creeks, collecting is generally best in late summer or early autumn when water levels are low and exposures are not obscured by falling leaves. In wooded areas, rocks can be seen more easily in early spring before the new growth appears; freshly plowed fields also may offer collecting opportunities in the spring.

Potential sites for mineralogical field trips exist wherever rock is exposed and include places such as hillsides, quarries, pits, strip mines, underground mines, highway and railroad cuts, cliffs along rivers and lakes, and the beds of rivers and lakes. Unfortunately, most quarries, pits, and mines are closed to the public because of enactment of the federal Mine Safety and Health Law. However, some quarry or mine operators permit entry after visitors have signed a document that releases the company from liability should an accident occur. The addresses and locations of active operations are published annually in the Ohio Division of Geological Survey *Report on Ohio mineral industries*.

Safety measures and good judgment must be observed on field trips at all times. Many sites have been closed because of accidents and the senseless actions of a few people. The following rules should be followed by field-trip participants.
 1. Always obtain permission well in advance of collecting on or crossing privately owned land.
 2. Wear safety glasses at all times.
 3. Wear steel-toed boots and hard hats in quarries and mines.
 4. Never climb quarry walls.
 5. Never climb steep slopes when people are directly below.
 6. Never hammer rocks when people are within range of flying chips.
 7. Always monitor oncoming traffic at road cuts.
 8. Park cars well off the road.
 9. Do not wade streams when water levels are high.
 10. Always keep livestock gates closed.
 11. Always remove litter.

TOPOGRAPHIC MAPS

Topographic maps published by the U.S. Geological Survey are especially useful on field trips because they accurately depict the configuration of the terrain. This configuration is shown by means of brown lines called contour lines. A contour line connects all points of equal elevation across the map area. Adjacent contour lines on a map are separated by a fixed vertical distance, such as 20 feet, called the contour interval. To imagine how contour lines are drawn, picture how an area would appear if it were covered by a lake at a particular elevation (fig. 46). The shoreline of this lake would mark the location on the map of a contour line at that elevation. Tracing a given contour line would form a ring, either within or off the map area, just as a traced shoreline would form a ring. If the lake level were raised 20 feet the new shoreline would form a ring outside the first one because more of the land would be covered with water. If the lake level had been lowered 20 feet instead, another shoreline would form inside the first because less of the land would be covered with water. A topographic map of the area could be constructed by drawing the configuration of a shoreline at different lake levels in steps corresponding to the contour interval. Every fifth contour line is drawn heavier than the rest as an aid to reading a map. Note that for steep terrain the contour lines are spaced close together and for flat terrain the contour lines are spaced farther apart. Steep cliffs are spotted readily by dense patterns of contour lines, and hills and ridges appear as loop-shaped patterns of nested contour lines. Thus, high hills and ridges, such as Flint Ridge, where exposures of resistant bedrock are observed, can be picked out easily on topographic maps. Quarries and natural depressions in the terrain are shown by depression contour lines, which are characterized by a series of short brown lines, called hachures, that are perpendicular to the contour line and point towards the center of the depression. The various symbols used on topographic maps are explained in the leaflet accompanying this bulletin.

The location of a field-trip site can be recorded in one of two ways: (1) the latitude-longitude method, or (2) the county-township-section method. The latitude-longitude system employs east-west lines of latitude that encircle the globe parallel to the equator and north-south lines of longitude that connect at the poles. Latitude is measured in degrees north (N) or south (S) from the equator and longitude is measured in degrees west (W) or east (E) from Greenwich, England. The borders of a topographic map, or quadrangle, are drawn parallel to latitude and longitude lines. A 7.5-minute quadrangle is 7.5 minutes of longitude wide from west to east and 7.5 minutes of latitude long from north to south. The latitude and longitude of a site

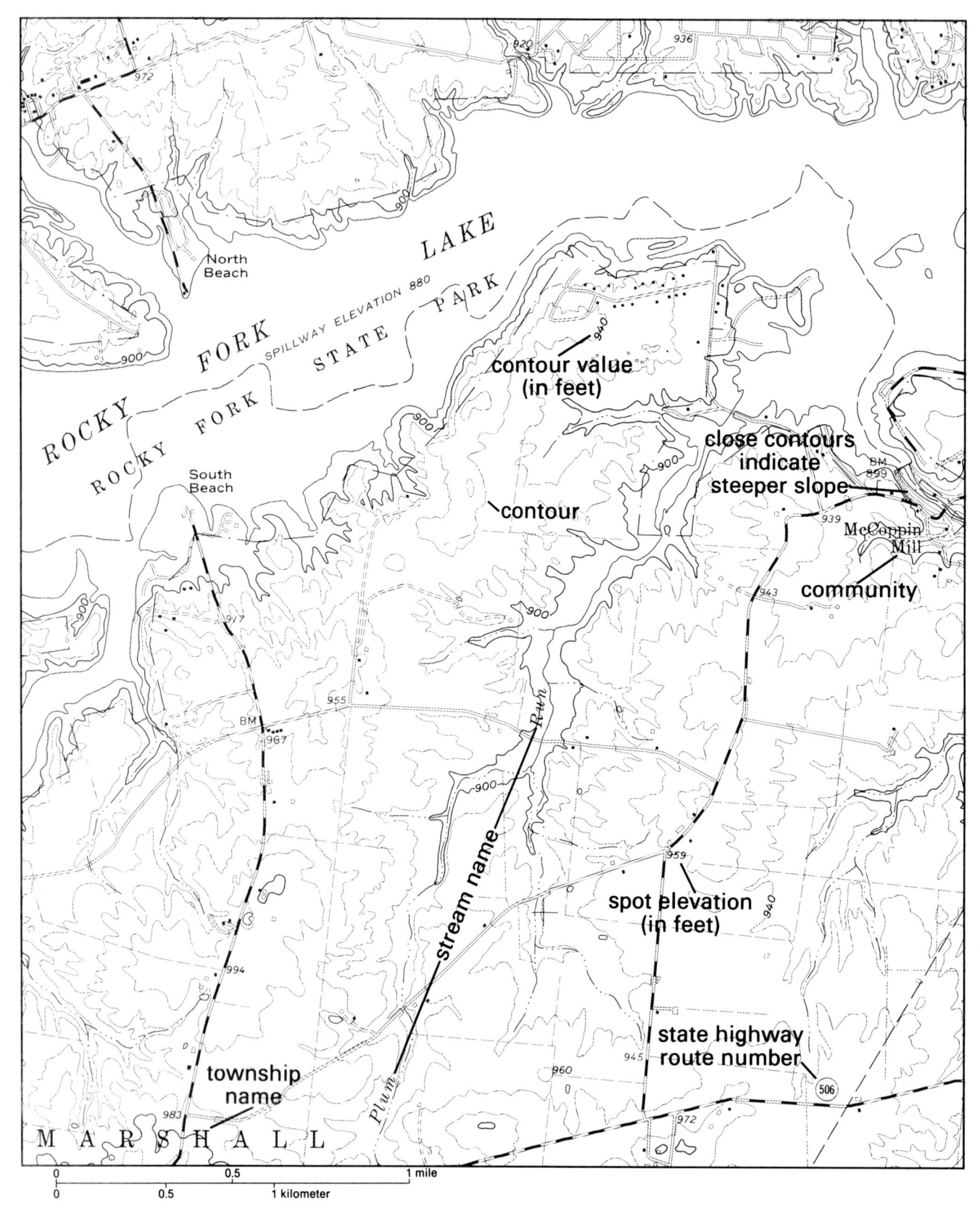

FIGURE 46.—Portion of the Rainsboro 7.5-minute quadrangle, Highland County, Ohio, illustrating features of a topographic map. (See also brochure on topographic map symbols accompanying this report.) Contour interval on this map is 20 feet. Approximate elevation of Rocky Fork Lake is 880 feet.

ordinarily are recorded to the nearest minute of a degree (60' = 1°) and are measured from the map borders with a ruler. Using this method, the Miller Blue Hole is located at 41°24'N latitude, 82°54'W longitude (fig. 47). Latitude-longitude is the most common method of location in mineralogical studies of national and international scope, such as meteorites (table 3).

The county-township-section method of location, although regional in extent, is easy and practical to use, and is the method used in this report. A township typically contains an area 6 miles by 6 miles square that is outlined by dashed black lines on a topographic map. There are 36 sections in a 6-miles-square township, and each section has an area of 1 square mile. Sections generally are numbered as shown in figure 47, but other numbering schemes also have been used in Ohio. To specify locations more precisely, sections can be subdivided into quarters, and quarters can be subdivided further into quarters. For example, the Miller Blue Hole is located in the NE¼ of the SW¼ of section 9, Townsend Township, Sandusky County (fig. 47). Although all counties in Ohio have been divided into townships, not all townships have been subdivided into sections. A location in an undivided township can be recorded by its compass bearing and distance from a prominent landmark such as a road or stream junction.

A site that has been spotted on a topographic map can be located easily in the field with a little practice. The most critical step is to align magnetic north on the map with the needle of a pocket compass and to find a landmark near the site such as a road intersection, stream junction, or hilltop that has a commanding viewpoint. Other map features then can be correlated with their field position if the map scale is noted. Be sure to observe the date of publication of the map because recent features such as new highways and new mine and quarry workings may not appear on the map. For protection in the field, a topographic map can be rolled up and transported in a cardboard map tube or folded and carried on a clip board.

A 7.5-minute quadrangle covers an area of about 50 square miles and is drawn to a scale of 1:24,000, where 1 inch of map distance is equivalent to 24,000 inches or 0.38 mile of land distance. An *Index to 7.5-minute topographic maps of Ohio*, which shows map coverage of the 7.5-minute quadrangles in the state, accompanies this bulletin. A 15-minute quadrangle depicts a larger land area and is drawn at a scale of 1:62,500. Although the latter maps have been out of print for many years, they provide an invaluable source of data, pinpointing old landmarks referred to in some reports, such as former schools; 15-minute maps can be examined at many of the larger public and university libraries in the state.

COLLECTING MINERALS

Techniques of mineral exploration and collecting vary according to the nature of the site. The following collecting and safety gear generally will be useful: (1) rock and sledge hammers, (2) rock chisels and wrecking bar, (3) protective eye glasses, (4) gloves, (5) steel-toed boots or work shoes, (6) wading boots or tennis shoes, (7) hard hat, (8) shovel, (9) bucket, (10) stiff brush, (11) gold pan, (12) pack sack, (13) sample bags, egg cartons, and boxes for transporting specimens, and (14) first aid kit. Distributors of some of these items are given in table 5. Rock hammers are made from specially tempered steel and are available with either pointed ends for chipping hard rock or chisel edges for splitting soft, layered rock. When breaking rock, safety glasses and gloves should be worn to shield the eyes and hands against flying rock chips. A hard hat and boots protect the head and feet from falling and rolling rock. Wading boots or tennis shoes (and a change of clothes) are needed for walking along or crossing streams.

In quarries that are cut in limestone or dolostone, crystals should be sought in the loose rock brought down by blasting; trips should be timed with recent blasts in order to examine a large volume of rock that has not been picked over. As stated previously, permission to enter private property should be obtained from the quarry operator or landowner. Because mineralization may be localized, large quarries should be explored to locate spots that warrant a more careful search. A concentration of mineralized pockets and crystal debris are the best signs of a favorable collecting site. If crystals are found in pockets of a particular rock type, for example, one should look for other pockets in similar rock. If the pockets are found in a particular bed, that bed should be traced to locate more specimens. Mineralized pockets may be hidden from view on the underside of a block or inside a block with broken crystals on the surface. Large blocks can be broken with a sledge hammer or wedged apart with a rock chisel or wrecking bar if the rock is cracked. Pockets lined with crystals can be removed intact only by the skillful use of a rock chisel on the rock matrix. Mineralized specimens can be trimmed in size either with a rock hammer in the field or with a rock saw later in the workshop.

Concretions typically weather free from the enclosing shale and can be picked up easily at a site. Collecting can be done at strip mines from the rock that has been moved by large earth shovels, and at cliffs along streams from piles of scree rock. Large concretions must be broken with sledge hammers and chisels before they can be explored for mineralization, but smaller concretions and geodes can be opened with a rock hammer. Several unopened ones should be saved for sawing, especially if specimens cannot be broken cleanly or if crystals are damaged when the rock is split.

One of the most rewarding methods of hunting for petrified wood is to slowly walk the bed of a stream when the water level is low and to look carefully for cylindrical masses of rock. Because heavy rains and the resulting increase in water flow will turn over new material, the same bed can be walked repeatedly with different results. Specimens of silicified wood and flint that are dug from soil can be scrubbed with a stiff brush and water.

Specimens should be sorted in the field so that only the best quality and the least weathered material is carried away. A few extra specimens should be taken for swapping with other collectors. Each specimen should be given an acquisition number that is recorded in a notebook along with other pertinent data such as mineral identity, associated minerals, type of occurrence, location, and date of collection. Masking tape and a waterproof marking pen are convenient for labeling specimens in the field. Many specimens can be transported in cloth sacks or paper bags; empty soda pop flats or egg cartons are convenient for transporting delicate specimens.

A gold pan is useful for obtaining sand-size grains of gold and other heavy minerals resistant to weathering from gravel deposits of an active stream. Gravel can be dug readily with a collapsible shovel. The gold pan should be filled with sand which has been washed through a garden screen (about ⅛ inch mesh) to remove the pebbles. The pan should be partially submerged in water and gently rocked back and forth with a continuous swirling action. The lighter minerals and organic debris that rise to the top of the pan are repeatedly washed off. As the volume of

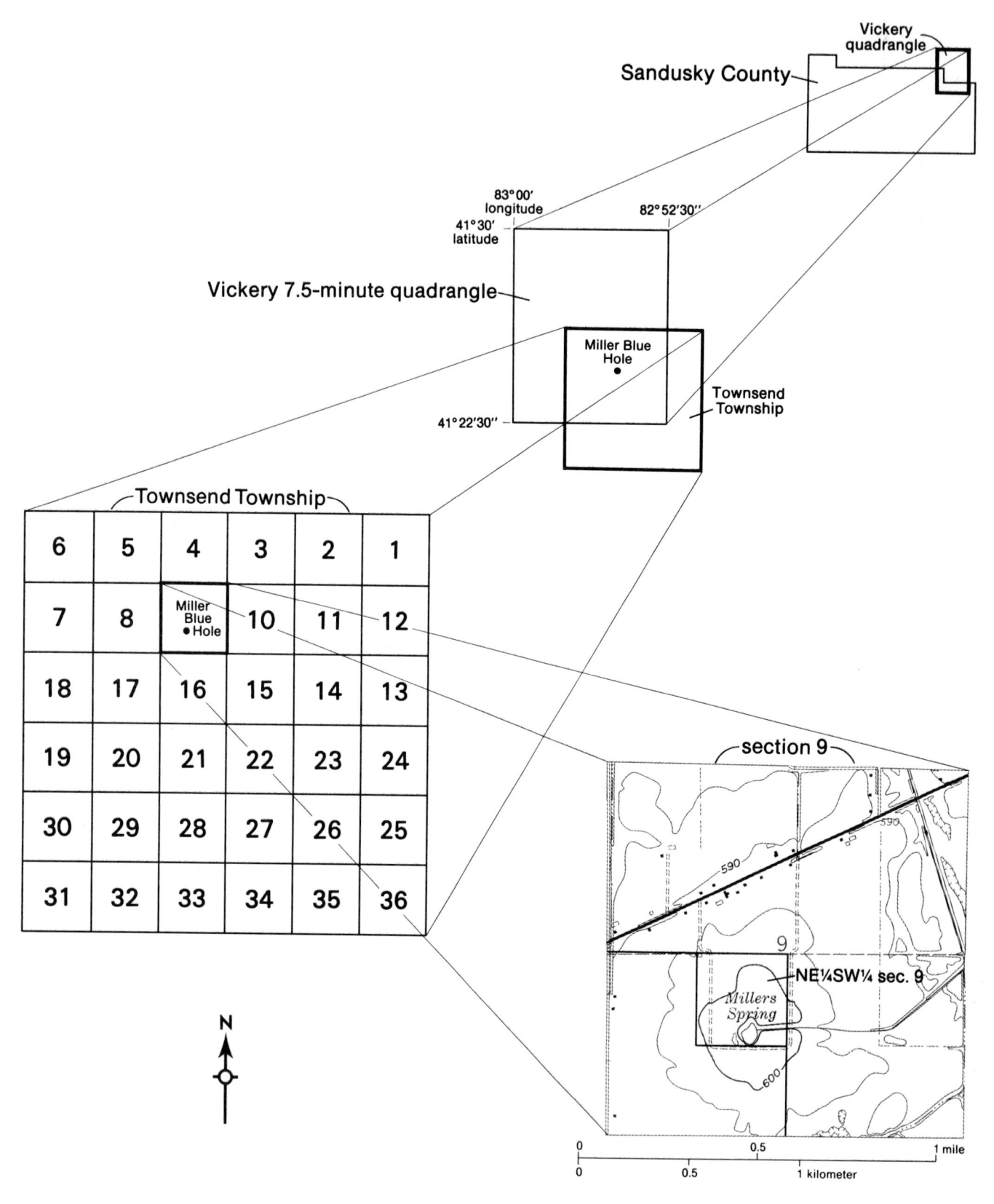

FIGURE 47.—Location of the Miller Blue Hole (Millers Spring), a small spring-fed lake in the northeast quarter of the southwest quarter of section 9 (NE¼SW¼ sec. 9), Townsend Township, Sandusky County, Vickery 7.5-minute quadrangle.

remaining sand decreases, the residue generally becomes black because of the greater concentration of heavy minerals. The heaviest minerals (see table 7) accumulate on the bottom of the pan, and, if gold is present, "colors" will appear when most of the black minerals are washed away. After the water is drained off, the panned concentrate can be dried in the pan and transferred to a small jar or empty medicine vial. A panned concentrate is fascinating to study under a microscope because interesting minerals such as magnetite and ilmenite, both black, red garnet, and possibly traces of gold will be found. These minerals are derived from the erosion of glacial deposits and are not native to exposures of bedrock in Ohio. Streams in unglaciated parts of Ohio, such as the Serpent Mound area of Adams County, yield panned concentrates that are brown because of an abundance of goethite.

PREPARATION AND PRESERVATION OF MINERALS

Cleaning and preparing minerals for display is an important activity after a successful field trip. A cleaning technique should always be practiced on imperfect samples and the results thoroughly evaluated before the technique is used on good material. For obvious reasons a cleaning agent that would react chemically with the desired mineral should be avoided. Caked mud and rock matrix can be washed from more delicate specimens with the gentle application of a toothbrush or scrub brush and from tough specimens with a wire brush. Coatings of clay or shale matrix can be cleaned from nonfragile specimens with an ultrasonic cleaner, a useful but moderately expensive laboratory instrument that uses high-frequency sound waves.

A bath solution of diluted acid can be used as a general cleaning agent for many minerals or to remove a specific type of coating or rock matrix. The solution, however, must be mixed, used, and stored in a well-ventilated room. The use of a glass tank, such as a wide-mouthed jar or fish bowl, allows the cleaning process to be closely monitored. After treatment, specimens must be washed well in running water to remove all traces of the acid and dried thoroughly in air. Baths of oxalic acid and acetic acid are used most commonly.

Oxalic acid baths are used to remove brown stains of iron oxide from pyrite, marcasite, flint, and other minerals. However, newly cleaned surfaces seldom achieve a luster comparable in quality to that of unstained material. Specimens are allowed to soak in the solution for 24 hours and, if necessary, the treatment is repeated with fresh solution until the stain is gone. Oxalic acid, a bleaching agent, can be purchased in crystalline form at some pharmacies and hardware stores. The bath solution is prepared by dissolving 2 tablespoons of crystals in a gallon of water, although a stronger solution may be needed on persistent stains.

Baths of acetic acid are used for general cleaning and for removing coatings of calcite or limestone and dolostone matrix. By varying the duration of treatment, crystals can be partially or completely freed from the matrix. A reactive specimen will effervesce slowly; when effervescence ceases the bath solution should be replaced. A 10 percent solution is prepared by carefully adding one part of concentrated acetic acid (available at a photographic supply house or a pharmacy) to nine parts of water. Vinegar, a 4 to 5 percent solution of acetic acid, can be used instead, but it contains impurities that could stain some minerals.

A bath of hydrochloric acid works well on dolostone matrix, but it attacks limestone so vigorously that crystals may be damaged; therefore, a hydrochloric acid bath should be used for cleaning only if acetic acid is ineffective. Effervescence should be continuous but slow and can be quieted by diluting the bath solution with water. Instructions for the preparation of dilute hydrochloric acid are given in the section on chemical testing in Chapter 4.

Special methods of preservation are required for some minerals. For example, pyrite and efflorescences such as melanterite are especially sensitive to changes in humidity and temperature and during storage may decompose into a mass of powder. Coal pyrite, noted for its instability, should be kept in an area of low humidity. Some efflorescences can be preserved by storage in a refrigerator or in sealed containers. Colorless varieties of vivianite, which are light sensitive and become blue on exposure, can be preserved in light-tight containers. As a general rule, most mineral specimens should be stored in a dry, dust-free area, using cabinets or boxes for protection. Further information on cleaning and preserving minerals is given in Sinkankas (1972) and Pearl (1980).

Lapidary techniques such as cutting and polishing are used on materials durable enough to keep a polish and hard enough to withstand scratching. Flint and silicified wood, composed of microcrystalline quartz, and quartz pebbles are ideally suited for this purpose. Flint is cut to show desirable color patterns, and silicified wood to exhibit its woody tissue structure. Large specimens are cut on slab saws and smaller ones on trim saws; they are shaped by sanding on grinding wheels and polished on lap wheels, using successively finer grades of abrasive grit until a high polish is obtained. Polished slabs can be made into attractive display specimens or into various ornamental objects such as book ends. Smaller pieces are generally made into cabochons, which are circular or oblong-shaped pieces with a polished convex surface. Irregularly shaped pieces and quartz pebbles are polished in a rotating drum, or tumbler, that has been partially filled with water and an abrasive. Cabochons and tumbled specimens are fashioned into pendants, necklaces, bracelets, bolo ties, and rings. Pyrite and hematite will take a high polish and are used to some extent as lapidary materials. Some prehistoric Indian burial sites, for example, contain ornaments that are made of locally obtained pyrite and hematite nodules. Geodes and concretions with cut and polished surfaces exhibiting internal structures make an attractive display (see figs. 11, 19, and 21).

Gemstones of faceting quality must be hard, transparent, durable, and have a pleasing color or display "fire." It is possible to learn to cut reasonably good faceted stones after a few hours of suitable instruction, although a special faceting instrument is required. More detailed information on lapidary techniques can be found in Quick and others (1977).

THE MINERAL COLLECTION

Building a mineral collection that can be displayed at science fairs, mineral and rock shows, or at home can be a rewarding project. Effective collections need to be systematically organized; each mineral should be provided with a label giving its identity, chemical composition, field locality, and acquisition number.

Many kinds of mineral collections can be made. Some collectors specialize in single crystals, and others in a particular mineral species. Some collectors attempt to assemble all known minerals from a particular mine, mining district, or state. Small beautifully crystallized specimens (micromounts) are favored by many collectors, but require special mounting procedures and access to a microscope.

Collections of fluorescent minerals can be displayed in specially constructed viewing boxes. Color patterns in flint or structures of silicified wood make attractive displays. Most mineral enthusiasts have obtained some specimens by trading and swapping at mineral and rock shows; dates and locations of mineral shows are listed in magazines such as *The Lapidary Journal*. There are many active mineral and lapidary clubs in Ohio that take field trips regularly, sponsor mineral and rock shows, and offer classes in lapidary techniques. Active clubs in Ohio are listed below.

ROCK AND MINERAL CLUBS IN OHIO

compiled from the 1990-1991 directory of the Midwest Federation of
Mineralogical and Geological Societies; 1990 Presidents/Liaisons are listed as contact persons

Akron Mineral Society
  Steven Farhat, President
  2891 S. Main St.
  Akron, Ohio 44319

Ashtabula Gem & Mineral Club
  Vince Gildone, President
  19 Clearview Dr.
  Conneaut, Ohio 44030

Brukner Gem & Mineral Club
  Jim Fisher, President
  4020 Ives Ct.
  Dayton, Ohio 45414

Brunswick High School Geology Society
  Brian Fallow, President
  Brunswick High School
  Brunswick, Ohio 44212

Chippewa Gem & Mineral Society
  Grancis Grim, President
  9765 Chatham Rd.
  Spencer, Ohio 44275

Cincinnati Mineral Society
  Carl Shadix, President
  2928 Saddleback Dr.
  Cincinnati, Ohio 45244

Columbus Rock & Mineral Society
  Fred Blyth, President
  9262 Worthington Rd.
  Westerville, Ohio 43081

Dayton Gem & Mineral Society
  John Steidle, President
  P.O. Box 33760
  Dayton, Ohio 45433-0760

East Ohio Lapidary Club
  Richard Lightbody, President
  742 Notre Dame
  Youngstown, Ohio 44515

Firelands Geological Club
  Everett Cole, President
  48 Pitt St.
  Norwalk, Ohio 44857

Fort Hamilton Gem & Mineral Society
  Frank Schrichter, President
  110 S. Brookwood
  Hamilton, Ohio 45013

Hancock Geological Society
  Chester Dangler, President
  154 W. Bigelow
  Findlay, Ohio 45840

The Heights Gem & Mineral Society
  Jeanette Schneider, President
  3091 Yorkshire Rd.
  Cleveland Heights, Ohio 44118

Lake Erie Gem & Geological Society
  Doris Fox, President
  10735 LaGrange Rd.
  Elyria, Ohio 44035

Lake Shore Mineral & Lapidary Society, Inc.
  John Van Sice, President
  12965 W. Geauga Trail
  Chesterland, Ohio 44026

Licking County Rock & Mineral Society
  Helen A. Smith, Liaison
  295 S. 21st St.
  Newark, Ohio 43055

Medina County Gem & Mineral Society
  Art Coley, President
  2351 Kellogg Rd.
  Hinckley, Ohio 47232

Miami Valley Mineral & Gem Club
  Glenn Russell, President
  113 S. Church St.
  Box 114
  South Charleston, Ohio 45368

Micromineral Society of Cleveland
  George Simmons, President
  9440 Headlands Rd.
  Mentor, Ohio 44060

Mineralogical Society of Cleveland
  John Blue, President
  16155 Shurmer Rd.
  Strongsville, Ohio 44136

Parma Lapidary Club
  Beatrice Jordan, President
  4100 Mapledale Ave.
  Cleveland, Ohio 44109

Port Clinton Earth Science Club
  Robert Meek, President
  507 Primrose
  Galion, Ohio 44833

Richland Lithic & Lapidary Society
  Richard Hull, President
  559 Park Ave. W.
  Mansfield, Ohio 44903

Rockport Lapidary Club
  John Blue, President
  16155 Shurmer Rd.
  Strongsville, Ohio 44136

Roehm Geology Club
  Peg Johnston, Liaison
  Roehm Middle School
  7220 Pleasant St.
  Berea, Ohio 44017

Stark County Ohio Gem & Mineral Club
  Lovene Rinn, President
  173 Tallmadge Ave.
  Akron, Ohio 44310

Summit Lapidary Club, Inc.
  Kenneth Lesniak, President
  1847 6th St.
  Cuyahoga Falls, Ohio 44221

Toledo Gem & Rockhound Club
  Suzanne Underwood, President
  11260 Monclova Rd.
  Monclova, Ohio 43542

Wayne County Gem & Mineral Club, Inc.
  Ray Mason, President
  239 Branstetter
  Wooster, Ohio 44691

West Central Ohio Rock Club, Inc.
  Alice Noble, President
  Rte. 3, Box 134
  St. Marys, Ohio 45885

Chapter 6

SELECTED MINERALOGICAL FIELD TRIPS

A good field trip is one of the most rewarding activities that a mineralogist or mineralogical organization can undertake. Participants in such a field trip have two major objectives: (1) to observe firsthand the geologic setting and characteristic features of the mineral occurrences, and (2) to obtain specimens that can be utilized in scientific studies or added to a mineral collection. Because almost all quarries and strip mines in the state are now closed to visitors, good field-trip sites are difficult to find. In order to help prevent additional site closings in the future, field-trip participants are urged to use good judgment at all times and to avoid such actions as climbing cliffs, littering, destroying property, blocking roadways, and trespassing.

Eleven mineralogical field trips are described in this chapter (fig. 48). These sites were selected to provide a fairly broad geographic distribution and to show a variety of mineral occurrences and associated geological features. Other considerations used in site selection were the anticipated accessibility of the site in the future, its educational value, and the presence of nearby accommodations. For this reason, several sites were chosen because of their proximity to state monuments and state and municipal parks, where science museums and camping facilities are available. Several of the included sites, such as Copperas Mountain, Crystal Cave, Flint Ridge, Serpent Mound, and Shade River, are known to mineralogists worldwide and are generally recognized as classic localities. Each of the 11 sites is discussed in terms of its location, geology, and mineralogy.

ALIKANNA, JEFFERSON COUNTY

Location

This locality is about 1.5 miles north of Steubenville near Alikanna, an unincorporated village in east-central Jefferson County. The collecting site is a road cut on the east side of Ohio Route 7 just north of the junction with Ohio Route 213 in the northern part of section 31, Island Creek Township, on the Knoxville 7.5-minute quadrangle (fig. 49). Because it is located on ground that was once part of old Stanton Park, the site was known for many years as the Stanton Park locality after the initial report of its discovery (Seaman and Hamilton, 1950). Vehicles should be parked along Backbone Ridge Road. The site is reached by a short walk across Ohio Route 7. Heavy traffic along Route 7 makes this site particularly hazardous and extreme caution should be observed at all times. Rock hammers are required to break open the concretions.

Geology

The Brush Creek shale is a widespread but erratically

EXPLANATION

Locality	Type of mineral occurrence
1. Alikanna site	ironstone septaria
2. Copperas Mountain	limestone septaria, pyrite nodules, efflorescences
3. Crystal Cave, South Bass Island	celestite crystals in cavernous dolostones
4. Flint Ridge	flint bed
5. West Branch Huron River area	limestone septaria, pyrite nodules, efflorescences
6. Mill Hollow-Bacon Woods Park	barite septaria, pyrite nodules, efflorescences
7. Nellie-Warsaw area	flint bed
8. Serpent Mound area	zinc mineralization in fractured dolostones
9. Shade River-Federal Creek area	silicified wood, hematite nodules
10. Stonelick Creek area	glacial gold
11. West Branch State Park	gypsum (selenite) crystals, ironstone septaria

FIGURE 48.—Location of selected field-trip sites.

59

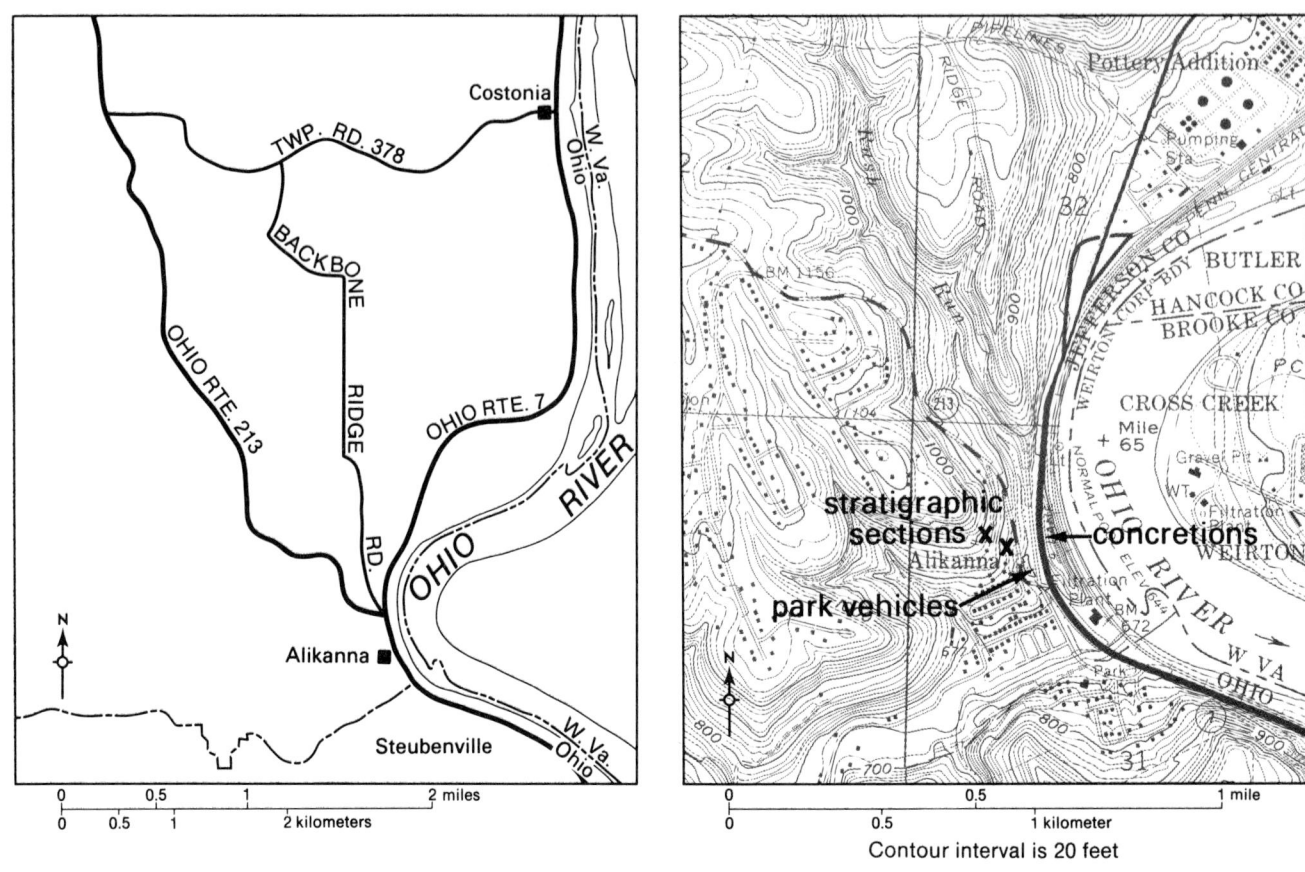

FIGURE 49.—Vicinity map (left) and southeastern part of the Knoxville 7.5-minute quadrangle (right) showing the Alikanna site, Jefferson County.

distributed marine unit in the lower Conemaugh Group (Pennsylvanian) of eastern Ohio and western Pennsylvania. Stratigraphic sections measured by Condit (1912) and Lamborn (1930) at old Stanton Park are representative of the strata at the road cut. Lamborn's section is given below.

Stratigraphic section of the Conemaugh Group at old Stanton Park, N½ of section 31, Island Creek Township, Jefferson County (from Lamborn, 1930, p. 123-124).

	feet	inches
Shale, arenaceous, green to red	62	0
Limestone, fossiliferous, *Cambridge*	1	2
Shale with limestone nodules	8	2
Shale, green, arenaceous	2	6
Sandstone, coarse-grained, *Buffalo*	10	4
Shale, gray to dark, arenaceous	29	0
Shale, fossiliferous, with ore nodules, *Brush Creek*	6	10
Shale, dark	1	4
Shale, bony, with shaly coal ⎫		11
Parting ⎬ *Brush Creek*		1
Coal ⎭		6
Clay, gray, arenaceous, ferruginous	4	0

The Brush Creek shale is a black, fossiliferous, concretion-bearing shale about 7 feet thick. This shale rests on the Brush Creek limestone, a thin, fossiliferous, black limestone 3 feet above the Brush Creek coal, which is a prominent horizon 6 inches thick that runs across the face of the exposure. Condit (1912) recorded the stratigraphic position of the Brush Creek limestone at the site, although it does not appear in Lamborn's section; this limestone is a well-known marker bed for mineralized concretions in eastern Ohio and western Pennsylvania (Seaman and Hamilton, 1950). The Brush Creek shale is overlain successively by a thick sequence of dark, concretion-free shale and a conspicuous sandstone (Buffalo sandstone).

Because of their resistance to weathering, the concretions weather out of the shale and accumulate in the loose rock along the slope or at the base of the road cut. They are slightly flattened, a few inches in diameter on average, and have a smooth outer surface. When broken open, many of the concretions display the networks of veinlets in their cores that are characteristic of septaria. The small, lustrous minerals of the veinlets in these septaria contrast markedly with the dull, massive matrix of the main body (see fig. 12). Brachiopods and other marine fossils appear to form nuclei at the centers of some of the septaria.

Mineralogy

The dark-brown to black bodies of the septaria are formed of finely crystalline aggregates of siderite, calcite, quartz, clay, and carbonaceous matter. Because siderite is the predominant constituent of the matrix, the concretions belong to the ironstone class of concretions, although some of the septaria exhibit limestone cores and ironstone shells. Insoluble residues, the material remaining after treatment with dilute hydrochloric acid, of the matrix contain quartz and a mixture of unidentified clay minerals.

The cracks of the septaria are filled with veinlets of well-crystallized minerals. Tabular crystals of lustrous, brown to black sphalerite and coarse platy aggregates of colorless to white barite are very abundant. Aggregates of granular, colorless calcite and small masses of iridescent pyrite also are common. Wurtzite is more rare, occurring in about one of every four septaria.

Wurtzite, an unusual, hexagonal form of zinc sulfide, occurs in well-formed reddish-brown crystals (Seaman and Hamilton, 1950; Hollenbaugh and Carlson, 1983). A hand lens is necessary to spot most of these crystals because they average less than 0.1 inch in length (see fig. 13). The wurtzite crystals are either embedded in the rock matrix or intergrown with other vein minerals; however, they can be freed from septaria with limestone cores using a bath of dilute acetic or hydrochloric acid. Most wurtzite crystals are hexagonal pyramids (see fig. 40K) and commonly occur in radiating groups in which the tips of individual pyramids point inward (see fig. 38I). Two types of six-sided pyramidal crystals are present: the most common type, with sides that slope 80°, is known as 6H wurtzite; the other type, with slopes of 75°, is known as 4H wurtzite. More rarely, the crystals form trigonal pyramids with sides that slope 86° and are known as 15R wurtzite (see fig. 40J). A detailed discussion of the terminology of wurtzite crystals can be found in Frondel and Palache (1950).

COPPERAS MOUNTAIN, ROSS COUNTY

Location

The Copperas Mountain site lies about 1 mile east of Seip Mound State Memorial on the southeast side of Paint Creek, in Paxton Township, Ross County, on the Morgantown 7.5-minute quadrangle (fig. 50). It is reached by going southwest on U.S. Route 50 from Bourneville for about 1 mile, turning south and following Jones Levee Road for about 1 mile, turning west and following Spargursville Road for about 1.5 miles, turning west and following Storms Road for about ¾ mile, and then turning west onto Copperas Mountain Road (Township Highway 530). Cars should be parked along the side of the road before the cliff is reached as the road ahead is narrow and treacherous because of falling rock. The site is particularly dangerous in the spring and after heavy rains when rock falls are frequent. Sledge hammers, rock hammers, and rock chisels are required to break open the concretions. A roadside park is located nearby along U.S. Route 50 at Seip Mound State Memorial.

Geology

Copperas Mountain, a classic geologic locality, is known for the unobstructed view it provides of the Ohio Shale (Briggs, 1838; Orton, 1874; Kepferle and others, 1981; Carlson, 1987b). Stream erosion at the site has produced a spectacular 350-foot cliff, of which the lower 150 feet rises nearly vertically above the bed of Paint Creek. Early settlers named this locality for the prominent efflorescence of melanterite, a mineral formerly known as copperas, that they collected and utilized in dyeing clothes.

The strata exposed at the Copperas Mountain site include the Ohio Shale (Devonian) and the overlying Bedford Shale and Berea Sandstone (Mississippian) (Kepferle and others, 1981) (fig. 51). The Ohio Shale, which constitutes three-fourths of the section and the vertical part of the cliff, consists of two major members, the Huron Shale Member and the Cleveland Shale Member. These shales are dark gray to black because of an abundance of carbonaceous matter and contain marine fossils of late Devonian age. *Foerstia*, a fossil alga with a restricted stratigraphic range, is found in the Huron Member (Kepferle and others, 1981). A few thin beds of dark-gray cone-in-cone limestone occur in the Huron Member; the cone-in-cone structure has an appearance of nested cones. The Three Lick Bed, an easily recognized thin unit consisting dominantly of green shale, separates the Huron and Cleveland Members. The Bedford Shale and Berea Sandstone form the upper slopes of Copperas Mountain, the latter forming the cap rock.

This site has been famous since the early 1800's (Briggs, 1838) for the unusually large limestone concretions in the lower portion of the Huron Member that is exposed at the level of the road. The concretions are massive, spherical to ellipsoidal in shape, and 1 to 5 feet in diameter (see fig. 14). The compaction of the shale around the concretions is quite dramatic at this locality (Rogers, M., 1935; Seyfried, 1953). Most of the larger concretions are characterized by "soft" septarian cores and resistant, crack-free rims, which are found as empty spherical shells after the cores have weathered away. Orton (1874) reported the occurrence of fossils in the centers of some of the septaria, and Seyfried (1953) noted thin outer bands of iron sulfide on others. The vein minerals, which fill the cracks and line the pockets of the cores, are coarse grained, light colored, and lustrous, contrasting conspicuously with the fine-grained, dark-colored, dull bodies of the concretions. After weathering out of the shale, the concretions roll down the slope towards Paint Creek, where they can be easily examined. Fragments of concretions are abundant and can be readily picked up along the slope and in the bed of the creek.

Pyrite nodules commonly weather out of the black shales at the Copperas Mountain site. These nodules, which range from 2 to 5 inches in diameter, occur in several layers distributed irregularly through the thickness of the Ohio Shale; one layer is reached easily at road level. Nearby banks of black shales, particularly those to the east and northeast along the valley of Paint Creek, are a well-known source of large nodules of pyrite (McAllister, 1941).

Mineralogy

The body of a typical large septarium is composed chiefly of finely crystalline dolomite and belongs to the limestone class of concretions (see definition of limestone concretions in Chapter 3). Smaller amounts of fine-grained quartz, calcite, unidentified clay minerals, pyrite, and carbonaceous matter also have been recognized in the matrix and its insoluble residue.

The chief vein minerals of the septaria are barite, calcite, dolomite, and quartz (Briggs, 1838; Dana, J. D., 1858, 1868; Dana, E. S., 1892; Carlson, 1987b). The barite is colorless and appears in large vitreous plates. Brown or colorless calcite and tan dolomite are closely associated, occurring in large, coarsely granular masses and aggregates of rhombohedral crystals. Colorless quartz, the least common of the vein minerals, is generally found in granular pod-shaped masses, although small crystals exhibiting a combination of rhombohedrons may be present.

Pyrite nodules appear either as fine-grained massive bodies or as radiating aggregates of acicular crystals. Both types commonly exhibit rough surfaces composed of coarsely granular, projecting crystals (see fig. 19). Although marcasite is commonly believed to occur at the site, its presence was not detected in several specimens examined by x-ray diffraction.

The site is especially famous for spectacular occurrences of efflorescences. Fibrous masses of silky, white halotrichite-pickeringite (see fig. 35), identified as alum in the earlier literature, and fibrous coatings of light-blue or light-green melanterite are most common.

62 MINERALS OF OHIO

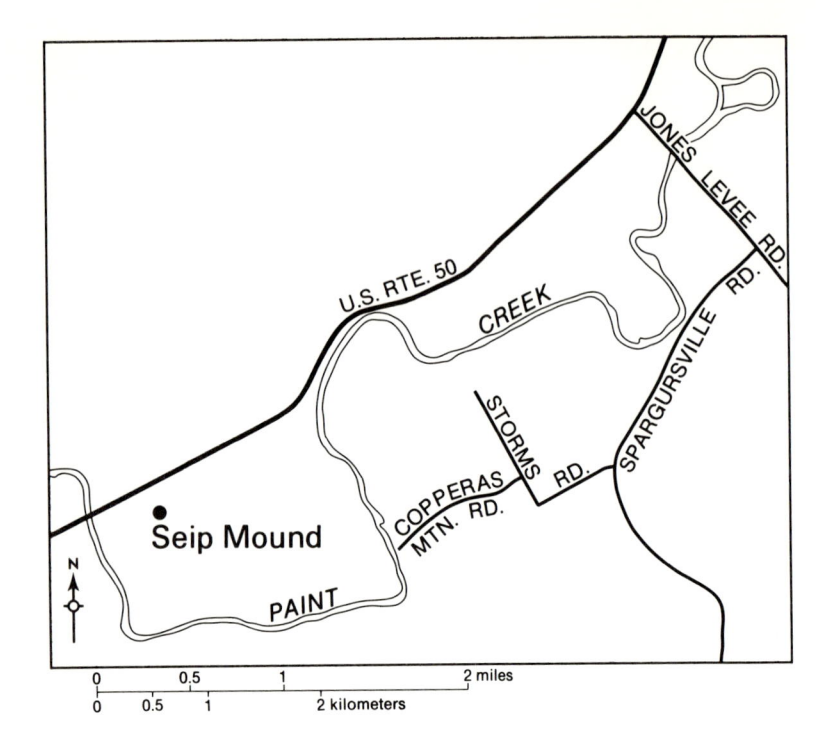

FIGURE 50.—Vicinity map (left) and north-central part of the Morgantown 7.5-minute quadrangle (below) showing the Copperas Mountain site, Ross County.

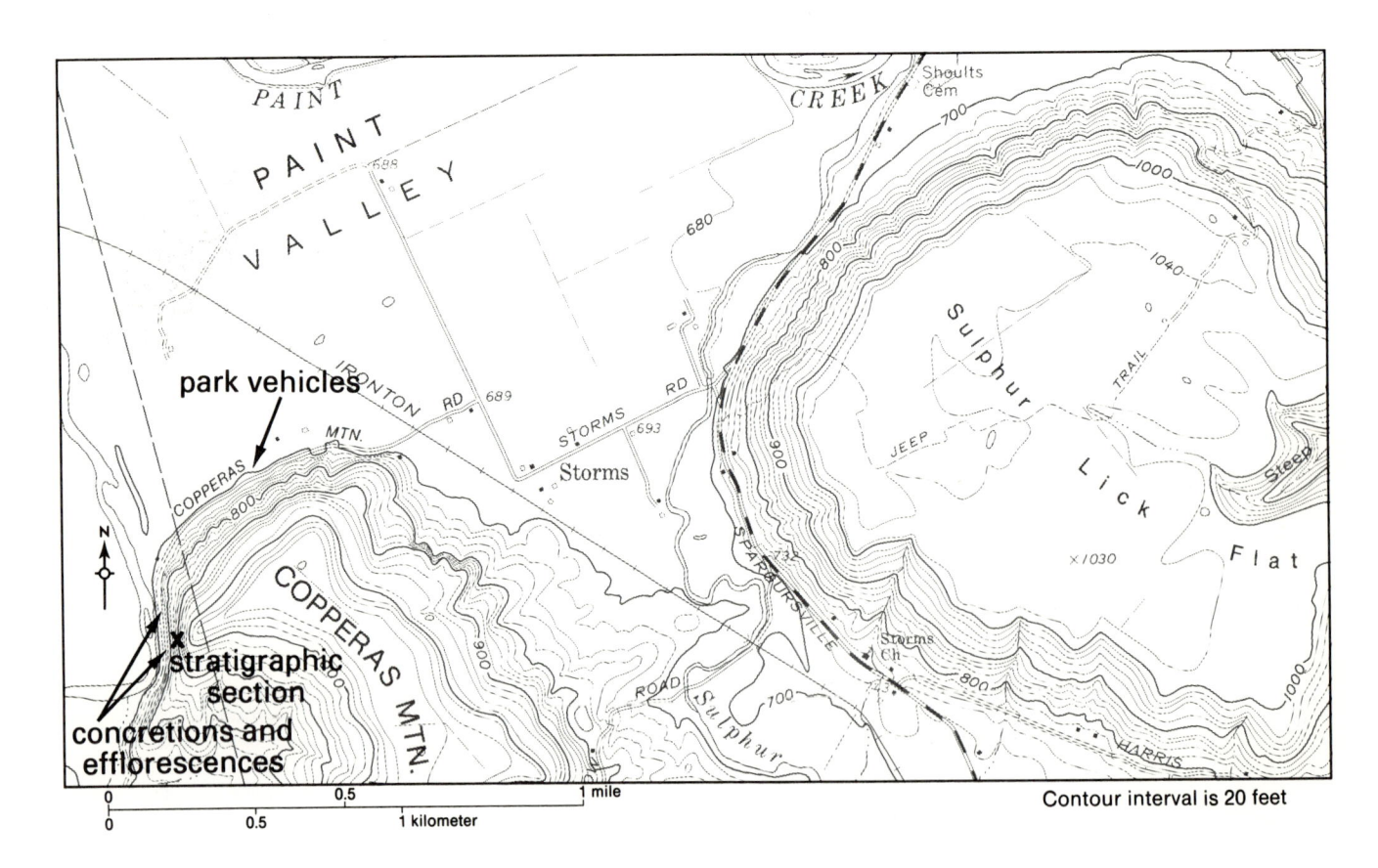

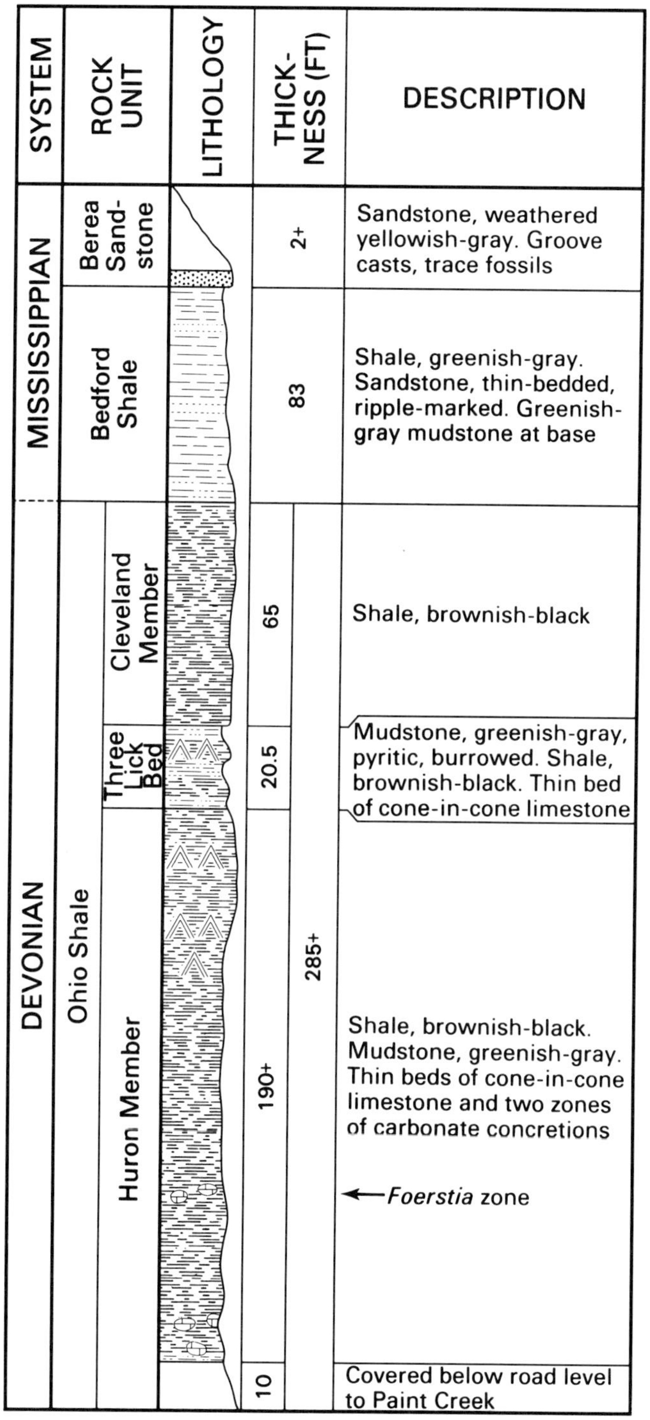

CRYSTAL CAVE, SOUTH BASS ISLAND, OTTAWA COUNTY

Location

South Bass Island, the largest of the three Bass Islands in the western part of Lake Erie, is located a few miles north of Catawba Point, in northeastern Ottawa County, on the Put-in-Bay 7.5-minute quadrangle (fig. 52). Lime Kiln Dock at the southern tip of South Bass Island and the docks at Put-in-Bay are reached by ferries from Catawba Point and Port Clinton, respectively, between May and September. Rental bicycles and bus transportation are available near the dock area during the tourist season for touring the island. Crystal Cave lies near the middle of South Bass Island on the south side of Catawba Avenue. The cave is located on the property of Louis V. Heineman, where a well-known winery is maintained. A fee is charged to enter the cave, and no collecting is allowed. Further information is available from: Louis V. Heineman, Put-in-Bay, Ohio 43456 (phone: 419-285-2811). A second cave, Perry's Cave, is located across the street from Crystal Cave and can be viewed for a fee. Rock exposures can be examined also at South Bass Island State Park on the west side of the island. Camping and picnic facilities are available there as well. Additional information can be obtained from the Manager, South Bass Island State Park, 4049 East Moores Dock Road, Port Clinton, Ohio 43452 (phone: 419-797-4530).

Geology

The upper Silurian Bass Islands Dolomite was named for the Bass Islands, where the formation achieves its best development (Sparling, 1970; Janssens, 1977). This fine-grained, gray to brown dolostone is well bedded, unfossiliferous, and about 60 feet thick in the region. The Bass Islands Dolomite is resistant to weathering and forms the rock exposures of the three islands everywhere except for the base of the cliffs along the southwest coast of South Bass Island, where the underlying strata of the Salina Group appear. These Salina rocks consist of a less resistant sequence of dolostones, shales, and evaporites that drill cores have proven to be about 600 feet thick. Gypsum is present in the Salina rocks beneath South Bass Island at shallow depths and has been dredged up from the waters off its southwestern shore (Newberry, 1874b; Kraus, 1905b). Structurally, the islands lie on the east flank of the Findlay Arch, and the Bass Islands rocks are gently inclined (less than 1 degree) towards the east. Figure 53 is a geologic cross section of the strata of South Bass and Kelleys Islands.

South Bass Island has numerous caves and sinkholes, and streams at the land surface are conspicuously absent (Newberry, 1874b; White, G. W., 1926). In addition to Crystal Cave and Perry's Cave, which are the only caves open to the public at present, several others have been discovered over the years. The sinkholes, which are funnel-shaped depressions on the land surface that form when the roofs of caves collapse, are as large as 600 feet across. The

FIGURE 51.—Stratigraphic section at Copperas Mountain (modified from Kepferle and others, 1981; Carlson, 1987b).

location of some of the larger sinkholes are outlined by depression contours on figure 52.

Crystal Cave, whose walls are lined with huge celestite crystals, is one of the most spectacular geological features in Ohio. It is a striking example of a mineral occurrence in a cavernous dolostone and is one of many similar deposits that compose the Findlay Arch district (Carlson, 1983). Formed in the Bass Islands Dolomite, this relatively small cave is about 30 feet below the surface (Sparling, 1970). According to Thorndale (1898), the cave was discovered in 1882 by Emiel Vanador, a lieutenant in the German army, who intended to develop the property into a strontium mine. Later, Gustav Heineman acquired the land, and in 1897 and 1898, the original 3-foot high cave was deepened so that visitors could stand erect. Enlargement was accomplished by removing approximately 150 tons of celestite

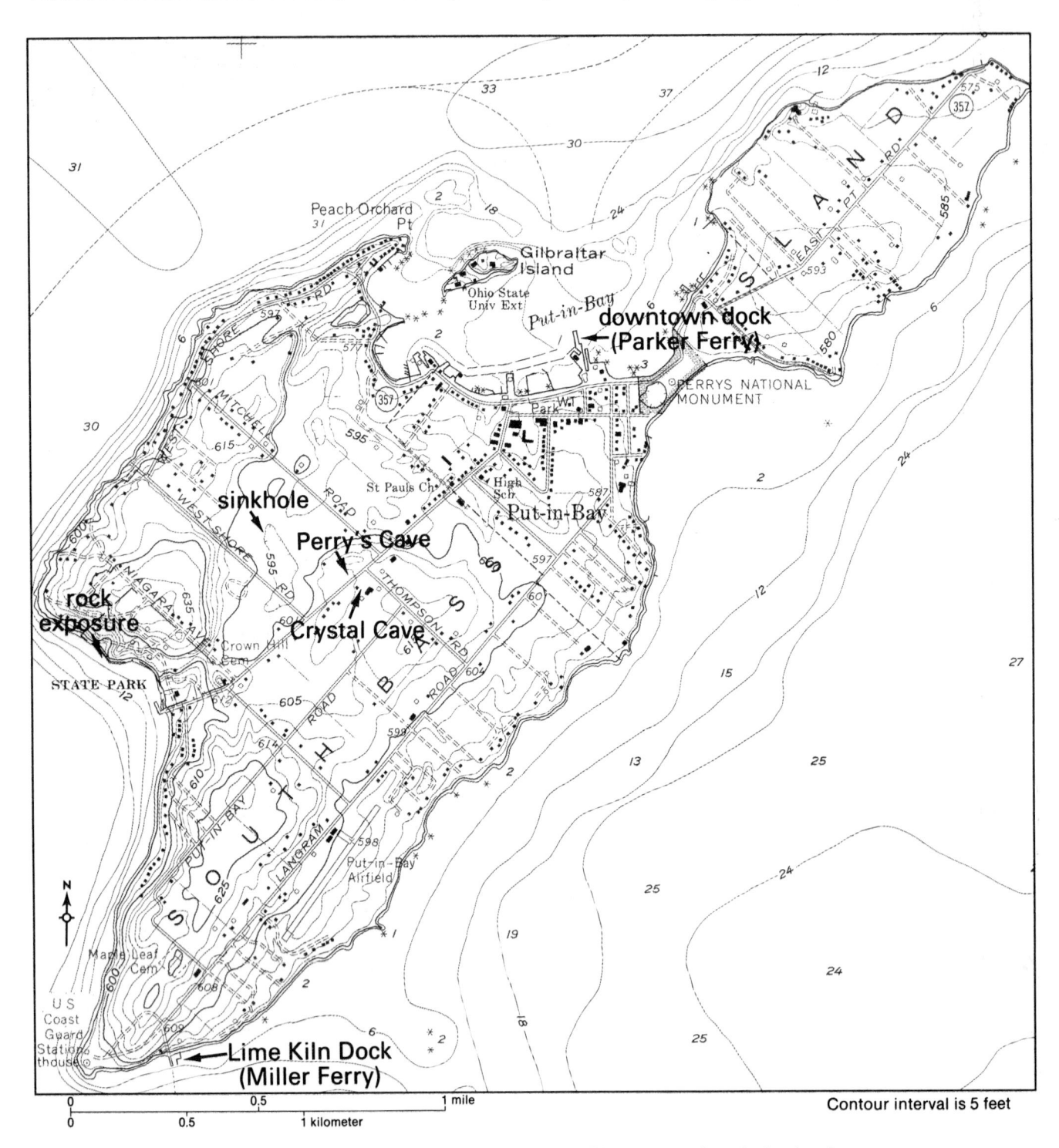

FIGURE 52.—South-central part of the Put-in-Bay 7.5-minute quadrangle showing the Crystal Cave site on South Bass Island, Ottawa County.

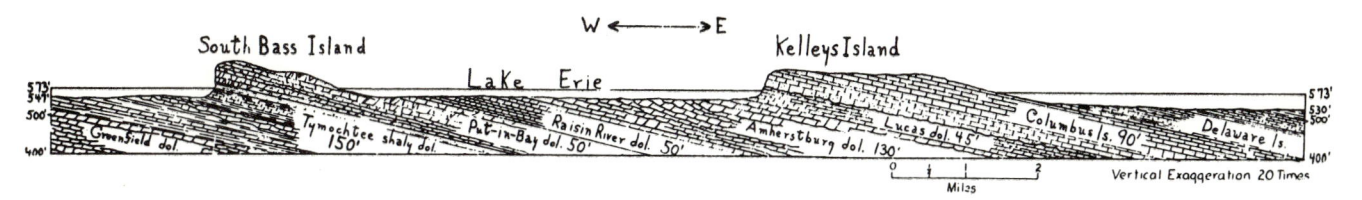

FIGURE 53.—Geologic cross section through South Bass Island and Kelleys Island (from Carman, 1946, fig. 37). The true angle of inclination of the strata is less than 1 degree.

crystals that once lined the floor (Kraus, 1905a; White, G. W., 1926).

Two hypotheses have been proposed to account for the caves of South Bass Island (White, G. W., 1926; Verber and Stansbery, 1953). According to the first idea, a cave originates when cracks in the rock, such as joints and bedding planes, are widened by underground waters, which have gradually dissolved the rock until the present shape of the roof and floor is attained. The roof and floor of a cave of this type do not match because the "missing" rock was removed by dissolution. Most caves in limestone terrain are believed to have originated in this manner, for example, Ohio Caverns, which are located east of West Liberty in Champaign County.

The second hypothesis of cave formation maintains that the roof and floor of a cave were separated along a bedding or joint plane when subsidence of the floor occurred. Because the shape of the roof and floor do match in a cave of this kind, it is assumed that a bed below the present floor was removed by selective dissolution, and the cave originated when the floor subsided into the void beneath it. Most caves on South Bass Island, including Perry's Cave, have roofs and floor that match and are believed to have originated in this manner. Although gypsum beds, which are invariably more soluble than the enclosing rocks, are not present in the Bass Islands Dolomite, they do occur in the Salina rocks which underlie the island beneath the Bass Islands Dolomite.

Because Crystal Cave is unique among the caves of South Bass Island, its origin is not known with certainty. The shape of its roof and floor, for example, cannot be matched because the roof and walls are covered with a 2-foot layer of crystals. By contrast, almost all of the other caves on the island are barren of mineralization. The only known exception is the celestite-bearing Kindt's Cave, formerly known as Smith's Cave, whose roof and floor match (White, G. W., 1926; Langlois, 1951; Stansbery, 1965). Furthermore, Crystal Cave remains dry even after heavy rains, unlike the other caves, which at least periodically contain some water. Crystal Cave originated sometime after the Bass Islands Dolomite was consolidated into solid rock (late Silurian) and before the area was scoured by glacial ice (Pleistocene). Evidence of the pre-Pleistocene age of Crystal Cave is provided by the celestite crystals. Sometime after the cave formed, the crystals began to grow along the walls by precipitation from mineralized waters that slowly moved through the opening. These waters were highly saline and hot, having temperatures that exceeded 68°C (see Roedder, 1969, 1979), in sharp contrast to the salt-free, cool ground waters of South Bass Island today. Such waters could have been present only in preglacial times when the Bass Islands Dolomite at Crystal Cave was deeply buried under Devonian (and younger) rocks. Subsequently, the cave was drained of water, the pore spaces of its walls were cemented tightly, and the Devonian (and younger) rocks were removed by erosion.

Mineralogy

The celestite crystals in Crystal Cave are exceptionally large, ranging from 8 to 18 inches in length, and are possibly the largest celestite crystals in the world (Kraus, 1905a; White, G. W., 1926). They are white to pale blue, particularly well formed, and display a tabular habit. Crystals of calcite also have been reported in the cave by Botoman and Stieglitz (1978).

Elsewhere on the island, sulfur, fluorite, barite, and hexahydrite are present in addition to calcite and celestite. Exceptionally fine crystals of calcite, celestite, and sulfur were found lining pockets in the dolostone as early as 1859 by local residents (Dana, J. D., 1868; Newberry, 1874b; Thorndale, 1898). Cubic crystals of brown fluorite, typical of the Findlay Arch mineral district, were reported by Kindt (1952). Small crystals of milky-white to colorless barite also were noted along the west shore north of the park (Stansbery, 1965). However, most parts of the island are presently closed to collecting. Fluffy coatings of white hexahydrite form efflorescences on sheltered exposures of the weathered dolostone along the cliff at the state park.

FLINT RIDGE AREA, LICKING AND MUSKINGUM COUNTIES

Location

The Flint Ridge area is northwest of Zanesville in Hopewell Township, Licking County, and western Hopewell Township, Muskingum County (fig. 54). The area is covered by the Glenford, Gratiot, Hanover, and Toboso 7.5-minute quadrangles. Flint Ridge State Memorial is about 3 miles north of Brownsville on Licking County Highway 668, in the western part of the ridge. The facilities include a nature museum, a trail that winds through old flint workings, and picnic tables; however, no collecting is allowed within the boundaries of the memorial. Further information is available from: The Ohio Historical Society, Ohio Historical Center, 1985 Velma Avenue, Columbus, Ohio 43211 (phone: 614-297-2300).

The flint bed is well exposed along Licking County Highway 668 just north of the boundary of the memorial and on several farms east and northeast of the memorial. The road cut (site 1), which is hazardous because of traffic, is reached by a quarter-mile walk north from the parking area at the memorial. Better quality flint can be collected on a fee basis on private properties in the area. As of the writing of this report, the following landowners allow collecting by permission for a fee: Clayton Mason (site 2), 15886 Flint Ridge Road S.E. (Licking County Highway 312), Newark, Ohio 43055 (phone: 614-787-2503); John Nethers (site 3), 3680 Flint Ridge Road (Muskingum County Highway 8), Hopewell, Ohio 43746 (phone: 614-787-2263); Basil Norris (site 4), 4695 Pert Hill Road (Hopewell Township Highway 413), Nashport, Ohio 43830 (phone: 614-787-2234);

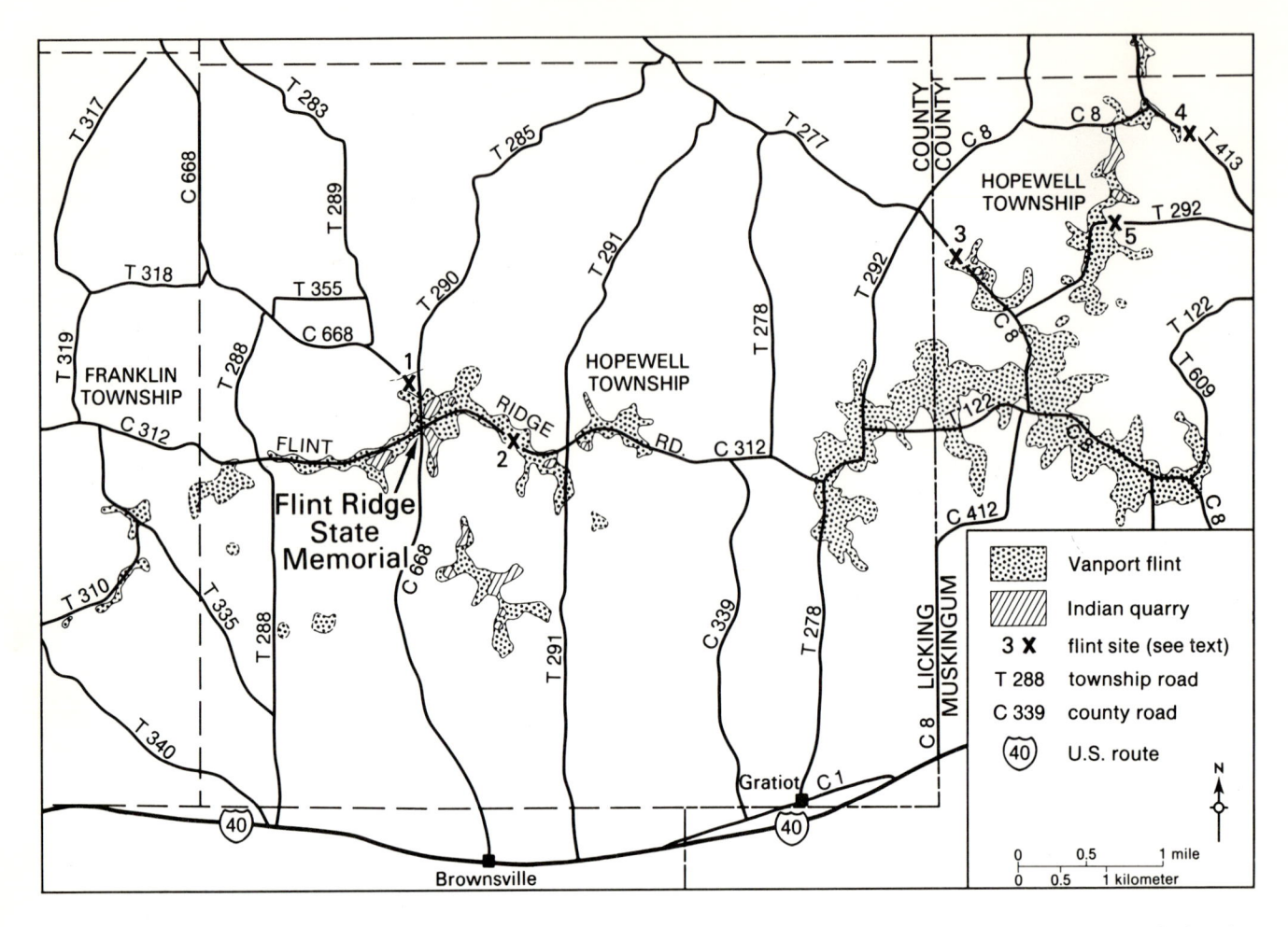

FIGURE 54.—Map of the Flint Ridge area, Licking and Muskingum Counties, showing the lower contact of the Vanport flint, the location of prehistoric Indian quarries, and the location of collecting areas described in the text (modified from Mills, 1921; DeLong, 1972; Carlson, 1987a).

and Gene Wyrick (site 5), 9305 Hidden Springs Road (Hopewell Township Highway 292), Hopewell, Ohio 43746 (phone: 614-787-2060). Collecting is best in early spring before the new growth obscures the ground surface. A shovel, wrecking bar, rock hammer, and chisel are needed to extract the flint, and a bucket, a stiff brush, and water are needed to clean it. Camping and recreational facilities are available a few miles east of Flint Ridge at Dillon State Park. Contact: Manager, Dillon State Park, P.O. Box 126, Nashport, Ohio 43830 (phone: 614-453-4377).

Geology

The Pennsylvanian Vanport limestone (Allegheny Group) has a widespread but patchy distribution across eastern Ohio and western Pennsylvania (Lamborn, 1951). This unit is well developed in the Flint Ridge area of Licking and Muskingum Counties, where it consists of 1 to 38 feet of shaly limestone, calcareous shale, and flint (Stout and Schoenlaub, 1945; DeLong, 1972). The flint rests on limestone or shale and forms a massive, nearly continuous sheet 8 miles long and 3 miles wide (fig. 54) at the top of the Vanport limestone (fig. 55). Across the ridge, the flint bed averages 5 feet thick; it reaches a maximum of 12 feet at the south end of the State Memorial and thins towards the edges (Stout and Schoenlaub, 1945). The characteristics of this sheet, the largest and purest deposit of flint in the state, can be seen at the road cut on Licking County Highway 668 (site 1), where the bed is 8 feet thick (see fig. 8). Porous tan flint of low quality, which was fashioned by pioneers into millstones, occurs at the western and southeastern margins of the sheet. The Vanport limestone lies between two sequences of continental (nonmarine) strata, the Clarion shale and sandstone below and the Kittanning shale and sandstone above (fig. 55); the Clarion (No. 4A) coal, which normally underlies the Vanport, is absent at Flint Ridge (DeLong, 1972).

The Vanport unit, particularly the shale, contains an abundant marine fauna. The flint and limestone bear a distinctive fusulinid about the size and shape of wheat grains that, when plentiful, gives the rock the appearance of worm-eaten wood (Smyth, 1957). Brachiopods, gastropods, bivalves, and even trilobites are less common in the flint (Stout, 1918). Spinelike sponge spicules are locally common in the flint and are highly significant because they probably were the source of the silica in the deposit (Mills, 1921; Cavaroc and Ferm, 1968; Carlson, 1987a). In general, the thick flint beds of high quality are less fossiliferous than the thinner, impure ones. The fossils in the pure flint are completely replaced by silica.

Because of the resistance of the flint to weathering and erosion, Flint Ridge stands high above the surrounding

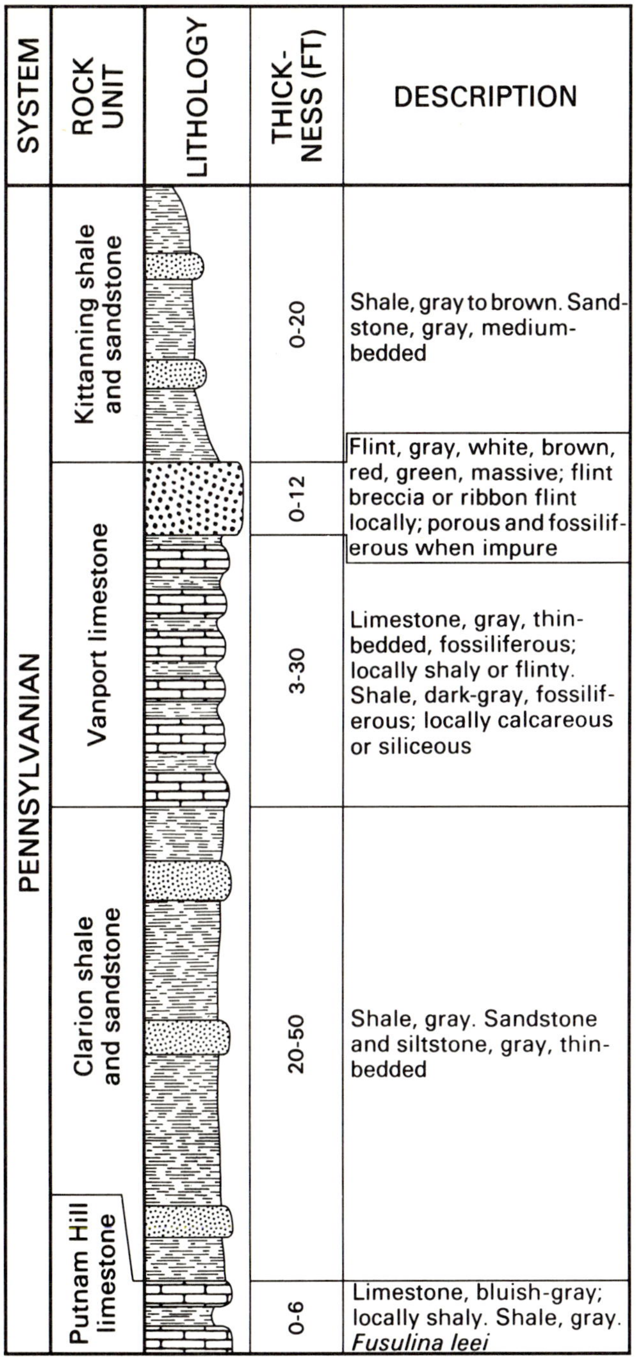

SYSTEM	ROCK UNIT	LITHOLOGY	THICK-NESS (FT)	DESCRIPTION
PENNSYLVANIAN	Kittanning shale and sandstone		0-20	Shale, gray to brown. Sandstone, gray, medium-bedded
	Vanport limestone		0-12	Flint, gray, white, brown, red, green, massive; flint breccia or ribbon flint locally; porous and fossiliferous when impure
			3-30	Limestone, gray, thin-bedded, fossiliferous; locally shaly or flinty. Shale, dark-gray, fossiliferous; locally calcareous or siliceous
	Clarion shale and sandstone		20-50	Shale, gray. Sandstone and siltstone, gray, thin-bedded
	Putnam Hill limestone		0-6	Limestone, bluish-gray; locally shaly. Shale, gray. *Fusulina leei*

FIGURE 55.—Generalized stratigraphic section of the Flint Ridge area (modified from DeLong, 1972; Carlson, 1987a).

terrain. For this reason, the ridge was not glaciated during the Pleistocene Ice Age, even though glacial ice surrounded it on the west and south during Illinoian time (Goldthwait and others, 1961; Forsyth, 1966b).

To the prehistoric Indians, Flint Ridge was probably the most important supply of flint for making tools and weapons in the eastern United States and possibly the entire country (Fowke, 1894; Wilson, T., 1899; Holmes, 1919). These Indians developed numerous quarries that were concentrated in the western and northeastern sections of the ridge (fig. 54), where the flint was relatively thick and the quality was high. One of the pits that the Indians dug can be observed in a unique display that occupies the floor of the museum at the State Memorial.

Mineralogy

Flint is the chief mineral of the deposit (Hildreth, 1829; Smith, C. M., 1885; Mills, 1921; Stout and Schoenlaub, 1945). High-quality material is dense and translucent to opaque and has a conchoidal fracture and a greasy luster. Although it ranges from white to black, the flint is typically light gray or milky white with darker gray patches and streaks (sites 1 and 2). However, the brightly colored red, yellow, blue, and green varieties are unique among the flints of Ohio and are known worldwide for their beauty. Ribbon flint (see fig. 9), with alternating dark- and light-gray layers, is locally abundant in the northeastern section of the ridge (site 3). Minerals that were introduced into the rock after the flint was deposited include chalcedony, quartz, barite, calcite, and an unidentified manganese oxide. Pockets and fractures in the flint are common and may be lined by or filled with fibrous, translucent, bluish-white chalcedony. Small, colorless, rhombohedrally terminated quartz crystals formed later than the chalcedony and commonly are perched on it. More rarely, the pockets contain crystals of barite and calcite. Thin coatings of a dendritic black manganese oxide are found on the surfaces of some fractured blocks of flint.

WEST BRANCH HURON RIVER, HURON COUNTY

Location

This locality is situated along the banks of West Branch Huron River in central Ridgefield Township, north-central Huron County, on the Kimball 7.5-minute quadrangle (fig. 56). The area is reached from U.S. Route 20 at Monroeville by traveling north on North St. and then northeast for about 2 miles along Peru Center Road, turning south then east on Lamereaux Road, and continuing to the river. The area can be reached from the north by traveling southwest on Ohio Route 113 from Milan, turning south onto Peru Center Road, and then south onto Lamereaux Road. Vehicles should be parked on the shoulder of the road on the west side of the bridge. The sites are reached by walking along the river banks. Do not cross the fields. The river banks are especially dangerous in the spring and after heavy rains when the river is high and the shale is slick; the area should be avoided at those times. Sledge hammers, rock hammers, and rock chisels are needed to break open the large concretions.

Geology

The Huron River area is noted for superb exposures of a black, carbonaceous, marine shale, appropriately named the Huron Shale by early geologists (Newberry, 1874b; Prosser, 1913). This rock unit, which is the lowest member of the upper Devonian Ohio Shale, is about 200 feet thick and is subdivided into lower, middle, and upper units by Broadhead and others (1980). Cliffs up to 65 feet high contain almost continuous exposures of these rocks along an 8-mile stretch of the river and its branches between Monroeville (north-central Huron County) and Milan (south-central Erie County). The shale is sparsely fossiliferous, but brachiopods, fish, and thin layers of shiny black coaly material up to ⅛ inch thick are present locally.

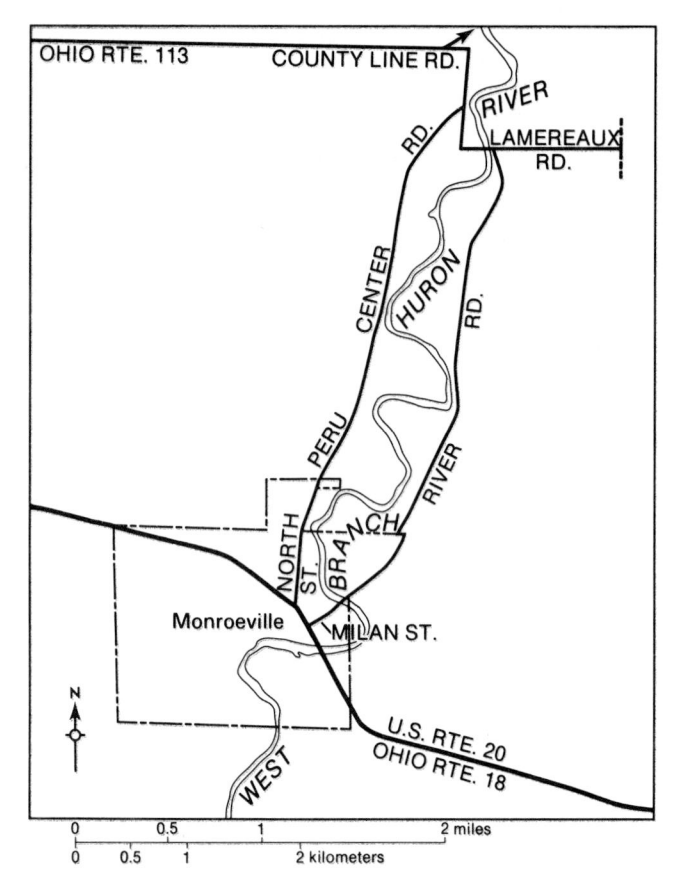

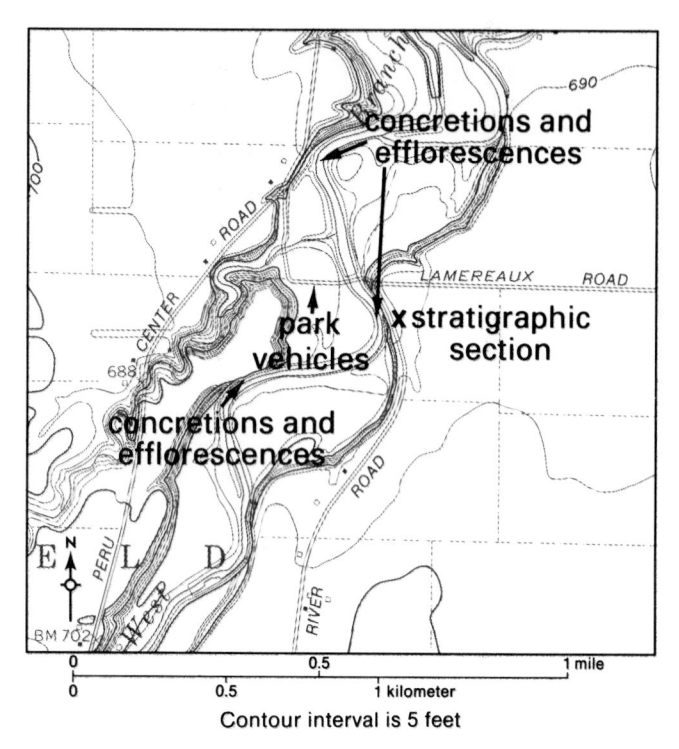

FIGURE 56.—Vicinity map (left) and south-central part of the Kimball 7.5-minute quadrangle (above) showing the West Branch Huron River site, Huron County.

Portions of the middle and upper units of the Huron Shale Member are particularly well exposed along the river at the Lamereaux Road site. The stratigraphic section of Broadhead and others (1980) for these rocks in the 54-foot-high cliff along the east side of the river (see fig. 56) is given below.

Stratigraphic section of the Huron Shale Member along the West Branch Huron River at Lamereaux Road (modified from Broadhead and others, 1980, p. 10-15).

Devonian (incomplete)
  Ohio Shale (incomplete, 54.3 ft+)
    Upper part of Huron Member
    (incomplete, 24 ft+)

	Thickness (ft) Unit	Cumulative
Shale, black; weathers grayish red and light brown; silt is present as sparse laminae a few grains thick or as disseminated grains; petroliferous; parts into brittle plates 1 to 10 mm thick. Lower contact is abrupt and planar. Top of unit is overgrown with grass and trees. Contains large, black, spheroidal to ovoid carbonate concretions 4 to 5 ft in diameter. Unit is a conspicuous bed of shale, which is more resistant to weathering than the interbedded units exposed. *Foerstia* found near base of unit	24.0	24.0

  Middle part of Huron Member
  (incomplete, 30.3 ft+)

Shale, medium-gray, containing sparse globular pyrite and some fine-grained, medium-gray carbonate concretions that have the form of flattened spheroids as much as 2 ft in diameter and 1 ft thick	1.7	25.7
Shale, black	0.2	25.9
Shale, medium-gray	0.6	26.5

	Thickness (ft) Unit	Cumulative
Shale, black	0.1	26.6
Shale, medium-gray	0.5	27.1
Shale, black	0.2	27.3
Shale, medium-gray	0.4	27.7
Shale, black	0.2	27.9
Shale, medium-gray	0.7	28.6
Shale, black	0.1	28.7
Shale, medium-gray	0.1	28.8
Shale, black	0.2	29.0
Shale, medium-gray	0.2	29.2
Shale, black	0.1	29.3
Shale, medium-gray	0.1	29.4
Shale, black, sparse pyrite	0.8	30.2
Shale, medium-gray	0.9	31.1
Shale, black	0.2	31.3
Shale, medium-gray	0.4	31.7
Shale, black	1.9	33.6
Shale, medium-gray, containing 5 percent black-shale laminae	5.3	38.9
Shale, black	0.2	39.1
Shale, medium-gray	0.2	39.3
Shale, black	0.2	39.5
Shale, medium-gray, containing 5 percent black-shale laminae, which pinch and swell	2.2	41.7
Shale, black	0.4	42.1
Shale, medium-gray	0.2	42.3
Shale, black	1.0	43.3
Shale, medium-gray	0.1	43.4
Shale, black	0.2	43.6
Shale, medium-gray	0.2	43.8
Shale, black	0.3	44.1
Shale, medium-gray, containing 5 percent black-shale laminae, which are laterally undulose and uniform in thickness	1.3	45.4
Shale, black	0.2	45.6
Shale, medium-gray	0.7	46.3
Shale, black	0.7	47.0

Middle part of Huron Member (continued)	Thickness (ft)	
	Unit	Cumulative
Shale, medium-gray	0.2	47.2
Shale, black	0.8	48.0
Shale, medium-gray	0.2	48.2
Shale, black	0.3	48.5
Shale, medium-gray	1.3	49.8
Shale, black	0.6	50.4
Shale, medium-gray	0.8	51.2
Shale, very dark gray	0.5	51.7
Shale, medium-gray	0.5	52.2
Shale, black	0.3	52.5
Shale, medium-gray	0.3	52.8
Shale, black	0.3	53.1
Shale, medium-gray, containing 5 percent thin to very thin black-shale beds, which are laterally undulose lenses 1 to 4 ft long and 0.1 to 0.3 ft thick	1.2	54.3

Here the upper unit of the Huron Member consists of a uniform sequence of black shale and is easily distinguished from the middle unit, which is characterized by interlayers of gray and black shale. *Foerstia*, a fossil alga with a restricted stratigraphic range, occurs near the base of the upper unit (Broadhead and others, 1980).

Because of their unusual size, the concretions of the Huron River area have excited the curiosity of residents and travelers alike since the 1800's (Newberry, 1874b). A zone of these large concretions is exposed above the bed of the river and forms a marker bed near the base of the Huron Member. At the Lamereaux Road site the concretions from this bed are up to 8 feet in diameter. This same concretion-rich bed can be traced northward to Lake Erie and southward to the Ohio River and is identical to the one at the Copperas Mountain site in Ross County described earlier in this chapter.

The concretions are more resistant than the enclosing shale and weather free and roll to the bed of the river, where they can be examined when water levels are low. Loose fragments of broken concretions litter the banks and the bed of the river and can be inspected easily. The concretions in the Lamereaux Road area are spherical to markedly flattened gray to grayish-black septaria 2 to 8 feet wide. The remains of fossil sharks or petrified wood are found at the centers of some of these septaria (Newberry, 1870, 1874b, 1889), suggesting that organic matter served as the nuclei around which the concretions developed. That the mud composing the matrix of the concretions was cemented into carbonate rock before the enclosing clay was compacted into shale is evidenced by the pronounced arching of the shale around the concretions (see fig. 14). The veins of the septaria originated sometime after the original concretionary mud shrank when mineralized waters moved through the resulting shrinkage cracks and deposited the vein minerals. These well-crystallized, lustrous vein minerals contrast sharply with the massive, dull bodies of the septaria.

Nodules of pyrite that average a few inches in diameter also weather out of the shale banks and can be picked up in scree rock at the base of the cliffs and in the bed of the river. These nodules, which may be septaria, are characterized by their heaviness and rough shiny surfaces of projecting crystals.

Mineralogy

The bodies of the large septaria consist of a fine-grained mixture of dolomite, calcite, quartz, unidentified clay minerals, pyrite, and carbonaceous matter, as determined from an examination of the matrix and its insoluble residue. Because dolomite is predominant, these rocks are limestone concretions (see definition in Chapter 3).

The veins of the septaria consist of coarse-grained aggregates of minerals that generally fill the cracks, although pockets with well-formed crystals may be found. The chief vein minerals are calcite, dolomite, ferroan dolomite, barite, and quartz; aragonite, pyrite, and sphalerite are more rare. The calcite, dolomite, and ferroan dolomite are closely associated and typically occur as granular masses or intergrowths of rhombohedral crystals. The minerals are distinguished as follows: calcite is white to brown and commonly displays an intense yellow fluorescence under both long and short wavelengths; dolomite is tan to pale yellow and is generally nonfluorescent; ferroan dolomite is brown, weathers darker brown or reddish brown, and generally shows a yellow fluorescence that is most intense under long wavelength. Barite characteristically occurs in lustrous, colorless, tabular plates up to 6 inches across (see fig. 15), although crystals with complex combinations of forms do occur. The quartz is colorless and typically appears in small granular masses or more rarely in doubly terminated crystals that display a combination of rhombohedrons (see fig. 16). Needles of colorless aragonite, tiny grains of pyrite, and small masses of lustrous, brown sphalerite are less common. Whewellite, which has been observed in large septaria west of Milan (Hyde, C., and Landy, 1966; Leavens, 1968), has not been identified at the Lamereaux Road site.

The nodular pyrite occurs in two forms, as knobby masses of finely crystalline equant grains and as disk-shaped bodies of radiating acicular crystals (see fig. 19). The knobby masses are commonly septaria and contain veinlets of barite and, less commonly, dolomite; the disk-shaped bodies are solid masses of pyrite.

The thin layers of coaly material in the shale exhibit tiny polygonal cracks that are filled with veins of white barite. Barite occurrences of this type were first reported from "asphaltic coal" in the Huron Shale Member at Monroeville by Leeds (1875) and Newberry (1875).

Efflorescences accumulate on the undersides of overhanging ledges of shale as coatings and porous ball-shaped masses up to 3 inches in diameter (see fig. 36). The efflorescences consist chiefly of silky, fibrous crystals of white halotrichite-pickeringite and acicular crystals of colorless gypsum.

MILL HOLLOW-BACON WOODS PARK, LORAIN COUNTY

Location

Mill Hollow-Bacon Woods Park, part of the Lorain County Metropolitan Park District, is located along the banks of the Vermilion River in Brownhelm Township, on the Vermilion East 7.5-minute quadrangle (fig. 57). The park is reached from Vermilion by traveling south along Vermilion Road for about 3.5 miles, turning west onto North Ridge Road, and continuing to the river. The park also can be reached from Ohio Route 60 at Axtel, in Erie County, by traveling east on North Ridge Road to the river. A nature museum and picnic and camping facilities are available in the park. Loose concretions may be collected but digging is not permitted. Further information is available from: Lorain County Metropolitan Park District, 126 Second Street, Elyria, Ohio 44035 (phone: 216-322-7800).

Geology

At Mill Hollow-Bacon Woods Park, vertical cliffs 100 feet high have been carved along the east bank of the Vermilion

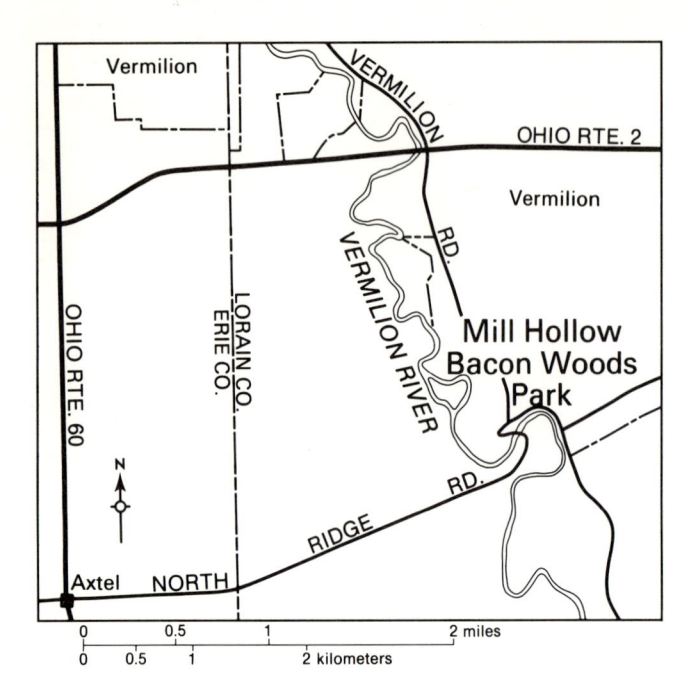

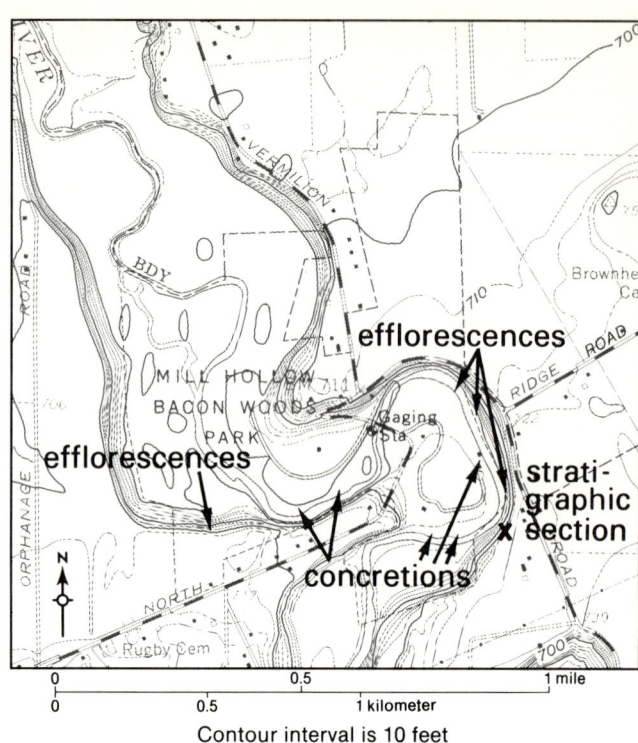

FIGURE 57.—Vicinity map (left) and south-central part of the Vermilion East 7.5-minute quadrangle (right) showing the Mill Hollow-Bacon Woods Park area, Lorain County.

River and provide a scenic panorama of the Cleveland Shale Member and the Bedford Shale (Prosser, 1913; Broadhead and others, 1980). The lower half of the cliffs to the bed of the river are cut in the Cleveland Member, the uppermost member of the upper Devonian Ohio Shale. The Cleveland Member is a sparsely fossiliferous, black, carbonaceous marine shale that is 48 feet thick at the Mill Hollow-Bacon Woods Park site (Broadhead and others, 1980). The Cleveland Member at this locality also contains a few thin beds of dark-gray limestone with cone-in-cone structure. The lower contact of the Cleveland Member with the underlying gray Chagrin Shale Member is gradational, and the rocks below this contact consist of interlayered beds of black (Cleveland) and gray (Chagrin) shale. These interlayered rocks are well exposed about 2 miles farther downstream in the lower part of the cliffs. The upper half of the cliffs at the park consists of the lower Mississippian Bedford Shale, which rests conformably on the Cleveland Shale Member. The Bedford rocks are about 40 feet thick and consist of a sequence of alternating red and gray shales and a few thin interbeds of a resistant brown siltstone (Prosser, 1913; Herdendorf, 1963). A stratigraphic section of the rocks exposed on the east bank of the Vermilion River is given below.

Stratigraphic section of Cleveland Shale Member and Bedford Shale at Mill Hollow-Bacon Woods Park, Lorain County (modified from Broadhead and others, 1980, p. 25-26).

	Thickness (ft)	
Mississippian and Devonian (incomplete) Bedford Shale (incomplete, 24.3 ft+)	Unit	Cumulative
Shale, grayish-red, silty, 3- to 6-mm-thick tabular partings	20.0	20.0
Siltstone, medium-gray, laterally traceable along meander cuts for at least 0.5 mile	0.3	20.3
	Thickness (ft)	
	Unit	Cumulative
Shale, medium-gray	4.0	24.3
Devonian (incomplete) Ohio Shale (incomplete) Cleveland Member (48.0 ft)		
Shale, black, weathers to dark-yellowish-orange; coating of sulfides. Silt is present as thin laminae a few grains thick and as disseminated grains. Some small, thin, medium-dark-gray cone-in-cone limestone lenses are in the lowermost 10 ft (0.1 ft thick and 2 to 4 ft long). Lower contact is abrupt and defines a very gentle syncline	48.0	72.3

The Vermilion River area is renowned for the septaria-bearing beds in the lower and upper parts of the Cleveland Shale Member (Holden and Carlson, 1979). At Mill Hollow-Bacon Woods Park, the best of the known sites, the lower part of the Cleveland Member is exposed in the low banks of the river opposite the cliffs. Large numbers of these septaria weather out of the shale on the west bank on the south side of the North Ridge Road bridge, and the east bank on the north side of the bridge.

The body of a typical septarium is dark gray with an internal network of light-colored veins that produce a distinctive ribbed appearance on the surface. The septaria are 1 to 4 inches in diameter, notably heavy, and typically disk shaped, although some are spherical. They are known popularly as "turtle rocks" because the ribbed surface superficially resembles the shell of a turtle. The veins, which do not reach the outermost surface of an unweathered septarian concretion, are resistant to weathering and become visible as ribs only after part of the less resistant shell has weathered away. Therefore, the appearance of the outer surface depends on the degree of weathering. An unweathered septarian concretion, for example, has a relatively smooth surface, but as weathering progresses the veins gradually produce a ribbed effect as they become increasingly exposed (see fig. 21).

Pyrite nodules also weather out of the Cleveland Shale Member in the Mill Hollow-Bacon Woods Park area. The nodules are 1 to 4 inches in diameter, disk shaped, and have knobby surfaces.

Mineralogy

The matrix of a typical septarium is composed of a fine-grained mixture of barite, quartz, pyrite, and carbonaceous material (Holden and Carlson, 1979). Because barite is the predominant constituent, the Vermilion River septaria are unique; barite septaria have not been reported elsewhere in Ohio. In unweathered septaria, a thin shell of fine-grained pyrite encloses the barite.

The veins of the septaria consist chiefly of barite, quartz, and chalcedony (see fig. 21); lesser amounts of pyrite and calcite are present. The outer margins of the veins characteristically exhibit thin layers of white chalcedony that parallel the walls. The interiors of the veins are composed predominantly of coarse-grained, granular intergrowths of colorless barite and quartz. Tiny grains of pyrite and, more rarely, masses of granular, white calcite also are found in the veins. Small pockets in the veins may be lined with terminated crystals of colorless barite and quartz.

The pyrite nodules are relatively pure and consist of radiating masses of acicular crystals. Pyritized fossils occur at the centers of some of the nodules.

Efflorescences are prominently developed on sheltered exposures of the Cleveland Member. White pickeringite, which occurs in porous masses of silky, fibrous crystals, is the most common efflorescence (Collins, R. F., 1924).

NELLIE-WARSAW AREA, COSHOCTON COUNTY

Location

The Nellie-Warsaw flint area borders the Walhonding River in Jefferson Township, in west-central Coshocton County (fig. 58); this area is on the Warsaw and Randle 7.5-minute quadrangles. Nellie and Warsaw lie on U.S. Route 36 and are reached by traveling west from Coshocton (Coshocton County) or east from Mount Vernon (Knox County). Road cuts provide good exposures of flint in the area and five sites are easily accessible: site 1, on the northeast side of Township Highway 53, 0.9 mile north of its intersection with Ohio Route 79; site 2, along County Highway 82, 0.6 mile west of its intersection with Township Highway 59; site 3, on the northeast side of Township Highway 81, 0.35 mile southeast of its intersection with County Highway 82; site 4, on Township Highway 41, approximately 0.6 mile east of its junction with Ohio Route 60; and site 5, on the west side of Township Highway 31, 1.1 miles north of the north edge of Warsaw. Extreme caution should be observed at these sites because the roads are quite narrow and some are unpaved and can be muddy. Little parking space is available. A bucket, water, and stiff brush are helpful for cleaning the flint. A roadside park is located at Mohawk Dam on the south side of Ohio Route 715 about 2 miles west of Nellie.

Geology

The Pennsylvanian Upper Mercer limestone (Pottsville Group) is a widespread unit in eastern Ohio and western Pennsylvania and averages a little over a foot in thickness (Lamborn, 1951). However, in the Jefferson Township area of Coshocton County, this unit attains its maximum development, and flint occupies part of the interval normally occupied by limestone. Here the Upper Mercer typically consists of a continuous sheet of flint up to 14 feet thick and an underlying dark-gray siliceous limestone (Hodge, 1878; Meyers, 1929; Lamborn, 1954). The Upper Mercer rocks lie 30 to 40 feet beneath the base of the Allegheny Group and crop out just below the ridge tops. Because the Upper Mercer flint occurs stratigraphically just below the Pottsville-Allegheny contact, this contact is useful for locating flint occurrences in the area (see fig. 58). A stratigraphic section near the head of Flint Run is given below. At this location the limestone and flint reach a combined thickness of 19 feet (site 3, fig. 58, is located just east of Lamborn's section); at sites 2 and 4 the Upper Mercer is 5 to 12 feet thick (Meyers, 1929; Lamborn, 1954). In other parts of the township (for example, sites 1 and 5) the unit is thinner and normally consists of 1 to 3 feet of flint. The sheetlike body of flint has an average thickness of about 5 feet over an area approximately 5 miles long, indicating the deposit is considerably smaller than the one at Flint Ridge in Licking and Muskingum Counties. The Upper Mercer limestone is underlain by the Bedford coal, a seam that averages 1 foot in thickness, and is overlain by the Upper Mercer ore, an ironstone bed that is less than 6 inches thick (Lamborn, 1954).

Most exposures of the flint are markedly fractured and fossiliferous. The fracturing together with the resistance of

Stratigraphic section of the Pottsville and Allegheny Groups on west side of valley near head of Flint Run (modified from Lamborn, 1954, p. 94).

		feet	inches
	Clay shale	12	0
	Clay shale, slightly ferruginous	31	4
	Limestone, gray, dense, fossiliferous, *Putnam Hill*	6	6
Allegheny Group	Covered interval	17	11
Pottsville Group	Flint, light	2	1
	Flint, gray-black, hard, fossiliferous } Upper	11	8
	Limestone, dark-blue, fossiliferous, with nodules of flint } Mercer	5	6
	Clay shale	-	8
	Coal, weathered	-	4
	Clay shale, light } Bedford	-	1
	Coal, cannel nature, shaly	-	11
	Clay, light, plastic, slightly siliceous	2	6
	Altitude, 1,008 ft		

the flint to weathering produces a litter of loose blocks on hillside or road-cut exposures. Both the limestone and the flint are distinguished by an abundant marine fauna, including brachiopods, bryozoans, cephalopods, corals, crinoids, foraminifera, and bivalves (Morningstar, 1922). These fossils, which are completely replaced with silica, are more abundant in the thinner flint beds than in the thicker ones.

The flint of Jefferson Township was shaped into tools and weapons by prehistoric Indians, who opened and developed quarries where the deposits were of good quality and adequate thickness. These quarries were operated chiefly in the ridges extending south of the Walhonding River, east of Mohawk and northwest of Flint Run (Smith, C. M., 1885; Moorehead, 1892; Fowke, 1894, 1902, 1928). Because the best quality material occurs near the base of the flint sheet, considerable excavation was required and the workings became quite extensive. Most of the old quarries still exist today, but are located on privately owned farmland that is not open to collecting. In contrast to the Flint Ridge area, where the flint was worked at the quarries, most of the Jefferson Township flint was carried to and fashioned at workshops located along the banks of the Walhonding River near Nellie (Prufer, 1963).

Mineralogy

The Jefferson Township deposit consists predominantly of flint (Morgan, R., 1929; Stout and Schoenlaub, 1945; Converse, 1972). The purest material, which is nearly comparable in quality to the flint from Flint Ridge, is massive, dense, lustrous, and translucent and has a conchoidal fracture. The flint ranges from white to black, but the vast majority is gray or slate blue. Although banding is uncommon, many specimens are streaked or mottled black and gray. Good-quality Jefferson Township flint is a prized lapidary material, even though it lacks the bright colors of Flint Ridge flint. The slate-blue variety is popularly known as Nellie blue flint. The dark color is believed to originate from trace amounts of carbonaceous matter and iron compounds in the flint (Stout and Schoenlaub, 1945). The surfaces of some weathered flint specimens are covered with a thin, chalky white layer, or patina, of finely crystalline

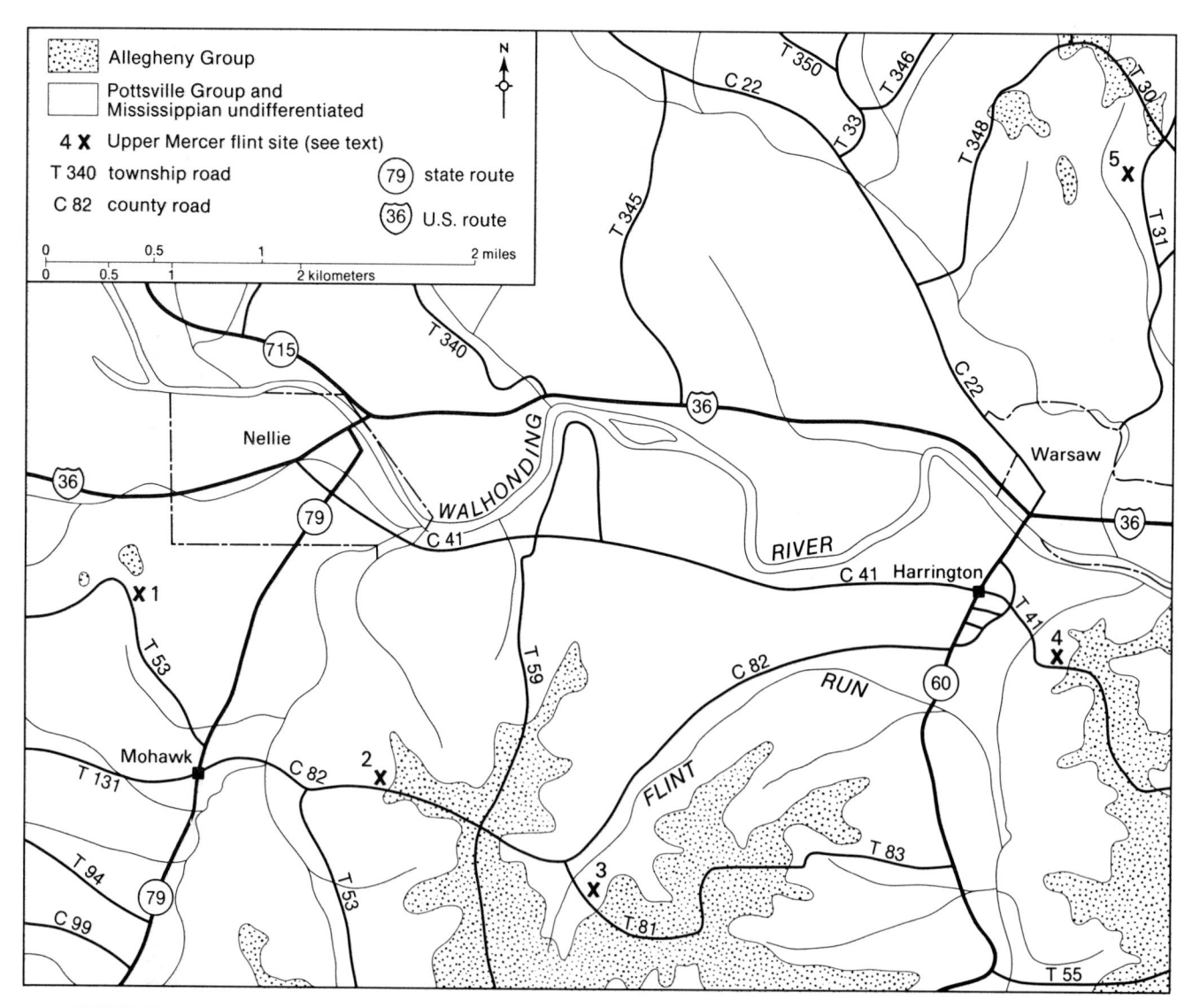

FIGURE 58.—Geologic map of the Nellie-Warsaw area, west-central Coshocton County, showing location of flint-collecting sites described in text. Pottsville-Allegheny contact from Lamborn (1954, pl. 1).

quartz.

Chalcedony and quartz line or fill the numerous small pockets and fractures in the rock and thus postdate the flint (Fowke, 1902). The fibrous, translucent, bluish-white chalcedony is the earlier of the two minerals, and small, drusy, colorless quartz crystals commonly are perched on the chalcedony. Chalcedony and quartz are less common and the quartz crystals are much smaller in the Jefferson Township flint than in the material from Flint Ridge. Joint surfaces in the flint may exhibit a black, dendritic coating of an unidentified manganese oxide.

SERPENT MOUND AREA, ADAMS COUNTY

Location

The Serpent Mound area is located at the mutual corners of Adams, Highland, and Pike Counties and lies mostly in Bratton and Franklin Townships, Adams County, on the Sinking Spring 7.5-minute quadrangle (fig. 59). Widely known both archaeologically and geologically, the Serpent Mound disturbance was designated as a National Natural Landmark in 1980 by the federal National Park Service. Serpent Mound State Memorial is about 4 miles northwest of Locust Grove (Adams County) on the north side of Ohio Route 73. The memorial includes the quarter-mile long mound-shaped serpent effigy, which reportedly is the largest and finest in the United States, as well as an observation tower, a natural science museum, and picnic tables. Further information can be obtained from the Manager, Serpent Mound State Memorial, Route 4, Peebles, Ohio 45660 (phone: 513-587-2897).

The rocks and mineralization can be observed at three easily accessible localities. Rock hammers are required to break open mineralized rock specimens. Site 1, a cliff exposure, is located at the north end of the memorial along the nature trail that starts near the tail of the serpent effigy. Site 2, a small abandoned roadside quarry, a gully just to the south, and the adjoining barren hillside, lies 0.7 mile east of the memorial entrance along Ohio Route 73

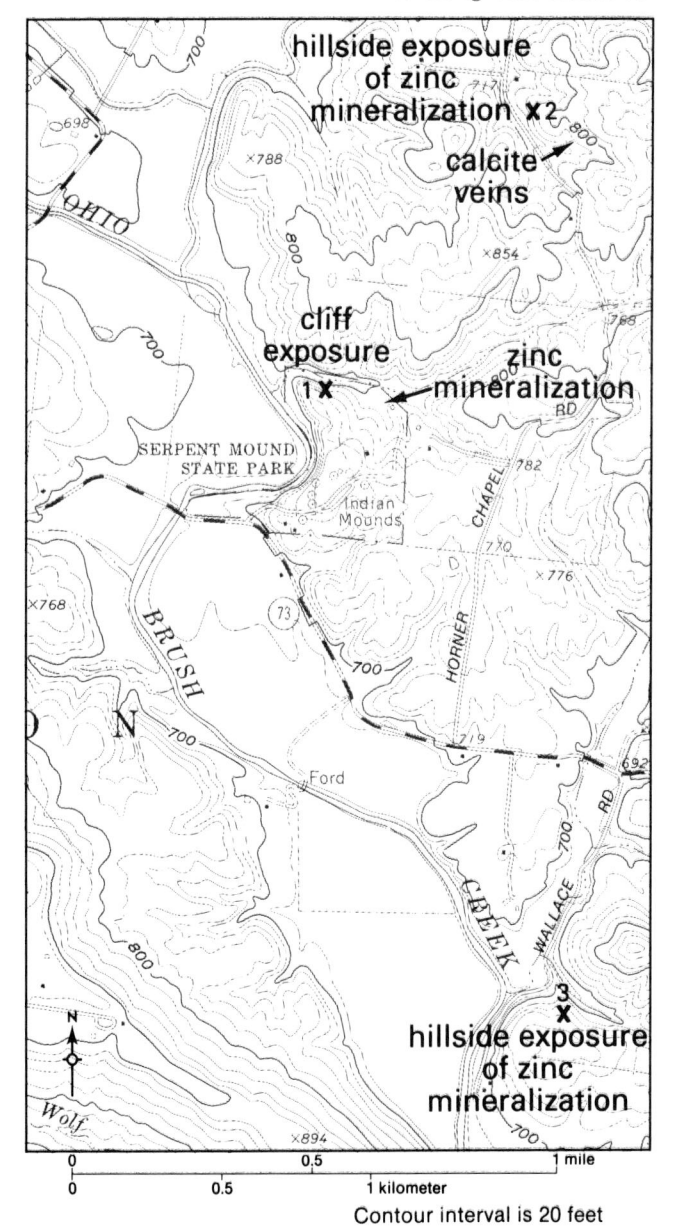

FIGURE 59.—Vicinity map (above) and south-central part of the Sinking Spring quadrangle (right) showing the Serpent Mound area, Adams County. Numbered sites are described in text.

and 1.4 miles north on Township Highway 116, on the east side of the road. The shoulder of the narrow road provides the only available parking at the latter site. Site 3, a hillside exposure, lies 1.0 mile east of the memorial entrance on Ohio Route 73 and 0.4 mile south on the east side of Wallace Road.

Camping facilities are available several miles to the north at Rocky Fork State Park in Highland County. Additional information can be obtained from the Park Manager, Rocky Fork State Park, Route 4, Box 363, Hillsboro, Ohio 45133.

Geology

The strata of the Serpent Mound area range from late Ordovician to early Mississippian in age; the Drakes Formation and the Cuyahoga Formation are the oldest and youngest beds, respectively. This thick sequence of rocks is quite varied and includes sandstones, siltstones, shales, limestones, and dolostones. However, the zinc mineralization is localized in a relatively narrow interval of middle and upper Silurian dolostones, specifically the Peebles Dolomite, Greenfield Dolomite, and Tymochtee Dolomite. These strata are composed of porous and in places reeflike gray to tan dolostones with a combined thickness of a little over 100 feet. Because these rocks have no distinguishing characteristics once they have been intensely deformed, they are commonly grouped into a single unit on geologic maps of the area (Reidel, 1975).

The region is renowned for a unique geological structure known as the Serpent Mound disturbance (fig. 60). This feature, first noted by Locke (1838) and later mapped by Bucher (1936) and again by Reidel (1975), is a circular area of strongly faulted and folded rocks 5 miles in diameter. The disturbance consists of a central up-faulted area marked by exposures of Ordovician rocks, and a surrounding, ring-shaped zone of younger, down-faulted beds. The abrupt change in the intensity of the deformation at its border, where essentially undisturbed strata appear, is one of the most remarkable aspects of the disturbance. Because resistant Mississippian sandstones crop out in the down-faulted zone, the structure forms a prominent topographic high in the region, with a relief of over 300 feet (Reidel and Koucky, 1981).

The disturbance is marked by closely spaced faults, zones of intensely brecciated rock called shatter breccia, and small, cone-shaped structures called shatter cones; the shatter cones are confined to the carbonate rocks of the central uplift (Heyl and Brock, 1962; Koucky, 1975; Reidel and Koucky, 1981; Koucky and Reidel, 1987). However, these structures are difficult to observe in the field because the rocks are commonly obscured by a cover of vegetation and soil. The characteristics of unbrecciated Peebles Dolomite are well-exposed at site 1, just inside the southwestern margin of the structure. Here, the bedding planes in a down-faulted block of the massive, thick-bedded, reeflike dolostone are tilted slightly towards the southwest. The features of the shatter breccia can be observed at site 2, in the west-central part of the disturbance. At this locality, deformation has entirely destroyed the bedding planes and other primary structures of the dolostone, producing a wide zone of intensely brecciated gray rock that can only be assigned generally to the Peebles-Greenfield-Tymochtee interval. Shattered and brecciated rocks of the Tymochtee Dolomite are exposed at site 3.

Vein-type zinc minerals are characteristic of the disturbed area and are localized in open spaces of the faulted and brecciated Silurian dolostones. Small vugs in the brecciated dolostones are also filled with these minerals. The locally intense mineralization is particularly well displayed in these rocks at sites 2 and 3 (Heyl and Brock, 1962; Reidel and Koucky, 1981; Koucky and Reidel, 1987). The zinc minerals also reportedly are present at site 1, in the gully behind the museum (Koucky, 1975; Koucky and Reidel, 1987). A number of other zinc sites in the disturbance are given by Koucky (1975), Reidel (1975), and Reidel and Koucky (1981). The ore minerals of the disturbance were introduced sometime after the main episode of faulting occurred because they fill the fractures and cement the shattered rock together and are only mildly brecciated themselves.

The origin of the Serpent Mound disturbance is problematical. Some researchers believe that it originated from the explosion of rising, deep-seated gases, while others think that it was produced from the explosion of a meteorite or comet that impacted on the earth's surface (Boon and Albritton, 1936; Bucher, 1936; Dietz, 1946, 1960; Heyl and Brock, 1962; McCall, 1979; Reidel and others, 1982). That an explosion or series of explosions occurred sometime in the geologic past is supported by the presence of the shatter cones, which are believed to result when strong shock waves pass through solid rock. However, reports of the existence of coesite (Cohen, A. J., and others, 1961, 1962), a high-pressure phase of silica (SiO_2) that is found in impact craters elsewhere, have not been confirmed in the Serpent Mound area (Reidel and others, 1982). Because no traces of igneous rocks or meteorites have been found in the deformed strata, the cause of this explosion cannot be proved and is still debated by geologists. The deformation is known to have occurred sometime after the early Mississippian, the age of the youngest deformed rocks, and before the Pleistocene (Illinoian), the age of the oldest undeformed materials in the structure.

Mineralogy

The vein-type minerals in the fault breccia at sites 2 and 3 are typical of the mineralization in the disturbance (Heyl and Brock, 1962; Koucky, 1975; Reidel and Koucky, 1981; Koucky and Reidel, 1987). Weathering is so extensive at these sites that choice specimens of the secondary zinc minerals can be readily obtained. Mineralized rock is recognized by its heaviness and by the presence of vugs lined with brown or white minerals in an otherwise gray rock. The vein-type minerals and their alteration products include dolomite, sphalerite, hydrozincite, smithsonite, sulfur, and calcite. The gray dolostone breccia is cemented together with veinlets of fine-grained tan dolomite and coarse-grained sphalerite (see fig. 32). The pockets of brecciated rock, less than an inch across on average, are partly filled or coated with sphalerite, hydrozincite, and smithsonite. The sphalerite occurs as coarse-grained, lustrous, yellowish-orange or brown aggregates that have partially or completely weathered to hydrozincite and smithsonite; sphalerite also commonly occurs as kernels within enclosing masses of the latter two minerals. The hydrozincite occurs in powdery white masses and displays a white fluorescence. The smithsonite is gray, yellowish orange, or brown and occurs as boxworks, linings of tiny crystals, and thin colloform layers. Rarely, tiny crystals of yellow sulfur are perched on the hydrozincite. Veins of coarsely granular, milky-white calcite an inch or less thick cut the dolostones locally; some of this calcite displays a yellow fluorescence.

SHADE RIVER-FEDERAL CREEK AREA, ATHENS COUNTY

Location

The Middle Branch Shade River flows across south-

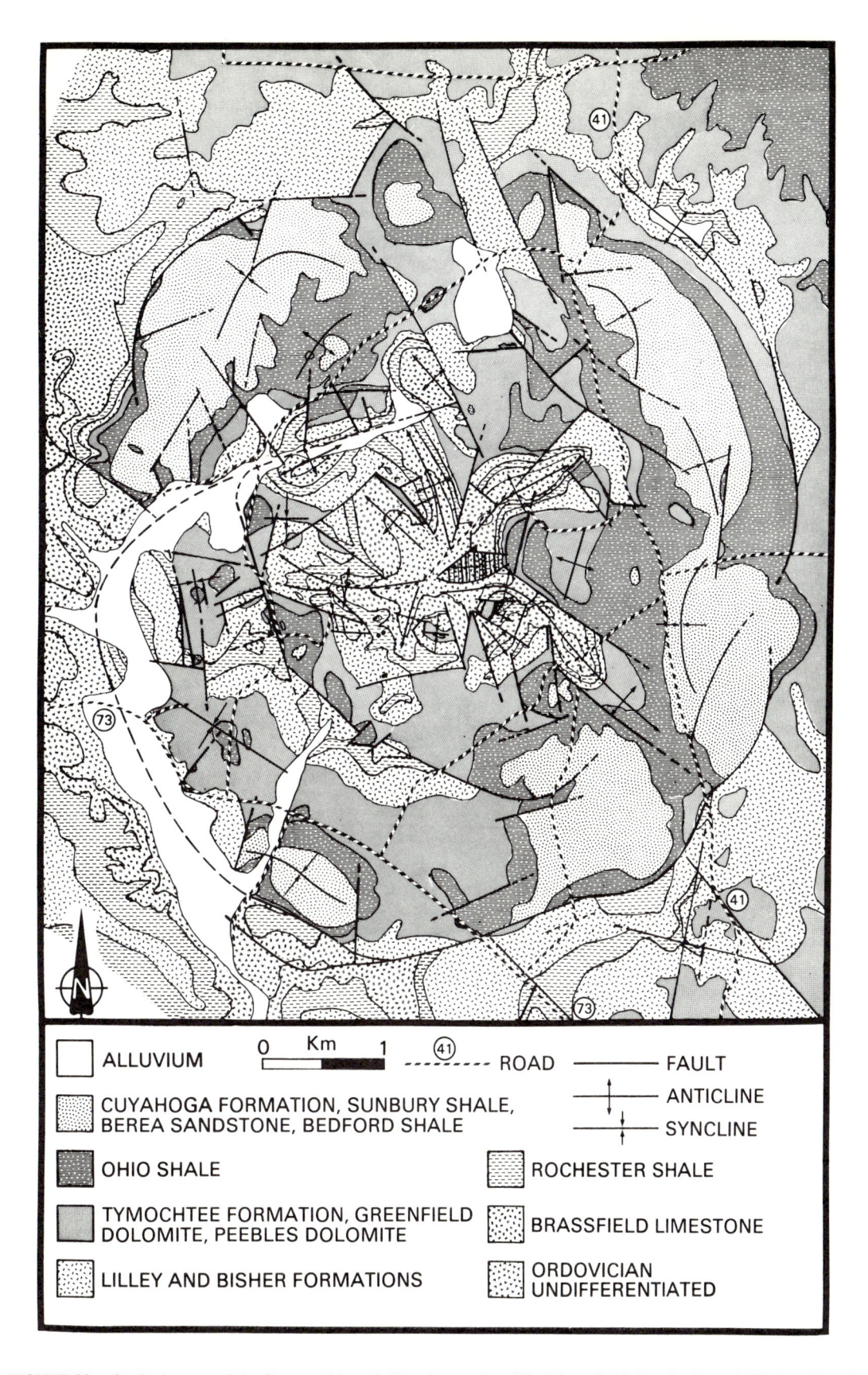

FIGURE 60.—Geologic map of the Serpent Mound disturbance (modified from Reidel and others, 1982, figs. 3 and 4; used with permission of the American Journal of Science).

central Athens County in southeastern Athens, northeastern Alexander, and Lodi Townships (fig. 61). The area is on the Athens and Shade 7.5-minute quadrangles. The silicified wood sites are reached from Athens by traveling southeast on U.S. Route 33. Site 1 is the southerly flowing headwaters of Middle Branch Shade River in the southeastern corner of Athens Township; it is most accessible from the intersection of U.S. Route 33 and Alexander Township Highway 62. Site 2 is Long Run, a southerly flowing tributary of Middle Branch that parallels County Highway 25 in southwestern Canaan and north-central Lodi Townships; it is reached from the intersection of U.S. Route 33 and County Highway 98, turning east and then north on Lodi Township Highway 84, and north on County Highway 25. Site 3 is Fossil Run, a northerly flowing tributary of Middle Branch that parallels County Highway 42 in central Lodi Township; it is reached from U.S. Route 33 at Shade by traveling east on County Highway 44 and turning north on County Highway 42. Site 4 is Rock Riffle Run, a northwesterly flowing tributary of the Hocking River that joins the main stream just southeast of Athens in eastern Athens Township; it is accessible from County Highway 25 near its intersection with U.S. Route 33 on the southeastern side of the Hocking River. The intersection of County Highway 25 and U.S. Route 33 is just west of the area shown in figure 61. Detailed information on the above sites is given by Hildreth (1838), Andrews (1873), Condit (1912), Stout (1945), Murphy (1973), and Good and Taylor (1974).

Silicified wood also has been reported along the tributaries of Federal Creek in Athens County, including the region of the hematite sites given below, and in the bordering area of southwestern Morgan County (Hildreth, 1838; Condit, 1912; Stout, 1945). Because walking out stream beds is one of the most effective methods of hunting for silicified wood, the field trip should be taken when water levels are low. A stiff brush, a bucket, and water are useful for cleaning mud or soil off specimens.

The Federal Creek drainage basin is in north-central and northeastern Athens County and the bordering parts of Morgan County. The hematite sites are all in the western part of the Federal Creek area in Ames Township, Athens County, on the Jacksonville and Amesville 7.5-minute quadrangles, and are reached from Athens by traveling northeast on Ohio Route 550. Site 5 is a road cut and hillside exposure along the north side of Ohio Route 550 about 1.25 miles east of its intersection with County Highway 36. Site 6 is a road cut and hillside exposure along the north side of the South Fork Dutch Creek; it is reached from Ohio Route 550 by turning south on County Highway 26 for 0.2 mile, turning southeast on County Highway 34 for about 2 miles, and then continuing straight ahead on County Highway 218 for 0.25 mile past the junction where County Highway 34 turns east. Site 7 is in the bed of Bryson Branch along its headwaters in the northwestern corner of Ames Township; it is reached from Ohio Route 550 by turning northwest on County Highway 28 for 0.3 mile, turning north on Township Highway 334, and proceeding about 2.5 miles to Bryson Branch. Site 8 is a road cut and hillside exposure along the northeast side of County Highway 37; it is reached from Ohio Route 550 by turning north at Amesville on Ohio Route 329, turning west on County Route 37, and continuing about 1 mile to the site. The intersection of Ohio Routes 550 and 329 is just east of the area shown in figure 61. Site 9 is a road cut and hillside exposure along the northeast side of Ohio Route 329, paralleling Federal Creek; it is reached from Ohio Route 550 by turning north at Amesville on Ohio Route 329 and continuing about 2.5 miles to the site. Condit (1912) noted an abundance of hematite nodules in northern Ames Township. Stout (1945), G. E. Smith (1951), and Sturgeon and associates (1958) provide additional data for

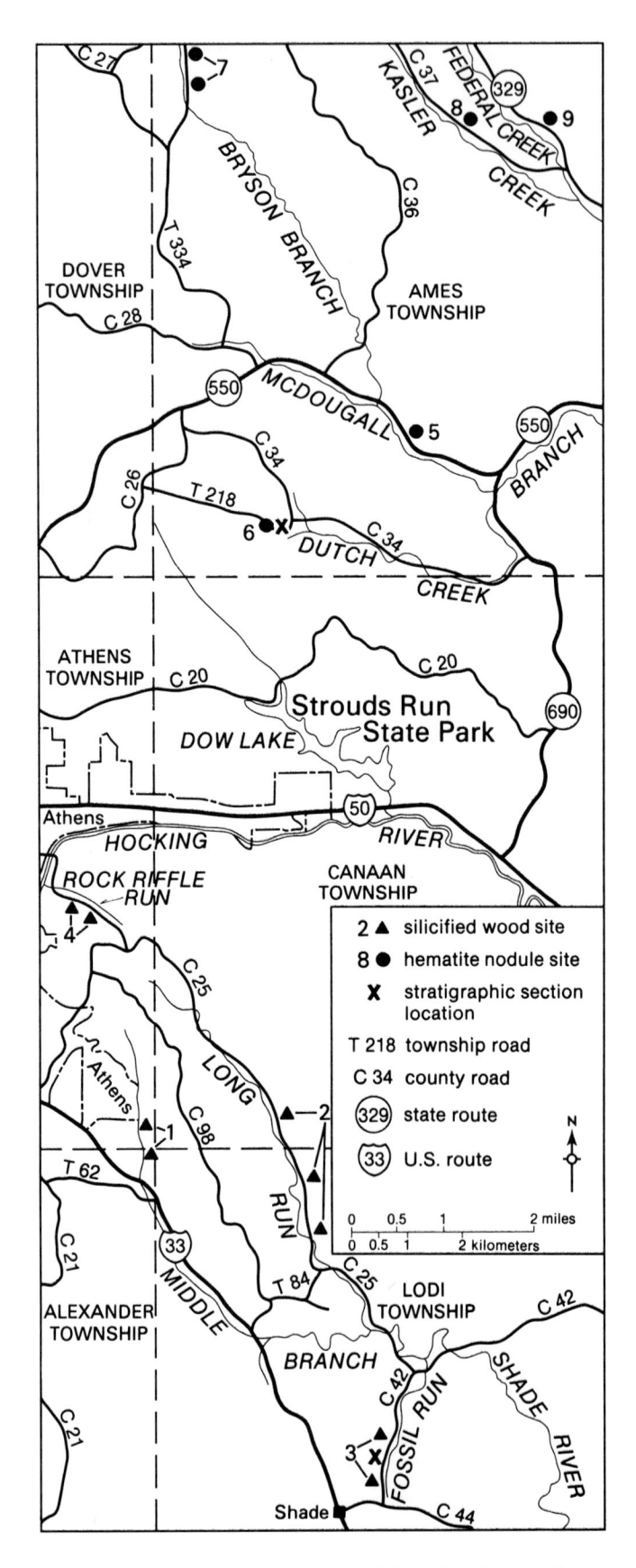

FIGURE 61.—Map of the Shade River-Federal Creek area, Athens County, showing silicified wood and hematite nodule sites described in text.

the above sites and other nodule localities in the region. Rock hammers are required to break open the hematite nodules.

Permission must be obtained prior to crossing private property at all of the Athens County sites noted above. Camping and picnic facilities are available 5 miles east of Athens on U.S. Route 50 at Strouds Run State Park. Further information is available from the Manager, Strouds Run State Park, 11661 State Park Road, Athens, Ohio 45701 (phone: 614-592-2302).

Geology

Pennsylvanian-age strata of the upper Conemaugh and lower Monongahela Groups compose the bedrock surface over much of southeastern Ohio (Condit, 1912; Sturgeon and associates, 1958; Collins, H. R., 1979). These rocks consist of a repetitious sequence of shales, sandstones, limestones, and coal seams. Many of the beds exhibit a fauna and flora, such as freshwater ostracodes and land plants, that are characteristic of continental conditions. The presence of red beds, whose pervasive color results from finely disseminated grains and nodular masses of sedimentary hematite, is also indicative of sediments deposited on land. In the Shade River area, the exposed rock strata belong entirely to the Monongahela Group, except at the bottom of the large valleys on the west, where the uppermost beds of the Conemaugh Group are exposed. On the western side of the Federal Creek area (northern Ames Township), the upper part of the Conemaugh Group is exposed in the main valleys to an elevation of about 200 feet above the valley floors. Stratigraphic sections typical of the upper Conemaugh rocks in the Federal Creek area and the lower Monongahela rocks in the Shade River area are given below.

Stratigraphic section of the Conemaugh Group in the creek bed and hillside along Township Highway 218, sec. 25, Ames Township, Athens County (modified from Sturgeon and associates, 1958, p. 325).

	feet	inches
Upper Grafton Member		
Sandstone, light-gray to tan, limonite-stained, weathers dark brown, coarse, micaceous, massive ledge, poorly exposed at top	27	0
Birmingham Member		
Shale, light-gray to olive-drab, limonite-stained, mottled red, silty to argillaceous, finely micaceous, thin-bedded	21	7
Skelley Member		
Limestone, blue-gray to greenish-blue, some red mottling, limonite-stained, dense to partly crystalline, nodules and irregular masses embedded in gray to buff, limonite-stained, micaceous shale showing slickensided surfaces, fossiliferous, marine	6	0
Shale and sandstone, light-gray to tan, limonite-stained, argillaceous, finely micaceous shale and thin bed of finely micaceous, fine sandstone in center	13	5
Duquesne Member		
Clay shale, light-gray, mottled tan, blue, green, and maroon, finely micaceous, containing limonite and freshwater limestone nodules, thin-bedded	7	4
Clay shale, red to maroon, finely micaceous, thin-bedded, containing flattened, septarian hematite nodules and masses	5	3

	feet	inches
Gaysport Member		
Limestone, blue-green to greenish-gray, mottled red, weathers dark brownish red, nodular and irregular bedded, dense, fossiliferous, marine	0	5
Clay shale, blue-green to maroon, silty, micaceous, thin-bedded, exposed	2	0

Stratigraphic section of the Monongahela Group along Fossil Run, sec. 21, Lodi Township, Athens County (modified from Sturgeon and associates, 1958, p. 480).

	feet	inches
Upper Pittsburgh Member		
Sandstone and shale, tan to light-olive-brown, fine- to medium-grained, shaly to massive-bedded, micaceous, becomes massive sandstone upward	11	5
Pittsburgh Member		
Clay shale, medium-gray, poorly bedded to laminated, slightly silty, some plant fossils, carbonaceous at base	2	2
Fusain	0	1
Coal, bright, blocky	0	3
Carbonaceous shale, some small zones of bright coal	2	½
Coal, bright, blocky	0	½
Clay shale, dark-gray to greenish-black, poorly bedded, silty, carbonaceous	0	6
Lower Pittsburgh Member		
Clay shale, gray, olive-green, nonbedded, breaks irregularly, silty, micaceous, contains nodular zone of dark-grayish-black limestone, thickness varies	0	4
Clay shale, dark-gray to greenish-black, poorly bedded, slightly silty, micaceous, carbonaceous	0	8
Clay shale, light- to dark-gray, mottled, maroon in part, nonbedded, breaks irregularly, calcareous, silty, micaceous, with abundant gray to greenish-gray limestone nodules, fossiliferous (ostracodes)	0	6

Ever since the early 1800's, fine specimens of silicified wood have been obtained from the Middle Branch Shade River and its tributaries in the region between Athens and Shade (sites 1 through 4). Only rarely is this wood found embedded in the lower Monongahela rocks of the area. Because of its resistance to weathering, most of the wood appears loose, having weathered out of the shale and sandstone beds that overlie a coal seam believed to be the Pittsburgh (No. 8) or Pomeroy (No. 8A) coal of the lower Monongahela Group (Andrews, 1873; Condit, 1912; Good and Taylor, 1974).

The two types of silicified material that are commonly obtained include sections of tree trunks and masses of rootlets. The trunk sections belong to an extinct giant tree fern that has been identified as the genus *Psaronius* (Lesquereux, 1880; Herzer, 1897; Arnold, 1947; Morgan, E. J., 1959). The fossil trunks generally range from 4 to 12 inches in diameter, although specimens as large as 2 feet in diameter have been observed. The rootlike masses characteristically occur with the trunk portions missing (Hildreth, 1838; Andrews, 1873; Lesquereux, 1880). Root specimens are disk shaped, with their central portions forming depressed areas. The masses of rootlets, believed to have supported the fossil ferns (*Psaronius*), are as large as 4 feet in diameter.

Hematite nodules are abundant in some of the red and green shales of the upper Conemaugh Group in the western part of the Federal Creek area (sites 5 through 9). These strata, a 200-foot interval between the Ames limestone and the Pittsburgh (No. 8) coal, were once known as the "Big Red" shales, and the hematite nodules in the "Big Red" shales were considered as ore (Stout, 1944). Within this sequence the hematite nodules are especially concentrated in the shale below the Gaysport limestone, the Duquesne shale, and the Birmingham shale (Smith, G. E., 1951; Sturgeon and associates, 1958). The nodules generally range from 1 to 2 inches in diameter, although they may reach 4 inches in length, and are characteristically flattened in the bedding planes of the enclosing rocks. Some of the nodules are septaria and others contain the remains of fossil plants, such as leaves, at their centers. Because of their resistance to weathering, the nodules commonly are found loose on the shale slopes or in stream beds, where they are easily recognized by their red color and heaviness.

Mineralogy

Chalcedony, a microcrystalline, fibrous variety of quartz, has replaced the original organic material of the wood and is now the chief constituent of it. This chalcedony lacks bright hues and is typically brown, reddish brown, gray, reddish gray, and black. However, trunk sections that are cut and polished display the well-preserved tissue structure of the wood prominently and make extremely attractive specimens. Fractures and small cavities in the replaced wood commonly are lined by tiny, colorless, rhombohedrally terminated quartz crystals.

The hematite nodules typically consist of a dull, fine-grained, red to brownish-red mixture of hematite, goethite, quartz, and clay. Some of the nodules are septaria, containing white veinlets of finely granular calcite and quartz. Hematite nodules of high purity are dense, quite hard, and red to reddish gray and have a metallic or submetallic luster.

STONELICK CREEK-BRUSHY FORK AREA, CLERMONT COUNTY

Location

Stonelick Creek and its tributary Brushy Fork are located about a mile north of Owensville in Stonelick Township, Clermont County, on the Goshen 7.5-minute quadrangle (fig. 62). Owensville lies east of Cincinnati at the intersection of U.S. Route 50 and Ohio Route 132. Stonelick Creek is reached by traveling north from Owensville 1.1 miles on Ohio Route 132; cars can be parked on the north side of the stream along Anstaett Road. Brushy Fork can be reached from Owensville by going north a short distance on either Whitmer Road, which deadends before the creek is reached, or Belfast-Owensville Road, which crosses the creek. The field trip should be taken when stream levels are low, and permission should be obtained before crossing private property. A small shovel, gold pan, garden screen, and hand magnet are required. Camping and picnic facilities are located about 8 miles northeast of Owensville on the east side of Ohio Route 727 at Stonelick State Park. Further information can be obtained from the Manager, Stonelick State Park, Route 1, Box 343, Pleasant Plain, Ohio 45162 (phone: 513-625-7544).

Geology

The Stonelick Creek area is covered with glacial drift of Illinoian age (Orton, 1873; Goldthwait and others, 1961; Caster and others, 1970). These deposits, which average 20 feet in thickness but locally are as thick as 50 feet, consist of both unstratified and stratified materials. The unstratified drift is a mixture of clay- to boulder-size particles, called till, that was deposited directly from the ice sheet. The stratified materials are chiefly outwash sands and gravels, and were deposited by meltwater streams flowing from the margin of the ice. Interbedded shales and limestones of Ordovician age underlie the glacial drift of the area.

Small amounts of placer gold have been recovered from the Stonelick Creek-Brushy Fork area; prospecting activity was particularly high in the area during the great economic depression of the 1930's and possibly earlier as well (Orton, 1873; Wuestner, 1938; Caster and others, 1970; Hansen, 1985b; Maslowski, 1986). This gold originated in eastern Canada from mineral deposits that were scoured and dispersed into the Great Lakes region by the southerly moving ice. Almost all of the more notable occurrences of gold that have been reported in Ohio come from the drift located along or near the glacial boundary (Newberry, 1874a; Wright, 1890; Hansen, 1985b). Exposures of this drift, which is chiefly Illinoian in age, were mapped by Goldthwait and others (1961); its distribution is shown in figure 3 of this report.

The gold-bearing outwash gravels rest on the Illinoian till and appear as flat-surfaced terraces above the floors and along the sides of the present stream valleys. A good exposure of the till and the overlying outwash gravels can be observed on the east bank of Stonelick Creek 0.3 mile east of Anstaett Road (Caster and others, 1970), and similar exposures are present near the mouth of Brushy Fork (Wuestner, 1938). A generalized columnar section (fig. 63) of the Illinoian drift along the Little Miami River in Warren County is representative of the deposits in the Stonelick Creek area. In addition to traces of gold in the terrace gravels, small amounts of gold are found in the gravel beds of Stonelick Creek and Brushy Fork, which are actively eroding their channels through the Illinoian till and the terrace gravels.

Mineralogy

The minerals to be found in the Stonelick Creek-Brushy Fork sediments include gold, ilmenite, magnetite, and garnet. Glacial gold is always associated with and masked by a number of black minerals that are also heavy and resistant to weathering. For this reason, the thin layers of black sand in the terrace gravels or the locally concentrated black sands of active stream gravels should yield the most gold. Panned samples will provide a black and red concentrate of sand-size grains that is rich in ilmenite (black, weakly magnetic or nonmagnetic), magnetite (black, strongly magnetic), garnet (red or brown, vitreous) and, perhaps, traces of gold.

WEST BRANCH STATE PARK, PORTAGE COUNTY

Location

West Branch State Park is located in the valley of West Branch Mahoning River in southeastern Charlestown and northeastern Edinburg Townships, Portage County, on the Ravenna and Windham 7.5-minute quadrangles (fig. 64). The park entrance is reached by traveling east from Ravenna or west from Warren along Ohio Route 5 and turning south onto Rock Spring Road. The site along the north shore is reached by turning east onto Esworthy Road and continuing to the visitors' parking lot, located just before the pay station at the campground. This site is apparently near the selenite locality originally reported by Birkheimer (1938) and later by Gettings (1955). For the Silver Creek locality along the south shore, follow Rock Spring Road south across the causeway, turn east onto Hughes Road, north onto Porter Road, east onto Calvin Road, north onto Alliance Road, and then west onto Cable Line Road, and follow the access road to the beach, where parking is available. The area along Silver Creek can be reached from the parking lot by either foot or boat. Because they are normally covered by water at other times, the north shore and south shore sites should be visited between the middle of October and the middle of March, when the water level of the reservoir is kept low; however, the lakeshore sites may be accessible in late summer if the season has been dry. Loose specimens can be collected if written permission is obtained from the Park Manager in advance of the trip, but digging is not allowed. Picnic grounds and primitive-type camping facilities are available and open year-round. Further information can be obtained from the Manager, West Branch State Park, 5708 Esworthy Road, Ravenna, Ohio 44266 (phone: 216-296-3239).

Geology

The West Branch State Park area was extensively

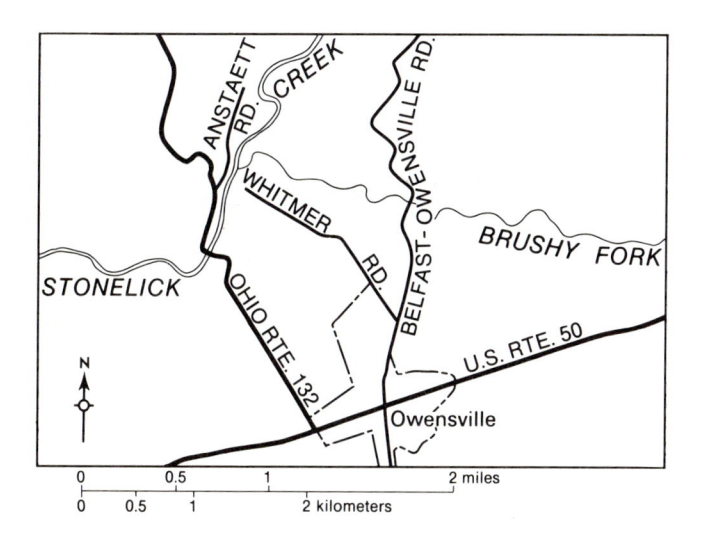

FIGURE 62.—Vicinity map (left) and southeastern part of the Goshen 7.5-minute quadrangle (below) showing the Stonelick Creek-Brushy Fork area, Clermont County.

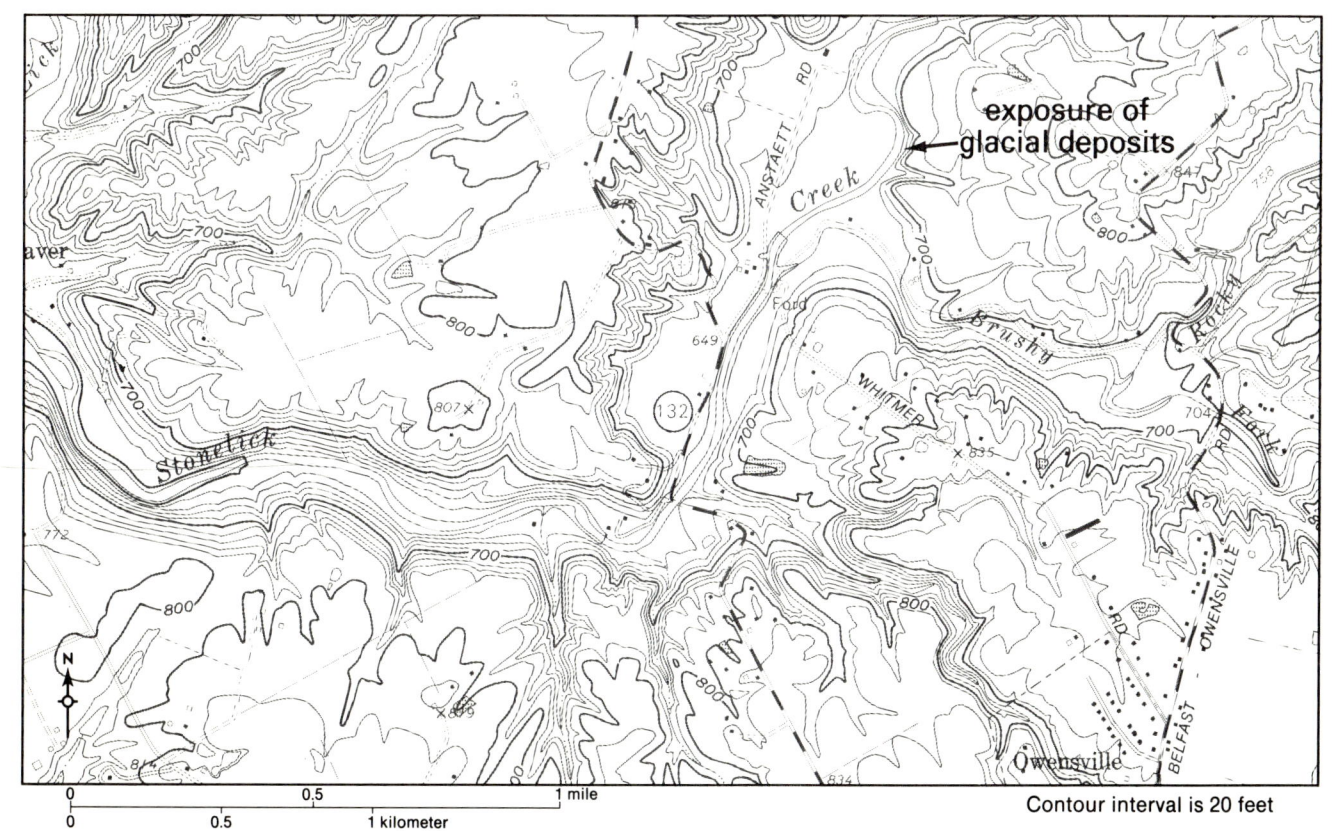

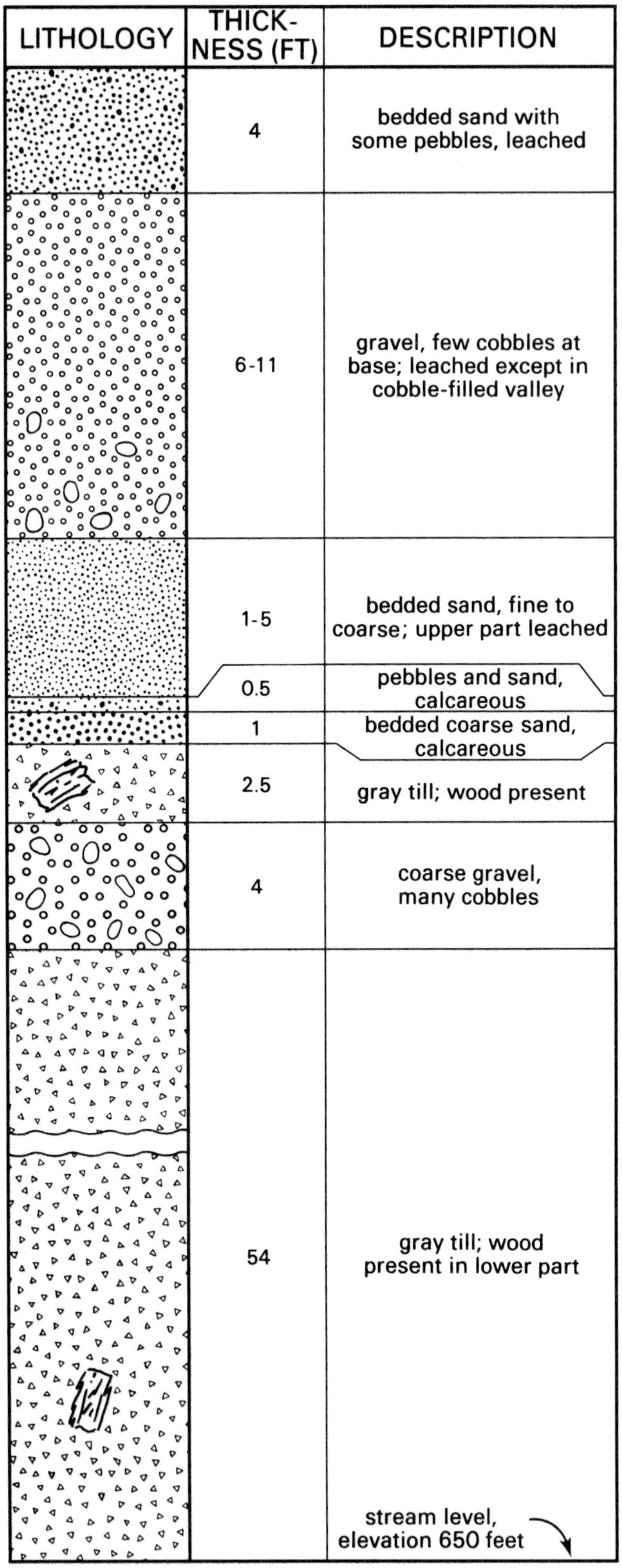

80 MINERALS OF OHIO

LITHOLOGY	THICKNESS (FT)	DESCRIPTION
	4	bedded sand with some pebbles, leached
	6-11	gravel, few cobbles at base; leached except in cobble-filled valley
	1-5	bedded sand, fine to coarse; upper part leached
	0.5	pebbles and sand, calcareous
	1	bedded coarse sand, calcareous
	2.5	gray till; wood present
	4	coarse gravel, many cobbles
	54	gray till; wood present in lower part
		stream level, elevation 650 feet

FIGURE 63.—Generalized stratigraphic section of the Illinoian deposits along the Little Miami River, Warren County (modified from Caster and others, 1970, p. 15).

glaciated during the Pleistocene (Winslow and White, 1966; Goldthwait and others, 1961; White, G. W., 1982). When the last ice sheet, the Wisconsinan, finally melted, a thick layer of unstratified glacial debris (till) was deposited across the entire region. This till now comprises the bulk of the glacial material exposed in the park area.

The ice sheet moved across a terrain dissected by deep stream valleys that formed an early, preglacial drainage system. One of these valleys ran east-west across southern Charlestown Township before turning north and was a tributary of the preglacial St. Lawrence River (Winslow and White, 1966). When the southerly moving Wisconsinan ice dammed the outlet farther north, this valley was periodically occupied by a meltwater lake. Eventually, this valley was filled with a combination of till and stratified silt and clay, the latter having been deposited in the lake at those times when the valley was ponded. Later, West Branch Mahoning River cut its modern valley through the till and stratified lake beds, which today are exposed along the banks of the reservoir. Both the till and the glacial lake deposits are unconsolidated and soft and erode quite easily. The lake beds are bluish gray to brownish gray and can be observed at low water levels along the north bank of the reservoir in the vicinity of the campground.

The selenite crystals occur in and are closely associated with the glacial lake beds. Before the reservoir was completed in 1966, crystals were dug from exposures along the north bank of West Branch where it was crossed by Esworthy Road. That segment of Esworthy Road is now flooded, but when the water level of the reservoir is low, crystals can be collected from the north bank near the campground. The crystals at the latter site are found loose on the surface after the bank has been washed and eroded by rain. This north shore site is similar geologically to the famous Ellsworth locality in Mahoning County (Silliman, 1821; Greene, 1937), which is now closed to collecting (see fig. 33).

The selenite formed much later than the lake beds and originated from underground waters that slowly moved through them. In this regard, the appearance of clusters of crystals near the roots of plants growing in the lake beds suggests that vegetation may play a role in the development of the selenite and that at least some selenite is forming today.

Pennsylvanian strata of the Pottsville Group form the bedrock of the park area at elevations above the water level of the reservoir (Winslow and White, 1966). Rocks older than Pennsylvanian were once exposed along the floor of the valley but are now flooded. The Pottsville rocks consist chiefly of interlayered black and gray shales; some beds of sandstone, coal, and ironstone are present. These strata are best exposed along the banks of streams, such as Silver Creek, that have eroded through the glacial cover. A stratigraphic section of the rocks along Silver Creek is given below.

Stratigraphic section of the Pottsville Group along Silver Creek just west of Alliance Road (modified from Winslow and White, 1966, p. 79).

	feet	inches
Pennsylvanian System, Pottsville Group		
Homewood member		
Sandstone, light-tan-gray, coarse-grained	5+	
Mercer member		
Covered	16	6
Shale, black, silty	0	6
Clay, sandy	3	0
Shale, black, sandy, blocky; in 1-ft ledges	6	0

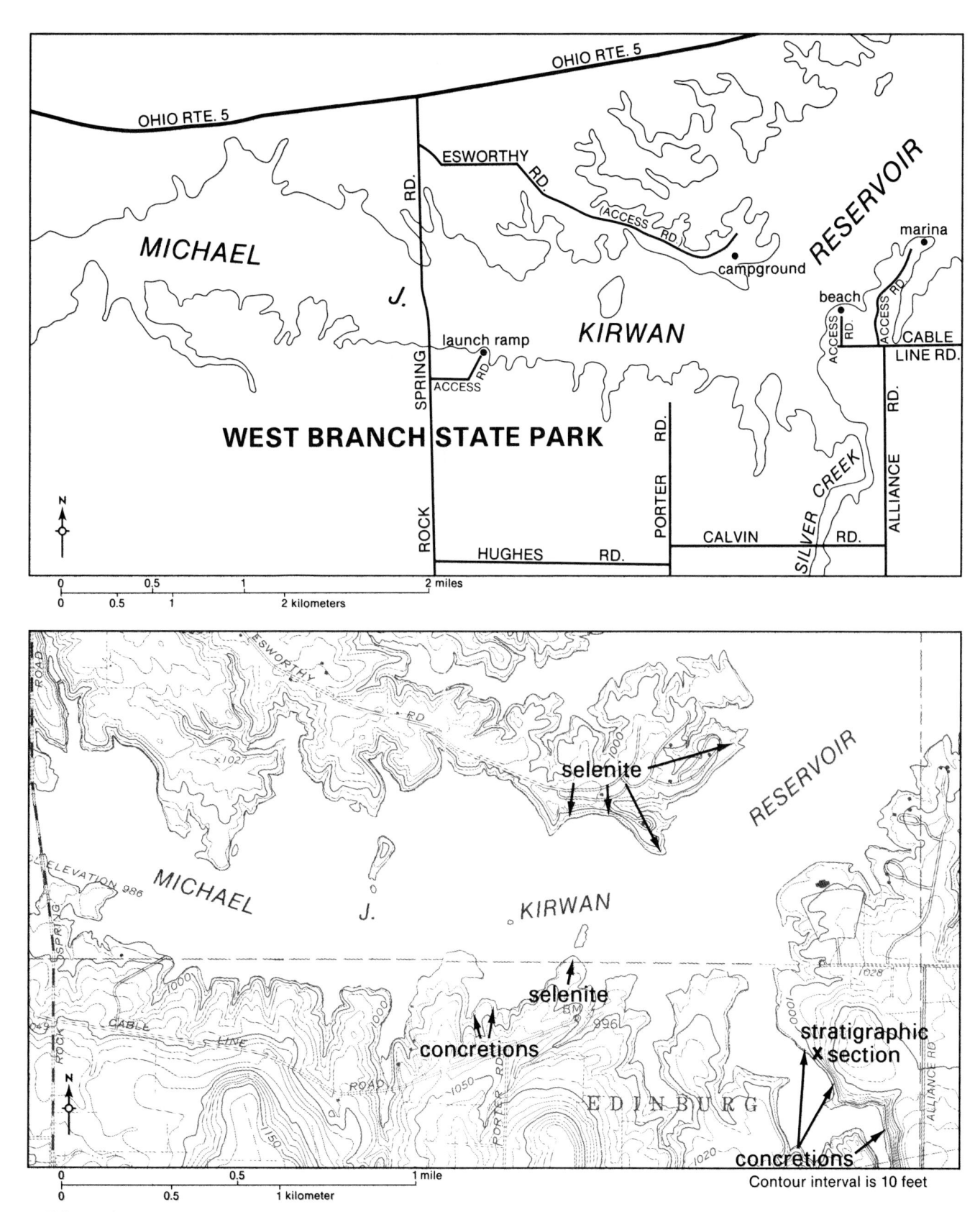

FIGURE 64.—Vicinity map (upper) and southeastern part of the Ravenna and southwestern part of the Windham 7.5-minute quadrangles (lower) showing the West Branch State Park area, Portage County. The stratigraphic section shown in the lower right of the topographic map extends for about a mile from the marked x southward along Silver Creek.

	feet	*inches*
Mercer member (continued)		
Siderite ore, nodular	0	8
Shale, black, silty, partly covered	2	0
Coal, bright and dull (Bedford)	3	0
Clay, silty to sandy	4	0
Shale, gray, silty to sandy, fissile	5	0
Siderite ore, nodular, continuous	1	8
Shale, gray to gray-black, silty, fissile	25	0
Siderite ore, nodular, continuous	0	3
Shale, gray, sandy, fissile	5	0
Connoquenessing member		
Sandstone, light-gray; contains flagstone layers	15	0
Shale unit of Sharon member		
Shale, gray to gray-black, silty, fissile; contains a few ironstone concretions	17	0
Covered interval. Possibly same as unit below	10-	0
Shale, black	1+	
Coal, blocky; in stream bottom (Sharon)	0	3
Covered interval	20+	
Conglomerate unit of Sharon member		
Sandstone, massive, light-tan-gray	20+	

Because this sequence was measured before the reservoir was built, the lower part of the Silver Creek section is now flooded.

Ironstone septaria occur in some of the dark-colored shale beds at the Silver Creek locality. Because of their resistance to weathering, the septaria weather out of the shale and accumulate along the slope and base of the stream banks; some septaria are found farther north, strewn loose on the beach of the inlet to Silver Creek. These septaria, which range from a few inches to a foot in diameter, are disk shaped and have a smooth outer surface. When broken open they exhibit a dense, dull, dark-brown matrix and veins of coarse-grained, lustrous minerals that fill a network of internal, shrinkage-type cracks in the matrix. Fossils, such as fragments of petrified wood, may occupy the centers of the septaria and apparently served as nuclei about which the concretionary bodies formed (see fig. 10).

Mineralogy

The gypsum in the silt and clay beds is the coarsely crystalline, colorless, transparent variety known as selenite. It occurs in well-formed single crystals that average an inch or so in length and typically display a combination of two monoclinic prisms and a side pinacoid (see fig. 40U), as well as in groups of interpenetrating individuals. However, the quality of the crystals varies greatly, and the material obtained at the site needs to be carefully inspected and sorted. Because of the high solubility of gypsum, some crystals may be corroded (see fig. 33), and because of its softness and perfect cleavage, others are scratched or broken. Phantom crystals are common, exhibiting internal bands of included silt and clay that are aligned parallel to the crystals faces. The selenite invariably displays a greenish-white fluorescence and phosphorescence of low intensity.

The body of an ironstone septarium, as determined from analysis of the matrix and its insoluble residue, is composed of a fine-grained mixture of siderite, quartz, unidentified clay minerals, and carbonaceous matter, with siderite being predominant. Some septaria exhibit a yellowish-brown weathering rind of goethite.

The vein minerals of the septaria include barite, calcite, sphalerite, kaolinite, and chalcopyrite. A typical vein is coarsely crystalline and consists of a solid intergrowth of colorless or white plates of barite, colorless to white masses of calcite, and brown to black aggregates of sphalerite. More rarely, well-formed crystals of these minerals are found in small pockets. Some concretions contain veins composed chiefly of powdery masses of white kaolinite, a clay mineral, in which small, isolated crystals of chalcopyrite and sphalerite are embedded.

Fluorite (largest crystal 7 mm on edge), Bluffton Stone Co. quarry, Bluffton, Allen County. Harris Precht specimen; Terry Huizing photo.

Fluorite (2 cm on edge), France Stone Co. Bellevue quarry, Bellevue, Sandusky County. Harris Precht specimen #398; Terry Huizing photo.

Fluorite (2.8 cm on edge) on calcite, Stoneco Lime City quarry, Lime City, Wood County. Joe Kielbaso specimen; Terry Huizing photo.

Fluorite (3.5 cm on edge), Charles Pfizer & Co., Inc., quarry, Gibsonburg, Sandusky County. Harris Precht specimen; Terry Huizing photo.

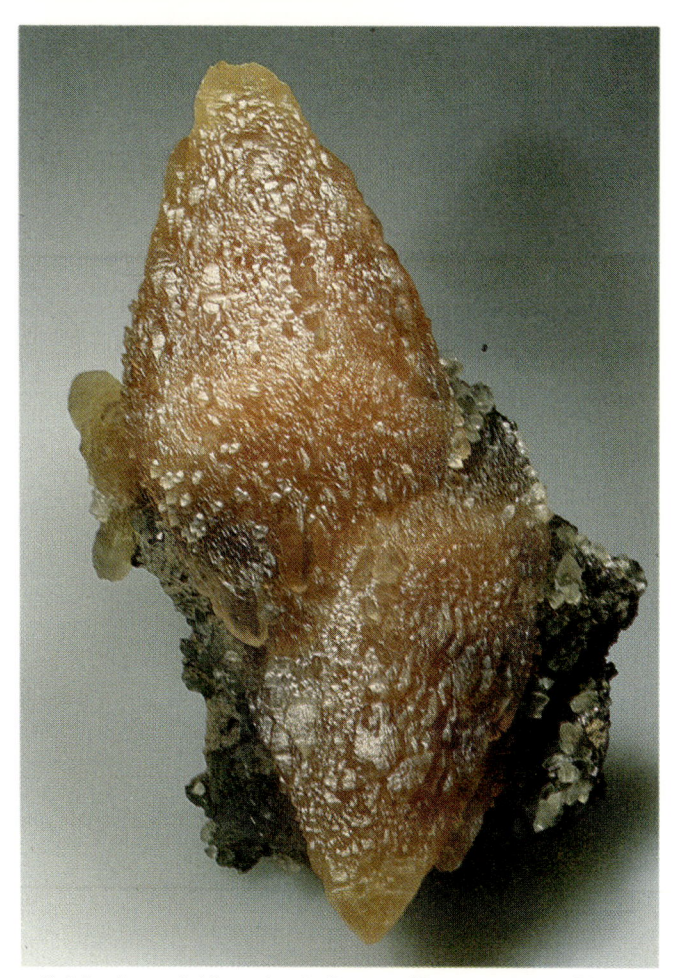

Calcite (crystal 16 cm long), Stoneco Maumee quarry, Maumee, Lucas County. Rick Russell specimen; Terry Huizing photo.

Fluorite (crystals 1 cm on edge), Stoneco Auglaize quarry, Junction, Paulding County. Harris Precht specimen #118; Terry Huizing photo.

Fluorite (2.3 cm on longest edge) with asphalt, Stoneco Maumee quarry, Maumee, Lucas County. Mark Kielbaso specimen; Terry Huizing photo.

Calcite on fluorite (specimen 2 cm high), Stoneco Auglaize quarry, Junction, Paulding County. Neal Pfaff specimen; Terry Huizing photo.

Calcite (largest crystal 9 cm high), Stoneco Auglaize quarry, Junction, Paulding County. Harris Precht specimen #292; Terry Huizing photo.

Celestite (3 cm long) and calcite, Edward Kraemer & Sons, Inc., White Rock quarry, Clay Center, Ottawa County. Harris Precht specimen #404; Terry Huizing photo.

Fluorite (2.5 cm on edge), calcite, and celestite, Edward Kraemer & Sons, Inc., White Rock quarry, Clay Center, Ottawa County. Mark Kielbaso specimen; Terry Huizing photo.

Pyrite (3.1 mm across), C. E. Duff & Son, Inc., quarry, Huntsville, Logan County. Dan Behnke specimen and photo.

Celestite (5 cm high), Stoneco Lime City quarry, Lime City, Wood County. Harris Precht specimen; Terry Huizing photo.

Fluorite (2 cm on edge) and strontianite, Stoneco Lime City quarry, Lime City, Wood County. Harris Precht specimen #38; Terry Huizing photo.

Calcite (6 cm long), Stoneco Maumee quarry, Maumee, Lucas County. Joe Kielbaso specimen; Terry Huizing photo.

Celestite and calcite (specimen 4 cm across), France Stone Co. Custar quarry, Custar, Wood County. Harris Precht specimen #402; Terry Huizing photo.

Fluorite (8 mm on edge) and pyrite, Suever Stone Co., Inc., Delphos quarry, Delphos, Van Wert County. Harris Precht specimen; Terry Huizing photo.

Celestite (1.5 cm long) and calcite, France Stone Co. Custar quarry, Custar, Wood County. Harris Precht specimen #346; Terry Huizing photo.

Fluorite (2.8 cm on edge), Stoneco Auglaize quarry, Junction, Paulding County. Harris Precht specimen #176; Terry Huizing photo.

Sphalerite (1.3 mm across) on dolomite, Bluffton Stone Co. quarry, Bluffton, Allen County. John Jaszczak specimen and photo.

Fluorite (3.8 cm on edge), Charles Pfizer & Co., Inc., quarry, Gibsonburg, Sandusky County. Harris Precht specimen #406; Terry Huizing photo.

Celestite (specimen 7 cm across), Edward Kraemer & Sons, Inc., White Rock quarry, Clay Center, Ottawa County. Harris Precht specimen #152; Terry Huizing photo.

Fluorite (specimen 3.5 cm across), Edward Kraemer & Sons, Inc., White Rock quarry, Clay Center, Ottawa County. Harris Precht specimen #411; Terry Huizing photo.

Celestite (11.5 cm high), Stoneco Portage quarry, Portage, Wood County. Cincinnati Museum of Natural History specimen; Terry Huizing photo.

Barite on calcite (specimen 8 cm high), France Stone Co. Custar quarry, Custar, Wood County. Terry Huizing specimen and photo.

Calcite (10 cm high), France Stone Co. Custar quarry, Custar, Wood County. Terry Huizing specimen #103 and photo.

Chapter 7

CATALOG OF MINERAL LOCALITIES

Minerals chosen for inclusion in the catalog generally must satisfy two criteria: (1) they must occur in a well-crystallized form, and (2) they must be native to Ohio. Under the first criterion, minerals such as kaolinite, siderite, goethite, and collophane (apatite) which invariably are poorly crystallized and impure have been excluded. Exceptions have been made for chalcedony and flint, both of which are microcrystalline varieties of quartz but are an important source of lapidary materials. Under the second criterion, displaced minerals such as those found in glacial drift are omitted. However, glacial diamonds and gold have been included because of the lore associated with those minerals. Meteorites are treated elsewhere (p. 32) in this publication. Localities are reported for mineralized specimens from natural outcrops and exposures in mines and quarries, but those from drill cores are excluded.

Each mineral species has an entry for chemical class, crystallization, habit, physical properties, and occurrence. Under crystallization, the crystal system is followed by the crystal class; both the name and the Hermann-Mauguin symbols are given for the latter. The crystal habits noted are typical for specimens that are found in Ohio. The physical properties are listed in the following order: (1) cleavage or fracture, (2) hardness (H), (3) specific gravity (G), (4) luster, (5) color, (6) streak, and (7) other properties such as luminescent character and behavior in acid. The crystallographic orientation of cleavage is given by bracketed Miller indices. An entry on chemistry is added for dolomite-ferroan dolomite and halotrichite-pickeringite, which form chemical series; and an entry on varieties is added for gypsum (selenite) and quartz (chalcedony, flint). Under occurrence, brief descriptions are given for the typical types of deposits that are encountered in Ohio.

Under each mineral, the locality entries are arranged alphabetically by county and township. Each entry has three parts: (1) the type of occurrence and closely associated minerals and compounds, (2) the location, and (3) important references. Under the type of occurrence, the formations that are exposed at the site are listed in order of decreasing geologic age; the name of the formation in which the mineral is known to occur is italicized at sites where more than one formation is exposed. Abandoned formation names that are cited in the source references have been replaced by current terminology (see *Generalized column of bedrock units in Ohio* that accompanies this report). Minerals that are found at the same site, but not in close association, are listed separately. Where source references do not indicate the nature of the association the minerals are listed separately. Hydrocarbon compounds such as asphalt that accompany mineralization are listed under associated minerals and compounds. Under location, the type of exposure, such as a cliff or quarry, and the name of the mine or quarry operator are provided. However, names and operators commonly change over time. The status of the quarry operation (whether active, inactive, or abandoned) is generally not indicated as it too can change over time. Locations are given by section (sec.) number or prominent map features, township (Twp.), and topographic-map name. Abbreviations are used for compass directions (N, S, E, W). Topographic-map names are indicated in capital letters and refer to 7½-minute quadrangles (see *Index to topographic maps* accompanying this report), although 15-minute quadrangle names also are given in parentheses for some localities. Stratigraphic-section descriptions for some locations are on file at the Ohio Division of Geological Survey and are noted as "OGS Section" plus the file number. The references are listed in alphabetical order and the sources are divided into two categories: mineral occurrence and general geology. All citations under mineral occurrence list the mineral in question; references under general geology describe the bedrock stratigraphy or structure or list other minerals at the site. Some unpublished mineralogical data are reported for new sites and newly found minerals from known sites; these data are based on information that has been gathered by the writer and his associates.

ALUNOGEN
$Al_2(SO_4)_3 \cdot 17H_2O$

Chemical class: Sulfate
Crystallization: Triclinic; pinacoidal; $\bar{1}$
Habit: Tiny scales; fibrous; powdery; massive
Physical properties: Cleavage: {010} perfect pinacoidal. H: 1½-2. G: 1.8. Luster: silky. Color: white. Streak: white. Taste: acid and sharp
Occurrence: Powdery efflorescence rare on coal and shale in eastern Ohio

MEIGS COUNTY
1. Efflorescence of white alunogen with copiapite and pickeringite in shales above Redstone (Pomeroy) (No. 8A) coal, Monongahela Group. Also botryogen. Old strip mine on E side of Twp. Hwy. 46 about 1 mile N of Langsville, Rutland Twp.; RUTLAND.
Mineral occurrence: Fisher, 1975, p. 416.
General geology: DeLong, 1955, p. 43-44.

ANHYDRITE
$CaSO_4$

Chemical class: Sulfate
Crystallization: Orthorhombic; dipyramidal; mmm
Habit: Crystals not common; tabular; granular

aggregates; commonly massive

Physical properties: Cleavage: {010}, {100}, and {001} well-developed pinacoidal at right angles. H: 3½. G: 3.0. Luster: vitreous if well crystallized or greasy if massive. Color: white, bluish white, blue, gray, colorless. Streak: white

Occurrence: Massive beds or nodules interbedded with dolomite or halite of evaporite origin in deeper quarry workings and mines in northern Ohio

CUYAHOGA COUNTY
1. Finely crystalline gray anhydrite in beds of Salina Group; may be associated with halite. AKZO Salt, Inc. (formerly International Salt Co.) mine, Whiskey Island, just S of mouth of Cuyahoga River along shore of Lake Erie, Cleveland; CLEVELAND SOUTH.
Mineral occurrence: Clifford, 1973, p. 16-17; Hall, 1963, p. 29; Heimlich and others, 1974, p. 9.

LAKE COUNTY
1. Finely crystalline gray anhydrite in beds of Salina Group; may be associated with halite. Morton Salt Co. mine on W side of Grand River in Fairport Harbor, Painesville Twp.; MENTOR.
Mineral occurrence: Andelfinger and Fiedelman, 1966, p. 365-368; Clifford, 1973, p. 16-17; Hall, 1963, p. 29.

OTTAWA COUNTY
1. Kernels of blue anhydrite in center of masses of white gypsum in dolostones of undifferentiated Salina Group. Also celestite. Deeper underground workings of old U.S. Gypsum Co. mine, SE¼ sec. 10 and SW¼ sec. 11, Portage Twp.; VICKERY.
Mineral occurrence: Janssens, 1977, p. 36-38; Jones, 1935, p. 494.
General geology: Newberry, 1873a, p. 133-134; Orton, 1888b, p. 696-702; Stout, 1941, p. 420-421.
2. Masses of blue anhydrite with gypsum in dolostones of undifferentiated Salina Group. Also pyrite. Deeper workings of Celotex Corp. quarry, W½ sec. 10, Portage Twp.; VICKERY.
Mineral occurrence: Botoman and Faure, 1976, p. 69; Janssens, 1977, p. 36-38; Sparling, 1965, p. 99; 1970, p. 11; 1971, p. 20-21.
General geology: Forsyth, 1971, p. 13-14.

ARAGONITE
CaCO₃

Chemical class: Carbonate
Crystallization: Orthorhombic; dipyramidal; mmm
Habit: Crystals commonly long prismatic or tabular in radiating aggregates; commonly in fibrous crusts
Physical properties: Cleavage: {010} distinct pinacoidal. H: 3½-4. G: 2.9. Luster: vitreous. Color: commonly colorless or white; also gray, yellow, blue, green. Streak: white. Effervesces vigorously in cold dilute hydrochloric acid
Occurrence: Fibrous aggregates rare as coatings on other minerals in cavities of dolostones from northwestern Ohio and in veins of limestone concretions from the Ohio Shale; most of the northwestern Ohio material with a fibrous habit is strontianite

ERIE COUNTY
1. Tiny fibrous, radiating aggregates of white aragonite coating calcite, dolomite, ferroan dolomite, and quartz in veins of large limestone concretions from lower Huron Shale Member, Ohio Shale. Also barite and sphalerite. Borrow pit at Huron just S of U.S. Rte. 6, 0.4 mile W of Rye Beach Rd. intersection, Huron Twp.; HURON.
General geology: Explorer, 1961, p. 5; Prosser, 1913, p. 324-341.

HURON COUNTY
1. Tiny bladed aggregates of colorless aragonite coating dolomite and quartz in veins of large limestone concretions from lower Huron Shale Member, Ohio Shale. Also barite, calcite, ferroan dolomite, pyrite, and sphalerite. Outcrop about 2 miles N of Monroeville at Lamereaux Rd. bridge on E side of West Branch Huron River, Ridgefield Twp.; KIMBALL.
Mineral occurrence: Carlson, 1977, p. 24-25.
General geology: Broadhead and others, 1980, p. 10-15; Prosser, 1913, p. 324-341.

WAYNE COUNTY
1. Tiny fibrous, radiating aggregates of white aragonite as efflorescence on ironstone nodules from shale of Wooster Shale Member, Cuyahoga Formation. Also calcite, galena, pyrite, and sphalerite. Old quarry E of County Rd. 22 behind City of Wooster Service and Maintenance Facility, NE¼ sec. 5, Wooster Twp.; WOOSTER.
General geology: Conrey, 1921, p. 62-63; Szmuc, 1957, p. 193-195.

WOOD COUNTY
1. Colloform, radiating aggregates of yellow aragonite with sphalerite and strontianite in vugs and fractures of Lockport Dolomite and *Greenfield Dolomite*. Also barite, calcite, celestite, dolomite, fluorite, galena, gypsum, marcasite, pyrite, and sulfur. Stoneco (formerly Maumee Stone Co.) quarry, Lime City, SW¼ sec. 11, Perrysburg Twp.; ROSSFORD.
Mineral occurrence: Strogonoff, 1966, p. 44.
General geology: Janssens, 1971, p. 35; 1974, p. 82, 84; 1977, p. 22; Kahle and Floyd, 1968, p. 28-30; 1972, p. 50-52.

BARITE
BaSO₄

Chemical class: Sulfate
Crystallization: Orthorhombic; dipyramidal; mmm
Habit: Commonly well crystallized, but may be massive; crystals commonly tabular; rarely in rosettes
Physical properties: Cleavage: {001} perfect pinacoidal and {210} good prismatic. H: 3-3½. G: 4.5. Luster: vitreous when well crystallized, dull when massive. Color: white, pale blue, pale yellow, colorless, gray, black, brown. Streak: white. May be fluorescent
Occurrence: Granular aggregates in veins of limestone-, ironstone-, pyrite-, and barite-matrix concretions from black shales of central and eastern Ohio; less common in crystals and granular aggregates, which may be perched on calcite and other minerals, in cavities and fractures of dolostones in northwestern and southwestern Ohio; interesting but rare occurrences in flint beds of Vanport limestone and in cracks in thin coal seams in the Ohio Shale

ADAMS COUNTY
1. Barite with fluorite and sphalerite in fractured Silurian dolostones. Unspecified locations within Serpent

Mound disturbance, Bratton and Franklin Twps.; SINKING SPRING.

Mineral occurrence: Heyl and Van Alstine, 1976, p. 79; Worl and others, 1974, p. 9.

General geology: Koucky and Reidel, 1987, p. 431-436; Reidel, 1975, map; Reidel and Koucky, 1981, p. 391-403; Reidel and others, 1982, p. 1343-1377.

2. Barite with calcite, pyrite, and quartz in veins of large limestone concretions from lower Ohio Shale. Abandoned Norfolk and Western Railroad cut at Beaver Pond, Franklin Twp.; JAYBIRD.

Mineral occurrence: Hoskins and Blickle, 1940, p. 474.

General geology: Seyfried, 1953, p. 30.

3. Tabular barite with asphalt, calcite, dolomite, and quartz in veins of large limestone concretions from lower Ohio Shale. Also pyrite. Old quarry and cliff exposure on W side of Hackleshin Rd. 4 miles NE of Locust Grove, Franklin Twp.; JAYBIRD.

Mineral occurrence: Wuestner, 1938, p. 259-261.

General geology: Kepferle and others, 1981, p. 290-293; Lamborn, 1927, p. 712-714; Seyfried, 1953, p. 28.

4. Barite. Near Locust Grove, Franklin Twp.

Mineral occurrence: Reidel, 1972, p. 129.

5. Tabular barite with calcite in veins of large limestone concretions from lower Ohio Shale. Also melanterite and pyrite. Outcrop at Blue Creek near Ohio Rte. 125, Jefferson Twp.; BLUE CREEK.

Mineral occurrence: Locke, 1838, p. 260-261, map.

General geology: Seyfried, 1953, p. 26.

6. Barite near top of Brassfield Formation. Also calcite and sphalerite. Exposure along Beasley Fork of Ohio Brush Creek about 1 mile S of West Union near Ohio Rte. 247, Tiffin Twp.; WEST UNION. OGS section no. 12667.

Mineral occurrence: Botoman and Stieglitz, 1978, p. 5.

BELMONT COUNTY

1. Tabular barite with kaolinite and pyrite in veins of limestone concretions from shale of the Sewickley sandstone, Monongahela Group. Outcrop about ¼ mile E of Ohio Rte. 9 and 2 miles N of Baltimore and Ohio Railroad crossing in Fairpoint, sec. 20, Wheeling Twp.; HARRISVILLE.

General geology: Berryhill, 1963, p. 32-33.

CARROLL COUNTY

1. Granular barite with pyrite, sphalerite, and wurtzite in veins of ironstone concretions from shales above Lower Kittanning (No. 5) coal, and Middle Kittanning (No. 6) coal, Allegheny Group. Also melanterite, rozenite, and szomolnokite. James Bros. Coal Co. strip mine about 3 miles SE of Mineral City, N½ sec. 25, Rose Twp.; MINERAL CITY.

General geology: Lamborn, 1942, p. 10, 13.

COLUMBIANA COUNTY

1. Tabular barite crystals with calcite, chalcopyrite, kaolinite, pyrite, sphalerite, and wurtzite in veins of ironstone concretions from shales above Lower Kittanning (No. 5) coal, Allegheny Group. Also copiapite and gypsum. Metrel, Inc., quarry S of Negley, sec. 13, Middleton Twp.; EAST PALESTINE.

Mineral occurrence: Hollenbaugh, 1979, p. 9, 16-22; Hollenbaugh and Carlson, 1983, p. 697-703.

General geology: Stout and Lamborn, 1924, p. 111.

CUYAHOGA COUNTY

1. Masses of tabular colorless barite with sphalerite in veins of pyrite nodules from Chagrin Shale Member, Ohio Shale. Cliff exposure along N side of Chippewa Creek in Brecksville Reservation about ½ mile downstream from Ohio Rte. 82 bridge, E Brecksville Twp.; NORTHFIELD.

General geology: Kent State University, in Frank, 1969, p. 1.4-1.9; Prosser, 1912, p. 119.

DELAWARE COUNTY

1. Crystalline masses of barite with calcite in veins of large limestone concretions from lower Ohio Shale. Outcrops along Bartholomew Run on W side of Olentangy River about 1½ miles ESE of Powell, SE Liberty Twp.; POWELL.

Mineral occurrence: Stauffer and others, 1911, p. 26, fig. 3.

2. Coarsely crystalline barite with calcite in veins of large limestone concretions from lower Ohio Shale. Outcrops along Olentangy River and small tributaries entering river from E; DELAWARE, POWELL, WALDO.

Mineral occurrence: Westgate, 1926, p. 54-55, 63.

ERIE COUNTY

1. Crystalline masses of barite with calcite in pyrite nodules from Cleveland Shale Member, Ohio Shale. Outcrop about 0.5 mile N of Birmingham on W bank of Vermilion River, Florence Twp.; KIPTON.

General geology: Herdendorf, 1963, p. 168-170.

2. Granular masses of white barite with quartz in veins of barite nodules from Cleveland Shale Member, Ohio Shale. Bank and bed of Vermilion River N and S of Garfield Rd. bridge about 0.6 mile S of Birmingham, Florence Twp.; KIPTON.

Mineral occurrence: Holden and Carlson, 1979, p. 227-232.

General geology: Herdendorf, 1963, map.

3. Coarsely crystalline aggregates of tabular colorless barite with calcite, dolomite, ferroan dolomite, and quartz in veins of large limestone concretions from lower Huron Shale Member, Ohio Shale. Also aragonite and sphalerite. Borrow pit at Huron just S of U.S. Rte. 6, 0.4 mile W of Rye Beach Rd. intersection, Huron Twp.; HURON.

General geology: Explorer, 1961, p. 5; Prosser, 1913, p. 324-341.

4. Coarsely crystalline aggregates of tabular colorless barite with calcite, dolomite, ferroan dolomite, pyrite, and whewellite in veins of limestone concretions from lower Huron Shale Member, Ohio Shale. Outcrop along Huron River about 1 mile W of Milan, Milan Twp.; KIMBALL.

Mineral occurrence: Hyde, C., and Landy, 1966, p. 228; Leavens, 1968, p. 456-457.

General geology: Prosser, 1913, p. 324-341.

5. Coarsely crystalline aggregates of tabular colorless barite with calcite, dolomite, ferroan dolomite, and quartz in veins of large limestone concretions from the lower Huron Shale Member, Ohio Shale. Also pyrite. Outcrop just W of Milan on N side of Huron River and W side of U.S. Rte. 250 bridge, Milan Twp.; MILAN.

Mineral occurrence: Feldmann and others, 1977, p. 48-49.

General geology: Prosser, 1913, p. 327-328.

FRANKLIN COUNTY

1. Crystalline masses of barite with calcite in veins of large limestone concretions from lower Ohio Shale. Also pyrite. Outcrops along Narrows of Olentangy River about 1¼ miles N of Worthington, Sharon Twp.; NORTHWEST COLUMBUS.

Mineral occurrence: Orton, 1878, p. 635; Stauffer and others, 1911, p. 26-27, pl. 4.

General geology: Foster, J. W., 1838, p. 105; Karhi, 1948, p. 26-27.

HANCOCK COUNTY

1. Small rosettes of white barite with pyrite in cavities of Tymochtee Dolomite. Also calcite, celestite, and fluorite. Tarbox-McCall Stone Co. quarry, Findlay, W½ sec. 24, Liberty Twp.; FINDLAY.

General geology: Janssens, 1977, p. 3.

HIGHLAND COUNTY
1. Barite in Brassfield Formation. Also calcite, pyrite, and sphalerite. Davon, Inc., Highland Plant quarry about 1 mile SE of Fairview on E side of Danville Rd., NE Hamer Twp.; NEW MARKET. OGS section no. 13610.
    Mineral occurrence: Botoman and Stieglitz, 1978, p. 5.
    General geology: Hopkins, 1954, p. 85.

HURON COUNTY
1. Crystals and platy aggregates of colorless barite with calcite, dolomite, ferroan dolomite, quartz, and sphalerite in veins of large limestone concretions from lower Huron Shale Member, Ohio Shale. Also aragonite and pyrite. Outcrop about 2 miles N of Monroeville at Lamereaux Rd. bridge on E side of West Branch Huron River, Ridgefield Twp.; KIMBALL.
    Mineral occurrence: Bingaman and others, 1978, p. 16; Carlson, 1977, p. 24-25.
    General geology: Broadhead and others, 1980, p. 10-15; Prosser, 1913, p. 324-341.
2. Colorless barite in veins of pyrite nodules and fracture fillings in thin coal seams in lower Huron Shale Member, Ohio Shale. Also gypsum and halotrichite-pickeringite. Cliff exposure about 2 miles N of Monroeville and ¼ mile SW of Lamereaux Rd. bridge on W side of West Branch Huron River, Ridgefield Twp.; KIMBALL.
    General geology: Broadhead and others, 1980, p. 10-15; Prosser, 1913, p. 324-341.
3. White barite veins in coal from lower Huron Shale Member, Ohio Shale. Outcrop at Monroeville along West Branch Huron River N of Penn Central Railroad bridge, Ridgefield Twp.; MONROEVILLE.
    Mineral occurrence: Leeds, 1875, p. 105; Newberry, 1875, p. 105-106; Read, 1878a, p. 308.
    General geology: Prosser, 1913, p. 330.

JEFFERSON COUNTY
1. Tabular colorless to white barite with calcite, pyrite, sphalerite, and wurtzite in veins of ironstone concretions from shales above Brush Creek coal, Conemaugh Group. Road cut near Alikanna on E side of Ohio Rte. 7 just N of Ohio Rte. 213 intersection, N½ sec. 31, Island Creek Twp.; KNOXVILLE.
    Mineral occurrence: Hollenbaugh and Carlson, 1983, p. 697-701.
    General geology: Condit, 1912, p. 204-205; Lamborn, 1930, p. 123; Seaman and Hamilton, 1950, p. 47.

LICKING COUNTY
1. Large barite crystal in flint beds of Vanport limestone, Allegheny Group. Also quartz. Prehistoric quarry near Flint Ridge State Memorial, intersection of County Hwy 668 and 312, Hopewell Twp.; GLENFORD.
    Mineral occurrence: Mills, 1921, p. 123-124.
    General geology: DeLong, 1972, map; Stout and Schoenlaub, 1945, p. 80-83.

LICKING AND MUSKINGUM COUNTIES
1. Barite crystals in flint beds of Vanport limestone, Allegheny Group. Also calcite and quartz. Prehistoric quarries and exposures along Flint Ridge, no specific localities given, Hopewell Twp., Licking Co., and Hopewell Twp., Muskingum Co.; GLENFORD, GRATIOT, TOBOSO.
    Mineral occurrence: Foster, J. W., 1838, p. 90-91; Moorehead, 1892, p. 35, 37; Smith, C. M., 1885, p. 859.
    General geology: DeLong, 1972, map; Mills, 1921, p. 90-161; Stout and Schoenlaub, 1945, p. 80-87.

LORAIN COUNTY
1. Crystals and granular masses of barite with calcite, pyrite, and quartz in veins of barite nodules from Cleveland Shale Member, Ohio Shale. Also pickeringite. Along banks of Vermilion River at Mill Hollow-Bacon Woods Park, Brownhelm Twp.; VERMILION EAST.
    Mineral occurrence: Holden and Carlson, 1979, p. 227-232.
    General geology: Broadhead and others, 1980, p. 23-30; Herdendorf, 1963, map; Prosser, 1913, p. 348.

LUCAS COUNTY
1. Small tabular white barite crystals with calcite in cavities of Silica Formation and *Tenmile Creek Dolomite*. Also celestite, dolomite, pyrite, sphalerite, and strontianite. W wall of France Stone Co. North quarry (formerly Medusa Portland Cement Co.), Sylvania, S-central sec. 7, Sylvania Twp.; SYLVANIA, BERKEY.
    Mineral occurrence: Carlson, 1983, p. 425, 429; Mychkovsky, 1978b, p. 36.
    General geology: Carman and others, 1962, p. 5-6; Ehlers, G. M., and others, 1951, p. 4.
2. Barite crystals in cavities of Sylvania Sandstone and dolostones of *Detroit River Group;* may be associated with calcite. Also fluorite. France Stone Co. East quarry, Sylvania, W½ sec. 17, Sylvania Twp.; SYLVANIA.
    Mineral occurrence: Carlson, 1983, p. 425, 429; Mychkosvky, 1978b, p. 26, 36.
    General geology: Ehlers, G. M., and others, 1951, p. 5-7.

MAHONING COUNTY
1. Barite with sphalerite in veins of ironstone concretions from shales below Lower Mercer limestone, Pottsville Group. Also calcite, chalcopyrite, kaolinite, and pyrite. Outcrop along West Branch Meander Creek just E of junction with Ohio Rte. 45 about ¾ mile S of Ellsworth, Ellsworth Twp.; CANFIELD.
    Mineral occurrence: Greene, 1935, p. 883.
    General geology: Lamb, 1910, p. 114.
2. Tabular barite with chalcopyrite, pyrite, and sphalerite in veins of ironstone concretions from shales below the Vanport(?) limestone, Allegheny Group. Keller mine S of Middletown Rd., NE¼ sec. 19, Smith Twp.; ALLIANCE.
    General geology: DeLong and White, 1963, p. 42, 45; Lamb, 1910, p. 109.

MUSKINGUM COUNTY (see also Licking County)
1. Tabular barite with chalcedony, flint, and quartz in flint bed of Vanport limestone, Allegheny Group. Exposure on John Nethers property, County Hwy. 8, NW¼ sec. 6, Hopewell Twp.; TOBOSO.
    General geology: Stout and Schoenlaub, 1945, p. 87.

OTTAWA COUNTY
1. Finely crystalline aggregates of white barite associated with celestite in cavities of Bass Islands Dolomite. Also calcite, fluorite, and pyrite. Fox Stone Products, Inc., quarry, N side of Langram Rd., S part of South Bass Island, Put-in-Bay Twp.; PUT-IN-BAY.
    General geology: Janssens, 1977, p. 27-30; Sparling, 1971, p. 19-22.

PORTAGE COUNTY
1. Tabular barite with calcite and sphalerite in veins of ironstone concretions from shales of lower Pottsville Group. Also chalcopyrite and kaolinite. Outcrop along SE shore of Michael J. Kirwan Reservoir at mouth of Silver Creek just W of Alliance Rd., NE Edinburg Twp.; WINDHAM.
    General geology: Winslow and White, 1966, p. 79.

ROSS COUNTY
1. Coarsely crystalline aggregates of tabular colorless barite with calcite, dolomite, and quartz in veins of large limestone concretions from lower Huron Shale Member, Ohio Shale. Also halotrichite-pickeringite, melanterite, and pyrite. Cliff exposure at Copperas Mountain about 1 mile ESE of Seip Mound State Memorial

on SE side of Paint Creek, Paxton Twp.; MORGAN-TOWN.
Mineral occurrence: Bingaman and others, 1978, p. 10; Briggs, 1838, p. 77-78; Carlson, 1987b, p. 428; Dana, E. S., 1892, p. 1085; Dana, J. D., 1858, p. 495; 1868, p. 784.
General geology: Kepferle and others, 1981, p. 294-295; Orton, 1874, p. 647; Seyfried, 1953, p. 18-25.

SANDUSKY COUNTY
1. Small white barite crystals with calcite, celestite, and strontianite in cavities of Lockport Dolomite. Also dolomite, fluorite, galena, pyrite, and sphalerite. Martin Marietta Chemicals quarry (S part formerly Woodville Lime & Chemical Co. quarry), Woodville, E½ sec. 21, W½ sec. 22, Woodville Twp.; ELMORE.
Mineral occurrence: Carlson, 1983, p. 425, 429; 1986, p. 9-13.
General geology: Stout, 1941, p. 375; Summerson and others, 1963, p. 42.
2. Small white to gray barite crystals in Lockport Dolomite. Also calcite, celestite, dolomite, fluorite, galena, pyrite, and sphalerite. Steetley Resources, Inc., Ohio Lime Co. quarry, Woodville, W½ sec. 34, Woodville Twp.; EL-MORE.
Mineral occurrence: Carlson, 1983, p. 425, 429; Mychkovsky, 1978b, p. 28, 35-36.
General geology: Floyd, 1971, p. 167-169; Kahle and Floyd, 1968, p. 31-35.

STARK COUNTY
1. Tabular barite with pyrite and sphalerite in veins of ironstone concretions in shales of Allegheny Group. Penn Central Railroad cut at Warren Rd. intersection about ½ mile NE of Paris, SW¼ sec. 4, Paris Twp.; ROBERTSVILLE.
General geology: DeLong and White, 1963, p. 75, 81.

TUSCARAWAS COUNTY
1. Barite with pyrite and sphalerite in veins of ironstone concretions from shales of Allegheny Group. Old strip mine on W side of Winfield Rd. about ½ mile NE of intersection with U.S. Rte. 250, Dover Twp.; DOVER.
General geology: Lamborn, 1956, p. 168, pl. 1.
2. Barite with pyrite and sphalerite in veins of ironstone concretions in shales above Lower Kittanning (No. 5) coal, Allegheny Group. Eberhart Coal Co., Inc., strip mine, Dover(?) Twp., specific location not given.
Mineral occurrence: Orr and others, 1982, p. 52-54.
General geology: Lamborn, 1956, p. 125-140.
3. Barite with sphalerite in veins of ironstone concretions from shales of Pottsville Group. Belden Brick Co. quarry just N of Dundee, Wayne Twp.; STRASBURG.
General geology: Lamborn, 1956, pl. 1.

WAYNE COUNTY
1. Tabular barite with calcite, chalcopyrite, galena, pyrite, and sphalerite in veins of ironstone concretions from shales of lower Pottsville Group. Penn Central Railroad cut N of Marshallville, W-central sec. 33, Chippewa Twp.; DOYLESTOWN.
Mineral occurrence: Ver Steeg, 1940, p. 259; 1942, p. 223.
General geology: Conrey, 1921, p. 92; Ver Steeg, 1948, p. 185.

WOOD COUNTY
1. Crystals and aggregates, some rosettes, of pale-blue to white barite in cavities in dolostones of *Detroit River Group* and Dundee Limestone; may be associated with calcite. Also asphalt, celestite, dolomite, fluorite, glauconite, hexahydrite, marcasite, pyrite, and sphalerite. France Stone Co. Custar quarry (formerly Pugh Quarry Co.) about 4 miles W of Weston, SW¼ sec. 6, Milton Twp.; MCCLURE.
Mineral occurrence: Carlson, 1983, p. 425, 429; Feldmann and others, 1977, p. 35-37; Gettings, 1950, p. 601; Green, R., 1970a, p. 584; Heinrich and Vian, 1967, p. 1186; Kessen and others, 1981, p. 913-918; Mychkovsky, 1978b, p. 26-28, 36; Nelson, 1967, p. 60; Parr and Chang, 1980, p. 20-26; Robbins, 1983, p. 125; Strogonoff, 1966, p. 48.
General geology: Forsyth, 1966a, p. 204-205; Janssens, 1970a, p. 7, 22; Orton and Peppel, 1906, p. 133; Stout, 1941, p. 395-396.
2. Small fine-grained masses of pale-yellow barite on sphalerite in cavities of *Lockport Dolomite* and Greenfield Dolomite. Also calcite, celestite, dolomite, fluorite, hexahydrite, pyrite, and strontianite. MacRitchie Materials, Inc., quarry (formerly Brough Stone Co.), West Millgrove, SE¼ sec. 4, Perry Twp.; FOSTORIA.
General geology: Janssens, 1971, p. 35; 1974, p. 82, 84; 1977, p. 22; Shaver, 1977, p. 1414; Stout, 1941, p. 392.
3. Layers of yellowish-brown barite on calcite crystals in *Lockport Dolomite* and Greenfield Dolomite. Also aragonite, celestite, dolomite, fluorite, galena, gypsum, marcasite, pyrite, sphalerite, stronianite, and sulfur. Stoneco quarry (formerly Maumee Stone Co.), Lime City, SW¼ sec. 11, Perrysburg Twp.; ROSSFORD.
General geology: Janssens, 1971, p. 35; 1974, p. 82, 84; 1977, p. 22; Kahle and Floyd, 1968, p. 28-30; 1972, p. 50-52.

BOTRYOGEN
MgFe(SO$_4$)$_2$(OH) · 7H$_2$O

Chemical class: Sulfate
Crystallization: Monoclinic; prismatic; 2/m
Habit: Commonly in colloform or rounded fibrous masses with a radial structure; prismatic crystals
Physical properties: Cleavage: {010} perfect pinacoidal. H: 2-2½. G: 2.1. Luster: vitreous to dull. Color: orange red. Streak: brownish yellow
Occurrence: Fine-grained aggregates rare as efflorescence associated with pyrite in coal and shale in eastern Ohio

MEIGS COUNTY
1. Efflorescence of small masses of orange botryogen on copiapite and pickeringite in shale above the Redstone (Pomeroy) (No. 8A) coal, Monongahela Group. Also alunogen. Old strip mine on E side of Twp. Hwy. 46 about 1 mile N of Langsville, Rutland Twp.; RUTLAND.
Mineral occurrence: Fisher, H. H., 1975, p. 416.
General geology: DeLong, 1955, p. 43-44.

CALCITE
CaCO$_3$

Chemical class: Carbonate
Crystallization: Hexagonal (Trigonal); ditrigonal scalenohedral; $\bar{3}$m
Habit: Commonly well crystallized; scalenohedral and rhombohedral forms most common; commonly granular or massive
Physical properties: Cleavage: {10$\bar{1}$1} perfect rhombohedral. H: 3. G: 2.7. Luster: vitreous. Color: white, colorless, yellow, brown, gray, black. Streak: white. May be fluorescent. Effervesces vigorously in cold dilute hydrochloric acid
Occurrence: Crystals and granular aggregates in cavities and fractures of dolostones and limestones in western Ohio; granular aggregates

commonly form veins in limestone concretions and less commonly in ironstone concretions from black shales in central and eastern Ohio; more rare as an efflorescence

ADAMS COUNTY
1. Veins of fluorescent white calcite in Bisher Dolomite. Also dolomite, hydrozincite, smithsonite, sphalerite, and sulfur. Outcrop in gully S of small quarry 0.7 mile E of entrance to Serpent Mound State Memorial on Ohio Rte. 73 and 1.4 miles N on E side of Twp. Hwy. 116, Bratton Twp.; SINKING SPRING.
Mineral occurrence: Koucky, 1975, p. 22.
General geology: Koucky and Reidel, 1987, p. 431-436; Reidel, 1975, map; Reidel and Koucky, 1981, p. 391-403; Reidel and others, 1982, p. 1343-1377.
2. Coarsely crystalline calcite in Brassfield Formation. Also hematite and sphalerite. Exposure on S side of Ohio Rte. 73, 1.5 miles W of Louden, Bratton Twp.; SINKING SPRING. OGS section no. 14350.
Mineral occurrence: Botoman and Stieglitz, 1978, p. 5.
General geology: Hopkins, 1954, p. 88; Koucky, 1975, p. 14-15.
3. Calcite with asphalt, hydrozincite, smithsonite, and sphalerite in fractures and pockets of undifferentiated Pebbles-Greenfield-Tymochtee Dolomites. Numerous exposures within the Serpent Mound disturbance, Bratton and Franklin Twps.; SINKING SPRING.
Mineral occurrence: Reidel, 1972, p. 72, 92, 98.
General geology: Reidel, 1975, map.
4. Crystals and aggregates of fluorescent calcite with quartz in cavities of Bisher Dolomite. Numerous outcrops within the Serpent Mound disturbance, Bratton and Franklin Twps.; SINKING SPRING.
Mineral occurrence: Reidel, 1972, p. 26, 92.
General geology: Reidel, 1975, map; Rogers, J. K., 1936, p. 72; Stout, 1941, p. 79.
5. Calcite in cavities of *Lilley Dolomite*, Peebles Dolomite, Greenfield Dolomite, Tymochtee Dolomite, and Ohio Shale. Also pyrite and sphalerite. Davon, Inc., Plum Run quarry about 1 mile S on Twp. Hwy. 126 from its intersection with Ohio Rte. 74 at Bacon Flat, Franklin-Meigs Twp. boundary; JAYBIRD.
Mineral occurrence: Schmidt and others, 1961, p. 285-288; Summerson and others, 1963, p. 18-23.
General geology: Rexroad and others, 1965, p. 29; Stith, 1983, p. 11-12, 15.
6. Fluorescent white calcite as breccia cement along two faults in Bisher or Lilley Dolomite. Also manganese oxides and pyrite. Outcrops about 1 mile N of Locust Grove on W and E sides of Ohio Rte. 41, Franklin Twp.; SINKING SPRING.
Mineral occurrence: Galbraith, 1968, p. 25, 32.
General geology: Reidel, 1975, map.
7. Calcite with barite, pyrite, and quartz in veins of large limestone concretions from lower Ohio Shale. Abandoned Norfolk and Western Railroad cut at Beaver Pond, Franklin Twp.; JAYBIRD.
Mineral occurrence: Hoskins and Blickle, 1940, p. 474; Seyfried, 1953, p. 30.
8. Crystals of calcite with asphalt, barite, dolomite, and quartz in veins of large limestone concretions from lower Ohio Shale. Also pyrite. Old quarry and cliff exposure on W side of Hackleshin Rd., 4 miles NE of Locust Grove, Franklin Twp.; JAYBIRD.
Mineral occurrence: Wuestner, 1938, p. 259-261.
General geology: Kepferle and others, 1981, p. 290-293; Lamborn, 1927, p. 712-714; Seyfried, 1953, p. 28.
9. Calcite with barite in veins of large limestone concretions from lower Ohio Shale. Also melanterite and pyrite. Outcrop at Blue Creek near Ohio Rte. 125, Jefferson Twp.; BLUE CREEK.
Mineral occurrence: Locke, 1838, p. 260-261, map; Seyfried, 1953, p. 26.
10. Veins of calcite in Brassfield Formation. Also hematite. Outcrop along Lick Creek 3½ miles S of Dunkinsville, Tiffin Twp.; WEST UNION.
Mineral occurrence: Hopkins, 1954, p. 90.
11. Calcite with sphalerite near base of Brassfield Formation. Also barite. Exposure along Beasley Fork of Ohio Brush Creek about 1 mile S of West Union near Ohio Rte. 247, Tiffin Twp.; WEST UNION. OGS section no. 12667.
Mineral occurrence: Botoman and Stieglitz, 1978, p. 5.

ALLEN COUNTY
1. White to colorless calcite in cavities of Tymochtee Dolomite and dolostones of undifferentiated Salina Group. Also asphalt, dolomite, fluorite, pyrite, and sphalerite. National Lime & Stone Co. quarry, Lima, sec. 29, Bath Twp.; LIMA.
Mineral occurrence: Botoman and Stieglitz, 1978, p. 5; Kessen and others, 1981, p. 913-918.
General geology: Janssens, 1977, p. 3.
2. Calcite in Tymochtee Dolomite. Also pyrite and sphalerite. National Lime & Stone Co. quarry (formerly Western Ohio Stone Co.), Lima, W½ sec. 29, Bath Twp.; LIMA.
Mineral occurrence: Botoman and Stieglitz, 1978, p. 5.
General geology: Janssens, 1977, p. 3; Stout, 1941, p. 305.
3. White to colorless calcite in cavities of *Tymochtee Dolomite* and dolostones of undifferentiated Salina Group. Also dolomite, fluorite, pyrite, and sphalerite. Bluffton Stone Co. quarry, Bluffton, NW¼ sec. 12, Richland Twp., BLUFFTON.
General geology: Janssens, 1977, p. 3; Stout, 1941, p. 310.

ATHENS COUNTY
1. Calcite veins in septarian ferruginous limestone from Gaysport(?) limestone, Conemaugh Group. Exposure on N side of U.S. Rte. 50, SW¼NW¼ sec. 28, Canaan Twp.; STEWART.
Mineral occurrence: Sturgeon and associates, 1958, p. 149, 406-407.
2. Calcareous veins in nodules from Lower Freeport limestone, Allegheny Group. Vaughn strip mine N of U.S. Rte. 33, SW¼SW¼ sec. 36, York Twp.; UNION FURNACE.
Mineral occurrence: Denton and others, 1961, p. 202; Sturgeon and associates, 1958, p. 581.
3. Calcite veins in ironstone nodules from Zaleski(?) flint, Allegheny Group. Exposures in gullies and mine entrance near N edge of Nelsonville on both sides of William St., NE¼NW¼ sec. 24, York Twp.; NELSONVILLE.
Mineral occurrence: Sturgeon and associates, 1958, p. 585-586.

AUGLAIZE COUNTY
1. Crystals of yellow calcite in cavities of *Lockport Dolomite* and *Greenfield Dolomite*. Also pyrite, quartz, and sphalerite. National Lime & Stone Co. quarry, Buckland, E½ sec. 10, Moulton Twp.; MOULTON.
Mineral occurrence: Botoman and Stieglitz, 1978, p. 5.
General geology: Janssens, 1971, p. 35; 1974, p. 82, 84; Shaver, 1974, p. 89-95.

CHAMPAIGN COUNTY
1. Hollow stalactites (soda straws) of calcite in Columbus Limestone. Ohio Caverns, 4 miles E of West Liberty, NE Salem Twp.; KINGSCREEK.
Mineral occurrence: Bassett and Bassett, 1962, p. 88-91; White, G. W., 1926, p. 97-98.

COLUMBIANA COUNTY
1. Calcite with barite, chalcopyrite, kaolinite, pyrite, sphalerite, and wurtzite in veins of ironstone concretions from shales above the Lower Kittanning (No. 5) coal, Allegheny Group. Also copiapite and gypsum. Metrel, Inc., quarry S of Negley, sec. 13, Middleton Twp.; EAST PALESTINE.
   Mineral occurrence: Hollenbaugh, 1979, p. 16-22; Hollenbaugh and Carlson, 1983, p. 697-703.
   General geology: Stout and Lamborn, 1924, p. 111.

CRAWFORD COUNTY
1. Crystals and granular masses of calcite in cavities of *Columbus Limestone* and Delaware Limestone. Also asphalt and fluorite. National Lime & Stone Co. quarry, Bucyrus (Spore), secs. 18 and 19, Holmes Twp.; OCEOLA.
   General geology: Hall and Alkire, 1956, p. 3, 32-33, 35-36; Janssens, 1970b, p. 3; Stauffer, 1909, p. 109-110; Summerson and others, 1957, p. 59.

CUYAHOGA COUNTY
1. Calcite efflorescences on Berea Sandstone. Deer Lick Cave about 1 mile S of Ohio Rte. 82 bridge over Chippewa Creek along park roads in Brecksville Reservation, E Brecksville Twp.; NORTHFIELD.
   Mineral occurrence: Connors, 1974, p. 38.
   General geology: Kent State University, *in* Frank, 1969, p. 1.4-1.9.

DELAWARE COUNTY
1. Calcite crystals in pockets of Columbus Limestone. Outcrop in gorge of Deer Run, a tributary on W side of Scioto River, SE corner Concord Twp.; POWELL.
   Mineral occurrence: Stauffer, 1909, p. 64.
2. Calcite crystals in pockets of Columbus Limestone. Outcrop in ravine of Monkey Run, a tributary on E side of Scioto River, SW corner Liberty Twp.; POWELL.
   Mineral occurrence: Stauffer, 1909, p. 62-63.
3. Calcite crystals coating joints in Columbus Limestone and *Delaware Limestone*. Also pyrite. Old Miami Stone Co. quarry on W side of Olentangy River W of Ohio Rte. 315, 1.8 miles N of Ohio Rte. 750 intersection, Liberty Twp.; POWELL.
   Mineral occurrence: Bernhagen and others, 1953, p. 4.
   General geology: Wells, 1944b, p. 299.
4. Crystalline masses of calcite with barite in veins of large limestone concretions from lower Ohio Shale. Outcrop along Bartholomew Run on W side of Olentangy River about 1½ miles ESE of Powell, SE Liberty Twp.; POWELL.
   Mineral occurrence: Stauffer and others, 1911, p. 26, fig. 3.
5. Calcite crystals in cavities of *Columbus Limestone* and Delaware Limestone. National Lime & Stone Co. Delaware (Klondike) quarry on E side of Scioto River about 2 miles N of Bellepoint, Scioto Twp.; OSTRANDER.
   Mineral occurrence: Stauffer, 1909, p. 74-75; Westgate, 1926, p. 24.
   General geology: Janssens, 1970b, p. 3; Stout, 1941, p. 229-230; Summerson and others, 1957, p. 59.
6. Coarsely crystallized calcite with barite in veins of large limestone concretions from lower Ohio Shale. Outcrops along the Olentangy River and small tributaries entering river from E; DELAWARE, POWELL, WALDO.
   Mineral occurrence: Westgate, 1926, p. 54-55, 63.

ERIE COUNTY
1. Masses of fluorescent white calcite with barite in pyrite nodules from Cleveland Shale Member, Ohio Shale. Outcrop about 0.5 mile N of Birmingham on W bank of Vermilion River, Florence Twp.; KIPTON.
   General geology: Herdendorf, 1963, p. 168-170.
2. Crystals and masses of colorless, pale-brown, and white calcite in cavities of dolostones of *Detroit River Group* and Columbus and Delaware Limestones; may be associated with fluorite, pyrite, and sphalerite. Also celestite. Sandusky Crushed Stone Co. quarry, Parkertown, just S of Portland Rd., Groton Twp.; BELLEVUE.
   Mineral occurrence: Nelson, 1967, p. 51-54.
   General geology: Janssens, 1970b, p. 10-12.
3. Granular masses of white to brown calcite with barite, dolomite, ferroan dolomite, and quartz in veins of large limestone concretions from lower Huron Shale Member, Ohio Shale. Also aragonite and sphalerite. Borrow pit at Huron just S of U.S. Rte. 6, 0.4 mile W of Rye Beach Rd. intersection, Huron Twp.; HURON.
   General geology: Explorer, 1961, p. 5; Prosser, 1913, p. 324-341.
4. Calcite crystals in cavities of Lucas Dolomite and *Columbus Limestone*. Also quartz and sphalerite. Kellstone (South Side) quarry, SW Kelleys Island, Kelleys Island Twp.; KELLEYS ISLAND.
   Mineral occurrence: Dana, E. S., and Ford, 1932, p. 516; Ford and Pogue, 1909, p. 186-187; Palache and others, 1951, p. 148, 156; Strogonoff, 1966, p. 59; Whitlock, 1910, p. 231-234.
   General geology: Feldmann and Bjerstedt, 1987, p. 395-398; Feldmann and others, 1977, p. 43-47; Fisher, M., 1922, p. 8, 41; Forsyth, 1971, p. 7; Stauffer, 1909, p. 136-137.
5. Calcite crystals in cavities of Lucas Dolomite and *Columbus Limestone*. Also quartz and sphalerite. North Side quarry N of Titus Rd., NW Kelleys Island, Kelleys Island Twp.; KELLEYS ISLAND.
   Mineral occurrence: Dana, E. S., and Ford, 1932, p. 516; Fisher, M., 1922, p. 8, 40; Ford and Pogue, 1909, p. 186-187; Palache and others, 1951, p. 148, 156; Whitlock, 1910, p. 231-234.
   General geology: Feldmann and Bjerstedt, 1987, p. 395-398; Feldmann and others, 1977, p. 43-47; Forsyth, 1971, p. 6; Stauffer, 1909, p. 139.
6. Calcite crystals in small pockets of Lucas Dolomite. Old Lake Shore quarry N of Glacial Grooves State Memorial on N shore of Kelleys Island, Kelleys Island Twp.; KELLEYS ISLAND.
   Mineral occurrence: Fisher, M., 1922, p. 38-39.
   General geology: Feldmann and Bjerstedt, 1987, p. 395-398; Feldmann and others, 1977, p. 43-47.
7. Calcite crystals in small pockets of Lucas Dolomite. Outcrop at NW side of Carpenter Point, W Kelleys Island, Kelleys Island Twp.; KELLEYS ISLAND.
   Mineral occurrence: Fisher, M., 1922, p. 38.
8. Calcite crystals in small pockets of Columbus Limestone. Also fluorite. Outcrop along N shore of Kelleys Island just W of N docks, Kelleys Island Twp.; KELLEYS ISLAND.
   Mineral occurrence: Fisher, M., 1922, p. 39.
   General geology: Feldmann and Bjerstedt, 1987, p. 395-398; Feldmann and others, 1977, p. 46-47.
9. White and brown calcite crystals in cavities of dolostones of Detroit River Group and *Columbus Limestone*. Also fluorite. Wagner Quarries Co. Castalia quarry 1½ miles SW of Castalia along E side of Ohio Rte. 101, Margaretta Twp.; CASTALIA.
   Mineral occurrence: Forsyth, 1971, p. 9-11; Nelson, 1967, p. 37.
   General geology: Janssens, 1970b, p. 14-16; Stout, 1941, p. 360-361.
10. Granular masses of white calcite in cavities of *Columbus Limestone* and Delaware Limestone. Erie Blacktop,

Inc., quarry 1½ miles NE of Castalia along E side of Bardshar Rd. just N of intersection with Ohio Rte. 101, Margaretta Twp.; CASTALIA.

General geology: Stout, 1941, p. 363-365.

11. Calcite crystals with fluorite in cavities of Bass Islands Dolomite. Small cave about ½ mile S of Crystal Rock along Crystal Road near Crystal Cave, NW Margaretta Twp.; CASTALIA.

General geology: Carman, 1927, p. 491; White, G. W., 1926, p. 86.

12. Crystalline masses of fluorescent white to brown calcite with barite, dolomite, ferroan dolomite, pyrite, and whewellite in veins of large limestone concretions from lower Huron Shale Member, Ohio Shale. Outcrop along Huron River about 1 mile W of Milan, Milan Twp.; KIMBALL.

Mineral occurrence: Hyde, C., and Landy, 1966, p. 228; Leavens, 1968, p. 456.

General geology: Prosser, 1913, p. 324-341.

13. Crystalline masses of fluorescent white to brown calcite with barite, dolomite, ferroan dolomite, and quartz in veins of large limestone concretions from lower Huron Shale Member, Ohio Shale. Also pyrite. Outcrop just W of Milan on N side of Huron River and W side of U.S. Rte. 250 bridge, Milan Twp.; MILAN.

Mineral occurrence: Feldmann and others, 1977, p. 48-49.
General geology: Prosser, 1913, p. 327-328.

FAYETTE COUNTY

1. Mottlings and veins of calcite in Tymochtee Dolomite. Fayette Limestone Co., Inc., quarry 4.3 miles S of Staunton on E side of U.S. Rte. 62, Green Twp.; MEMPHIS.

Mineral occurrence: Summerson and others, 1963, p. 28.

General geology: Stout, 1941, p. 131-132.

2. Calcite in Greenfield Dolomite. Also pyrite, quartz, and sphalerite. American Aggregates Corp. Blue Rock quarry about ¾ mile N of intersection of Ohio Rtes. 41 and 753, SE corner Perry Twp.; NEW MARTINSBURG.

Mineral occurrence: Botoman and Stieglitz, 1978, p. 5, 9.
General geology: Stout, 1941, p. 133-134.

FRANKLIN COUNTY

1. Calcite crystals in cavities of dolostones of undifferentiated Salina Group, *Columbus Limestone*, and Delaware Limestone. Marble Cliff Quarries Co. Hobo quarry on Trabue Rd. just W of U.S. Rte. 33 intersection, NE Franklin Twp.; SOUTHWEST COLUMBUS.

Mineral occurrence: Janssens, 1969, p. 1.5-1.6; 1970b, p. 5-6.

General geology: Janssens, 1977, p. 29; Stout, 1941, p. 213.

2. Calcite in Columbus Limestone. Exposures along Scioto River near Griggs Dam, NW of Columbus, Norwich Twp.; NORTHWEST COLUMBUS.

Mineral occurrence: Haden, 1977, p. 25, 28.
General geology: Stauffer and others, 1911, p. 19-21; Stout, 1941, p. 211-213.

3. Calcite crystals in cavities of Columbus Limestone. Cliff exposure on S side of Little Darby Creek about ½ mile W of Georgesville, Pleasant Twp.; GALLOWAY.

Mineral occurrence: Stauffer, 1909, p. 41; Stauffer and others, 1911, p. 18.

4. Calcite crystals in cavities of Columbus Limestone. Old quarry on W bank of Big Darby Creek 2 miles N of Georgesville, Pleasant Twp.; GALLOWAY.

Mineral occurrence: Stauffer, 1909, p. 41-42.

5. Granular masses of calcite with barite in veins of large limestone concretions from lower Ohio Shale. Also pyrite. Outcrops along Narrows of Olentangy River about 1¼ miles N of Worthington, Sharon Twp.; NORTHWEST COLUMBUS.

Mineral occurrence: Orton, 1878, p. 635; Stauffer and others, 1911, p. 26-27, pl. 4.

General geology: Foster, J. W., 1838, p. 105; Karhi, 1948, p. 26-27.

6. Calcite with whewellite in veins of large limestone concretions from lower Huron Shale Member, Ohio Shale. Also pyrite. Road cut along Interstate 270 about 2 miles N of Worthington, Sharon Twp.; NORTHWEST COLUMBUS.

Mineral occurrence: Criss and others, 1988, p. 4.

GREENE COUNTY

1. Crystals and masses of colorless and white calcite in cavities of Cedarville Dolomite. Also dolomite, marcasite, pyrite, and quartz. American Aggregates Corp. quarry 1 mile SE of Cedarville on N side of Turnbull Rd., Cedarville Twp.; CEDARVILLE.

General geology: Stith, 1983, p. 11-12, 14.

HANCOCK COUNTY

1. Granular white, green, and purple calcite in cavities and fractures of *Tymochtee Dolomite* and dolostones of undifferentiated Salina Group; may be associated with fluorite and pyrite. Also asphalt, celestite, gypsum, and sphalerite. National Lime & Stone Co. quarry, Findlay, sec. 24 and NE¼ sec. 25, Liberty Twp.; FINDLAY.

Mineral occurrence: Strogonoff, 1966, p. 56.
General geology: Janssens, 1971, p. 35; Stout, 1941, p. 342-343.

2. Small crystals and large granular masses of colorless to white and yellow calcite with celestite, fluorite, and pyrite in cavities of Tymochtee Dolomite. Also barite. Tarbox-McCall Stone Co. quarry, Findlay, W½ sec. 24, Liberty Twp.; FINDLAY.

General geology: Janssens, 1977, p. 3.

3. Granular aggregates of white calcite in cavities of Tymochtee Dolomite. Also fluorite and pyrite. Pifer Stone Co. quarry, Williamstown, SE¼ sec. 24, Madison Twp.; DUNKIRK.

General geology: Janssens, 1977, p. 3; Stout, 1941, p. 338-340.

HARDIN COUNTY

1. Granular masses of white and colorless calcite in cavities of Lockport Dolomite. Also dolomite and pyrite. Standard Slag Co. quarry, Forest, SW¼ sec. 19, Jackson Twp.; FOREST.

General geology: Cumings, 1930, p. 203; Janssens, 1974, p. 81-86; 1977, p. 3, 22; Stout, 1941, p. 270-272; Summerson and others, 1963, p. 38-39.

2. Granular masses of white and colorless calcite in cavities of Tymochtee Dolomite. Also asphalt, dolomite, fluorite, pyrite, and sphalerite. Hardin Quarry Co., Inc., quarry, Blanchard, NW¼ sec. 6, Pleasant Twp.; FORAKER.

General geology: Janssens, 1977, p. 3; Stout, 1941, p. 274-276.

HENRY COUNTY

1. Calcite with pyrite in Dundee Formation or dolostones of Traverse Group. Old quarry along W bank of Maumee River a short distance SW of Florida, Flatrock Twp.; FLORIDA.

Mineral occurrence: Stout, 1941, p. 399; Winchell, 1874, p. 417.

HIGHLAND COUNTY

1. Fluorescent white calcite with sphalerite in a fault breccia of Bisher-Lilley Dolomites. Outcrop about ½ mile S of Sinking Spring on E side of Ohio Rte. 41, Brush Creek Twp.; SINKING SPRING.

Mineral occurrence: Galbraith, 1968, p. 25-26, 32.
General geology: Reidel, 1975, map.
2. Coarsely crystallized calcite in cores of large limestone concretions from lower Ohio Shale. Exposure along Ohio Rte. 41 a little more than 2 miles N of Sinking Spring, Brush Creek Twp.; SINKING SPRING.
Mineral occurrence: Rogers, J. K., 1936, p. 85, 117.
3. Calcite in cavities of *Bisher Dolomite* and *Lilley Dolomite*. Road cut along Sinking Spring Rd. near Countryman Cemetery about 2 miles NNW of Elmville, Brush Creek Twp.; SINKING SPRING. OGS section no. 12957.
Mineral occurrence: Bowman, 1956, p. 116-117.
4. Calcite in cavities of Lilley Dolomite and Peebles Dolomite. Also pyrite. Outcrop along Sinking Spring Rd. on W bluff above Baker Fork of Ohio Brush Creek 0.5 mile W of Sinking Spring, Brush Creek Twp.; SINKING SPRING. OGS section no. 12683.
Mineral occurrence: Bowman, 1956, p. 111-113.
General geology: Summerson and others, 1963, p. 3-4.
5. Coarsely crystalline masses of white calcite with sphalerite in fossil cavities of Lilley Dolomite. Also quartz. Abandoned quarry on N side of County Hwy. 54 and exposures along and near road 1 mile W of Elmville a short distance SW of Dunkard Ridge Church, Brush Creek-Jackson Twp. boundary; SINKING SPRING. OGS section no. 12961.
Mineral occurrence: Bowman, 1956, p. 114-115.
General geology: Rogers, J. K., 1936, p. 101.
6. Calcite with sphalerite in Brassfield Formation. Also hematite. Outcrop along a tributary of Little West Fork of Ohio Brush Creek near intersection of Pondlick and Richardson Rds. about 2¼ miles SE of Sugartree Ridge, central Concord Twp.; SUGAR TREE RIDGE. OGS section no. 9732.
Mineral occurrence: Botoman and Stieglitz, 1978, p. 5.
General geology: Hopkins, 1954, p. 87; Rogers, J. K., 1936, p. 95.
7. Calcite in Greenfield Dolomite. Also asphalt, quartz, and sphalerite. Havens Limestone Co. quarry about 2 miles SW of Leesburg, S Fairfield Twp.; LEESBURG.
Mineral occurrence: Botoman and Stieglitz, 1978, p. 5, 9.
8. Calcite in Brassfield Formation. Also barite, pyrite, and sphalerite. Davon, Inc., Highland Plant quarry about 1 mile SE of Fairview on E side of Danville Rd., NE Hamer Twp.; NEW MARKET. OGS section no. 13610.
Mineral occurrence: Botoman and Stieglitz, 1978, p. 5.
General geology: Hopkins, 1954, p. 85.
9. Crystals of calcite with sphalerite in Brassfield Formation. Road cut on Peach Orchard Rd. just E of bridge across Ohio Brush Creek 1 mile NW of Belfast, Jackson Twp.; BELFAST. OGS section no. 13609.
Mineral occurrence: Botoman and Stieglitz, 1978, p. 5; Rogers, J. K., 1936, p. 93.
10. Calcite in cavities of Lilley Dolomite. Old Beecher quarry near E edge of Hillsboro between Ohio Rte. 138 and U.S. Rte. 50, Liberty Twp.; HILLSBORO. OGS section no. 9750.
Mineral occurrence: Bowman, 1956, p. 96-97.
11. Veins of calcite in *Lilley Dolomite* and Peebles Dolomite. Exposures on N and S sides of Rocky Fork below mouth of dam and upstream from McCoppin Mill, NE Marshall Twp. and S Paint Twp.; RAINSBORO. OGS section no. 12882.
Mineral occurrence: Bowman, 1956, p. 106-107; Summerson and others, 1963, p. 25-26.
12. Crystals of calcite with quartz in silicified stromatoporoids in Lilley Dolomite. Exposure along Franklin Branch of Rocky Fork at intersection of Marshall Twp. Rd. 250A about 0.6 mile S of McCoppin Mill, NE Marshall Twp.; RAINSBORO.
Mineral occurrence: Bingaman and others, 1978, p. 17.
General geology: Bowman, 1956, p. 106-107; Summerson and others, 1963, p. 25-26.
13. Calcite in cavities of Lilley Dolomite and *Peebles Dolomite*. Also quartz. Exposures in a stream bed, an abandoned quarry, and a road cut along Ohio Rte. 124, 2.8 miles SSE of Marshall and 0.5 mile NE of Harriett, Marshall Twp.; RAINSBORO, SINKING SPRING. OGS section no. 12748.
Mineral occurrence: Bowman, 1956, p. 126-127.
General geology: Rogers, J. K., 1936, p. 106-107; Summerson and others, 1963, p. 5-6.
14. Calcite in cavities of Bisher Dolomite. Outcrop along a tributary to Smith Branch of Rocky Fork at intersection of Chestnut Rd. about 1.5 miles N of Marshall, Marshall Twp.; RAINSBORO. OGS section no. 12965.
Mineral occurrence: Bowman, 1956, p. 105.
15. Calcite in *Lilley Dolomite* and *Peebles Dolomite*. Also asphalt and sphalerite. Marshall Quarry, Inc., quarry about 1¼ miles W of Marshall on S side of Ohio Rte. 124, W Marshall Twp.; HILLSBORO.
Mineral occurrence: Botoman and Stieglitz, 1978, p. 5, 9.
16. Crystals of calcite in Lilley Dolomite. Also pyrite. Exposure S of old woolen mill along Factory Branch of Rocky Fork, about 2 miles SE of Rainsboro, SE Paint Twp.; RAINSBORO (BAINBRIDGE 15-minute).
Mineral occurrence: Rogers, J. K., 1936, p. 108.
17. Calcite in cavities of Bisher Dolomite. Exposure along Blinco Branch of Rocky Fork 0.7 mile S of old Beaver School, Paint Twp.; RAINSBORO (BAINBRIDGE 15-minute). OGS section no. 12883.
Mineral occurrence: Bowman, 1956, p. 105.

HURON COUNTY
1. Colorless crystals and granular aggregates of fluorescent white to brown calcite with barite, dolomite, ferroan dolomite, quartz, and sphalerite in veins of large limestone concretions from the lower Huron Shale Member, Ohio Shale. Also aragonite and pyrite. Outcrop about 2 miles N of Monroeville at Lamereaux Rd. bridge on E side of West Branch Huron River, Ridgefield Twp.; KIMBALL.
Mineral occurrence: Bingaman and others, 1978, p. 16; Carlson, 1977, p. 24-25.
General geology: Broadhead and others, 1980, p. 10-15; Prosser, 1913, p. 324-341.

JEFFERSON COUNTY
1. Fibrous white calcite in veins of ironstone nodules from shales above Brush Creek coal, Conemaugh Group; may be associated with barite, pyrite, sphalerite, and wurtzite. Road cut near Alikanna on E side of Ohio Rte. 7 just N of Ohio Rte. 213 intersection, N½ sec. 31, Island Creek Twp.; KNOXVILLE.
Mineral occurrence: Hollenbaugh and Carlson, 1983, p. 697-701.
General geology: Condit, 1912, p. 204-205; Lamborn, 1930, p. 123; Seaman and Hamilton, 1950, p. 47.

LICKING AND MUSKINGUM COUNTIES
1. Calcite crystals in cavities of flint bed in Vanport limestone, Allegheny Group. Also barite and quartz. Prehistoric quarries and exposures along Flint Ridge, no specific localities given, Hopewell Twp., Licking Co., and Hopewell Twp., Muskingum Co.; GLENFORD, GRATIOT, TOBOSO.
Mineral occurrence: Foster, J. W., 1838, p. 90-91; Smith, C. M., 1885, p. 859.
General geology: DeLong, 1972, map; Mills, 1921, p. 90-161; Stout and Schoenlaub, 1945, p. 80-87.

LOGAN COUNTY

1. Calcite crystals in cavities of *Lucas Dolomite* and Columbus Limestone. Old quarry W of Bellefontaine, SE part of sec. 5, Harrison Twp.; BELLEFONTAINE.
   Mineral occurrence: Moses, 1922, p. 11; Stout, 1941, p. 249, 252.
   General geology: Stauffer, 1909, p. 101-102; Summerson and others, 1957, p. 60.
2. Granular masses of white calcite in cavities of Columbus Limestone. Also dolomite and quartz. Connolly Construction Co., Inc., quarry 1¼ miles W of East Liberty on N side of Ohio Rte. 347 near intersection with U.S. Rte. 33, Perry Twp.; EAST LIBERTY.
   General geology: Stout, 1941, p. 255-257.
3. Granular masses of white calcite with pyrite in cavities of dolostones of undifferentiated Salina Group. Also asphalt, dolomite, fluorite, and sphalerite. C. E. Duff & Son, Inc., quarry just E of Ohio Rte. 117 about 2 miles N of Huntsville, Richland Twp.; HUNTSVILLE.
   Mineral occurrence: Fisher, H. H., 1976, p. 293; Richards and Chamberlain, 1987, p. 391-392.
   General geology: Janssens, 1971, p. 35.
4. Crystals and granular aggregates of white to colorless calcite in cavities of dolostones of undifferentiated Salina Group. Also asphalt, dolomite, fluorite, and pyrite. Northwood Stone & Asphalt Co. quarry ½ mile W of Northwood on S side of County Hwy. 105 just W of intersection with County Hwy. 106, Richland Twp.; RUSHSYLVANIA.
   General geology: Summerson and others, 1963, p. 37; Stout, 1941, p. 245-247.

LORAIN COUNTY

1. White calcite with barite and quartz in veins of barite nodules from Cleveland Shale Member, Ohio Shale. Also pickeringite and pyrite. Along banks of Vermilion River at Mill Hollow-Bacon Woods Park, Brownhelm Twp.; VERMILION EAST.
   Mineral occurrence: Holden and Carlson, 1979, p. 227-232.
   General geology: Broadhead and others, 1980, p. 23-30; Herdendorf, 1963, map; Prosser, 1913, p. 348.

LUCAS COUNTY

1. Calcite in cavities of dolostones of undifferentiated Salina Group, Sylvania Sandstone, and dolostones of *Detroit River Group*. Old France Stone Co. Holland quarry N of Monclova, S½ sec. 29, Monclova Twp.; MAUMEE.
   Mineral occurrence: Gilbert, 1873, p. 575-577, 581, 583.
   General geology: Carman, 1936, p. 259; 1960, p. 1-5; Carman and others, 1962, p. 6-7; Janssens, 1977, p. 25-30; Stout, 1941, p. 404-405.
2. Calcite crystals in cavities of the Sylvania Sandstone and dolostones of *Detroit River Group*. Old Toledo Stone and Glass Sand Co. quarry, Silica, NW¼ sec. 20, Sylvania Twp.; SYLVANIA.
   Mineral occurrence: Carman, 1922, p. 125; 1927, p. 500; Carman and others, 1962, p. 2, 4; Ehlers, G. M., and others, 1951, p. 5-6.
3. Colorless crystals and white aggregates of calcite in cavities of Silica Formation and *Tenmile Creek Dolomite;* may be associated with barite, celestite, and sphalerite. Also dolomite, pyrite, and strontianite. W wall of France Stone Co. North quarry (formerly Medusa Portland Cement Co.), Sylvania, S-central sec. 7, Sylvania Twp.; SYLVANIA, BERKEY.
   General geology: Carman and others, 1962, p. 5-6; Ehlers, G. M., and others, 1951, p. 4.
4. Colorless and yellow calcite crystals in vugs and fractures of *Sylvania Sandstone* and dolostones of *Detroit River Group*. Also barite and fluorite. France Stone Co. East quarry, Sylvania, W½ sec. 17, Sylvania Twp.; SYLVANIA.
   Mineral occurrence: Ehlers, G. M., and others, 1951, p. 5-7; Strogonoff, 1966, p. 28-30.
5. Calcite in pockets of Tenmile Creek Dolomite. Also pyrite. Outcrop along Tenmile Creek, SE¼ sec. 19, Sylvania Twp.; SYLVANIA.
   Mineral occurrence: Ehlers, G. M., and others, 1951, p. 21.
   General geology: Stauffer, 1909, p. 145-146.
6. Crystals of calcite in cavities of dolostones of Detroit River Group. Old quarry 2 miles N of Silica, Sylvania Twp.; SYLVANIA.
   Mineral occurrence: Carman, 1922, p. 128.
7. Crystals and granular aggregates of colorless to brown calcite in cavities and faults and as pseudomorphs of gypsum in *Tymochtee Dolomite* and dolostones of undifferentiated Salina Group. Also asphalt, celestite, fluorite, gypsum, halite, pyrite, sphalerite, and sulfur. France Stone Co. quarry, Waterville, secs. 38 and 39, Waterville Twp.; BOWLING GREEN NORTH.
   Mineral occurrence: Kahle and Floyd, 1972, p. 65-68; Mychkovsky, 1978b, p. 9, 14; Strogonoff, 1966, p. 38.
   General geology: Janssens, 1977, p. 25-30; Kahle and Floyd, 1968, p. 21-24; 1971, p. 2082-2086; Stout, 1941, p. 402-404.
8. Calcite with celestite in cavities of dolostones of Detroit River Group. Old Loeb's quarry 2 miles E of Whitehouse, Waterville Twp.; WHITEHOUSE.
   Mineral occurrence: Dana, E. S., 1892, p. 1085; Gilbert, 1873, p. 576-577, 581, 583; Sanford and Stone, 1914, p. 148.
   General geology: Ehlers, G. M., and others, 1951, p. 1.
9. Crystals of yellow calcite in Tymochtee Dolomite. Outcrop on Roche de Boeuf Island in Maumee River about 1 mile SW of Waterville, Waterville Twp.; BOWLING GREEN NORTH.
   Mineral occurrence: Silliman, 1824, p. 47.
   General geology: Gilbert, 1873, p. 573-574; Kahle and Floyd, 1972, p. 55-64.
10. Calcite with asphalt in cavities of Tymochtee Dolomite. Exposure along the Maumee River at Waterville, Waterville Twp.; BOWLING GREEN NORTH.
    Mineral occurrence: Gilbert, 1873, p. 578, 583.
    General geology: Kahle and Floyd, 1971, p. 2075-2082.
11. Large pseudomorphs of calcite after gypsum in Tymochtee Dolomite. Exposure on Granger Island in Maumee River, E edge of Waterville, Waterville Twp.; BOWLING GREEN NORTH.
    Mineral occurrence: Kahle and Floyd, 1971, p. 2080-2081.
12. Calcite with celestite in Greenfield Dolomite or Tymochtee Dolomite. Presque Isle on W side of Maumee River about 2 miles N of Waterville, Waterville and Monclova Twps.; MAUMEE (TOLEDO 15-minute).
    Mineral occurrence: Silliman, 1824, p. 46.
    General geology: Gilbert, 1873, p. 574; Kahle and Floyd, 1971, p. 2075-2077.
13. Crystals and granular aggregates of colorless to brown calcite in cavities and fractures and as pseudomorphs of gypsum in *Lockport Dolomite* and *Greenfield Dolomite;* may be associated with asphalt, fluorite, or sulfur. Also celestite, dolomite, gypsum, pyrite, and sphalerite. Stoneco quarry (formerly Maumee Stone Co.), Maumee, sec. 35, Waynesfield Twp.; MAUMEE.
    Mineral occurrence: Botoman and Stieglitz, 1978, p. 5; Kahle, 1974, p. 34; 1978, p. 63-115; Strogonoff, 1966, p. 31-33; Summerson, 1966, p. 222; Textoris and

Carozzi, 1966, p. 1377.

General geology: Kahle and Floyd, 1972, p. 70-81; Summerson and others, 1963, p. 44-45.

14. Granular masses of white to colorless calcite in cavities of dolostones of undifferentiated Salina Group. Also celestite, fluorite, and gypsum. Outcrop on E side of West Sister Island in Lake Erie; METZGER MARSH.

General geology: Gilbert, 1873, p. 589-590; Herdendorf and Braidech, 1972, p. 9-12; Sparling, 1965, p. 95; 1970, p. 11.

MADISON COUNTY

1. Crystals of calcite in cavities of dolostones of *undifferentiated Salina Group* and Columbus Limestone. Old Madison Stone Co. quarry 2 miles SE of West Jefferson on N side of Little Darby Creek, Jefferson Twp.; WEST JEFFERSON.

Mineral occurrence: Summerson, 1959, p. 426-427.

General geology: Stout, 1941, p. 209.

MAHONING COUNTY

1. Granular masses of white calcite with sphalerite in veins of ironstone concretions from shales below Lower Mercer limestone, Pottsville Group. Also barite, chalcopyrite, kaolinite, and pyrite. Outcrop along West Branch Meander Creek just E of junction with Ohio Rte. 45 about ¾ mile S of Ellsworth, Ellsworth Twp.; CANFIELD.

Mineral occurrence: Greene, 1935, p. 883.

General geology: Lamb, 1910, p. 114.

MARION COUNTY

1. Granular aggregates of white and colorless calcite in cavities of *Lockport Dolomite* and Greenfield Dolomite. Also celestite, dolomite, fluorite, marcasite, sphalerite, and strontianite. Tri-County Limestone Co. quarry (formerly Laubis Stone Co.) 2 miles SW of Marseilles, center sec. 19, Grand Twp.; MARSEILLES.

General geology: Cumings, 1930, p. 202-203; Hall and Alkire, 1956, p. 5, 32-35; Stith, 1983, p. 15; Stout, 1941, p. 281-282.

2. Granular masses of white and colorless calcite in cavities of *Columbus Limestone* and *Delaware Limestone*. Also fluorite and pyrite. National Lime & Stone Co. Marion quarry, secs. 2 and 3, Marion Twp., and sec. 34, Grand Prairie Twp.; MONNETT.

General geology: Hall and Alkire, 1956, p. 5, 32-35; Janssens, 1970b, p. 3.

3. Sparry calcite in cavities of *Columbus Limestone* and Delaware Limestone. J. M. Hamilton & Sons Co., Inc., quarry, N edge of Marion, NW¼ sec. 10, Marion Twp.; MARION WEST, MORRAL.

Mineral occurrence: Janssens, 1970b, p. 8.

General geology: Hall and Alkire, 1956, p. 5, 32-35; Stauffer, 1909, p. 97.

MERCER COUNTY

1. Crystals of white calcite in cavities of Lockport Dolomite. Also dolomite. Rockford Stone Co. quarry 1½ miles NW of Rockford on N side of U.S. Rte. 33, Dublin Twp.; ROCKFORD.

General geology: Janssens, 1971, p. 35; Shaver, 1974, p. 97-102; Stout, 1941, p. 267-268.

2. Crystals of white to colorless calcite in cavities of Lockport Dolomite and Greenfield Dolomite. Also asphalt, dolomite, pyrite, quartz, and sphalerite. Stoneco quarry (formerly John W. Karch Stone Co.) 4 miles W of Celina, E½ sec. 8, Jefferson Twp.; ERASTUS.

General geology: Shaver, 1974, p. 95-97; Stout, 1941, p. 265-266.

MIAMI COUNTY

1. Crystals and masses of colorless and white calcite in cavities of *Brassfield Formation* and *Dayton Formation*. Also dolomite, glauconite, and pyrite. Armco, Inc., quarry (formerly Piqua Stone Products Co.), Piqua, W½ sec. 29, Spring Creek Twp.; PIQUA EAST, TROY.

General geology: Stith, 1983, p. 11-12, 16; Stout, 1941, p. 187-190.

2. Calcite with sphalerite in Brassfield Formation. Road cut on N side of Ohio Rte. 571 about 0.3 mile E of West Milton, sec. 21, Union Twp.; WEST MILTON. OGS section no. 12771.

Mineral occurrence: Botoman and Stieglitz, 1978, p. 5.

General geology: Stout, 1941, p. 190.

MONROE COUNTY

1. Thick layer of calcite on face of sandstone in Greene Formation, Dunkard Group. Exposure along Clark Hill Rd. S of junction with Ohio Rte. 7 and near mouth of Opossum Creek, sec. 16, Salem Twp.; NEW MARTINSVILLE.

Mineral occurrence: Cross and others, 1950, p. 6, 46, 48.

MUSKINGUM COUNTY (see also Licking County)

1. Calcite with sphalerite in ironstone nodules from shales above Lower Mercer limestone, Pottsville Group. Outcrop at Zanesville along E side of Muskingum River; ZANESVILLE EAST, ZANESVILLE WEST.

Mineral occurrence: Foster, J. W., 1838, p. 86-88.

General geology: Stout, 1918, p. 84.

OTTAWA COUNTY

1. Crystals of colorless to brown calcite in cavities and fractures of *Lockport Dolomite* and *Greenfield Dolomite*; may be associated with celestite, galena, and pyrite. Also dolomite, fluorite, gypsum, and sphalerite. Edward Kraemer & Sons, Inc., White Rock quarry, Clay Center, SE¼ sec. 9 and NE¼ sec. 16, Allen Twp.; GENOA.

Mineral occurrence: Botoman and Stieglitz, 1978, p. 5; Carman and others, 1962, p. 13-14; Kessen and others, 1981, p. 913-918; Morrison, 1934, p. 19-20; 1935, p. 784; Roedder, 1967, p. 355; 1979, p. 92; Strogonoff, 1966, p. 9-10; White, J. S., 1977, p. 60-61.

General geology: Janssens, 1974, p. 82, 84; 1977, p. 22; Sparling, 1965, p. 239-240; 1971, p. 19; Stout, 1941, p. 415-418.

2. Crystals of colorless to yellow calcite in cavities of *Lockport Dolomite* and Greenfield Dolomite; may be associated with celestite and pyrite. Also asphalt, dolomite, fluorite, sphalerite, and sulfur. Stoneco quarry (formerly Maumee Stone Co.), N of Rocky Ridge, sec. 23, Benton Twp.; OAK HARBOR.

Mineral occurrence: Botoman and Stieglitz, 1978, p. 6.

General geology: Forsyth, 1971, p. 14; Sparling, 1965, p. 172.

3. Crystals of calcite in dolostones of *undifferentiated Salina Group* and *Bass Islands Dolomite*. Also celestite, fluorite, and gypsum. Cliff exposure on NW edge of Catawba Island, Catawba Island Twp.; GYPSUM.

Mineral occurrence: Anonymous, 1936, p. 462; Treesh, 1970, p. 9.

General geology: Carman, 1927, p. 488-491; Janssens, 1977, p. 27-30; Sparling, 1970, p. 3, 19-21; 1971, p. 19-22.

4. Crystals of colorless to brown calcite in cavities and fractures of Lockport Dolomite; may be associated with celestite, fluorite, and sphalerite. Also dolomite, galena, marcasite, and pyrite. GenLime Group, L. P., quarry (formerly U.S. Gypsum Co.), Genoa, W½ sec. 3, Clay Twp.; GENOA.

Mineral occurrence: Carlson, 1986, p. 9-13; Strogonoff, 1966, p. 18.

General geology: Forsyth, 1971, p. 15-16; Janssens, 1977, p. 3, 22; Sparling, 1965, p. 236-237; Stout, 1941, p. 413-414.

5. Granular white to brown calcite in vugs and fractures of dolostones of *Detroit River Group* and *Columbus Limestone*. Standard Slag Co. Marblehead quarry just S of Marblehead on S side of Ohio Rte. 163, E Danbury Twp.; GYPSUM, KELLEYS ISLAND.

Mineral occurrence: Forsyth, 1971, p. 11-13; Janssens, 1970b, p. 19-21; Sparling, 1965, p. 255-256; Strogonoff, 1966, p. 23.

General geology: Stauffer, 1909, p. 134-135; Stout, 1941, p. 424-425.

6. Calcite in Bass Islands Dolomite. Also celestite. Crystal Cave, near middle of South Bass Island, Put-in-Bay Twp.; PUT-IN-BAY.

Mineral occurrence: Botoman and Stieglitz, 1978, p. 6.

General geology: Janssens, 1977, p. 27-30; Sparling, 1970, p. 12; 1971, p. 19-22; White, G. W., 1926, p. 84.

7. Calcite with celestite and sulfur in Bass Islands Dolomite. South Bass Island, no specific location given, Put-in-Bay Twp.; PUT-IN-BAY.

Mineral occurrence: Dana, E. S., 1892, p. 1085; Dana, J. D., 1868, p. 784; Kindt, 1952, p. 256; Newberry, 1874b, p. 202.

General geology: Janssens, 1977, p. 27-30; Mohr, 1931, p. 28; Sparling, 1971, p. 19-22.

8. Calcite crystals in dolostones of undifferentiated Salina Group and *Bass Islands Dolomite*. Also celestite and gypsum. Cliff exposure at South Point, South Bass Island, Put-in-Bay Twp.; PUT-IN-BAY.

Mineral occurrence: Treesh, 1970, p. 9.

General geology: Janssens, 1977, p. 27-30; Mohr, 1931, p. 33-34; Sparling, 1971, p. 19-22; Stout, 1941, p. 421-422.

9. Granular masses of white and colorless calcite in cavities and fractures of Bass Islands Dolomite. Also barite, celestite, fluorite, and pyrite. Fox Stone Products, Inc., quarry, N side of Langram Rd., S part of South Bass Island, Put-in-Bay Twp.; PUT-IN-BAY.

General geology: Janssens, 1977, p. 27-30; Sparling, 1971, p. 19-22.

PAULDING COUNTY

1. Crystals and aggregates of colorless to yellow calcite in vugs and fractures of dolostones of *Detroit River Group* and *Dundee Formation;* may coat fluorite or be coated with asphalt. Also pyrite, quartz, and sphalerite. Stoneco Auglaize quarry (formerly Maumee Stone Co.), Junction, NW¼ sec. 32, Auglaize Twp.; JUNCTION.

Mineral occurrence: Botoman and Stieglitz, 1978, p. 6; Feldmann and others, 1977, p. 32-33; Kessen and others, 1981, p. 913-918; Nelson, 1967, p. 43; Strogonoff, 1966, p. 60-61.

General geology: Janssens, 1970a, p. 21; Stauffer, 1909, p. 152-153; Stout, 1941, p. 324-325.

2. Crystals of orange calcite in cavities of dolostones of undifferentiated Salina Group. Old quarry S of mouth of Blue Creek on W side of Auglaize River about ½ mile S of Charloe, Brown Twp.; OAKWOOD.

Mineral occurrence: Winchell, 1874, p. 340, 382.

General geology: Carman, 1927, p. 482; Janssens, 1977, p. 3.

PICKAWAY COUNTY

1. Crystallized calcite with globules of asphalt in veins of large septarian limestone concretions from lower Ohio Shale. Also pyrite. Outcrops along banks and in bed of Deer Creek at Williamsport, Deer Creek Twp.; CLARKSBURG, WILLIAMSPORT.

Mineral occurrence: Andrews, 1874b, p. 591.

General geology: Hildreth, 1834, p. 249-250.

2. Granular masses of white calcite in Columbus Limestone. Also dolomite, marcasite, and pyrite. Melvin Stone Co. quarry (formerly F. H. Brewer Co.) about 1 mile E of Crownover Mill on N side of Williamsport-Crownover Mill Rd., N Perry Twp.; CLARKSBURG.

General geology: Stout, 1941, p. 140-141.

PORTAGE COUNTY

1. Crystalline masses of colorless to white calcite with sphalerite and barite in veins of ironstone concretions from shales of lower Pottsville Group. Also chalcopyrite and kaolinite. Outcrop along SE shore of Michael J. Kirwan Reservoir at mouth of Silver Creek just W of Alliance Rd., NE Edinburg Twp.; WINDHAM.

General geology: Winslow and White, 1966, p. 79.

PREBLE COUNTY

1. Calcite in Brassfield Formation. Also sphalerite. Exposure along N side of a branch of Twin Creek on E side of Ohio Rte. 503 about 1/3 mile N of intersection with Brennersville-Pyrmont Rd.; NW¼SW¼ sec. 10, Twin Twp.; LEWISBURG. OGS section no. 15772.

Mineral occurrence: Botoman and Stieglitz, 1978, p. 6.

PUTNAM COUNTY

1. Calcite in Tymochtee Dolomite and dolostones of undifferentiated Salina Group. Also fluorite, pyrite, and sphalerite. Ottawa Stone Co., Inc., quarry, W½ sec. 27, Blanchard Twp.; LEIPSIC.

Mineral occurrence: Botoman and Stieglitz, 1978, p. 6.

General geology: Janssens, 1971, p. 35; 1977, p. 29.

2. Calcite in cavities of Tymochtee Dolomite and dolostones of undifferentiated Salina Group. Also asphalt, fluorite, pyrite, and sphalerite. Putnam Stone Co. quarry, NW¼ sec. 6, Riley Twp.; BLUFFTON.

Mineral occurrence: Botoman and Stieglitz, 1978, p. 6.

General geology: Janssens, 1971, p. 35; 1977, p. 29.

3. Calcite in Tymochtee Dolomite and dolostones of undifferentiated Salina Group. Also fluorite and sphalerite National Lime & Stone Co. Rimer quarry, sec. 6, 7, and 8, Sugar Creek Twp.; KALIDA.

Mineral occurrence: Botoman and Stieglitz, 1978, p. 6.

General geology: Janssens, 1971, p. 35; 1977, p. 29; Stith, 1983, p. 11-13; Stout, 1941, p. 327-328.

ROSS COUNTY

1. Calcite in Greenfield Dolomite. Also asphalt, quartz, and sphalerite. Old Rucker quarry E of Greenfield and just E of Paint Creek about ¼ mile N of Ohio Rte. 4, Buckskin Twp.; SOUTH SALEM.

Mineral occurrence: Wuestner, 1938, p. 262.

General geology: Napper, 1916, p. 155-159; 1917, p. 7-13; Rogers, J. K., 1936, p. 113-114, 135; Stout, 1941, p. 71; Summerson and others, 1963, p. 27.

2. Granular masses of calcite with barite, dolomite, and quartz in veins of large limestone concretions from lower Huron Shale Member, Ohio Shale. Also halotrichite-pickeringite, melanterite, and pyrite. Cliff exposure at Copperas Mountain about 1 mile ESE of Seip Mound State Memorial on SE side of Paint Creek, Paxton Twp.; MORGANTOWN.

Mineral occurrence: Briggs, 1838, p. 77-78; Carlson, 1987b, p. 428; Dana, E. S., 1892, p. 1085; Dana, J. D., 1858, p. 495; 1868, p. 784; Seyfried, 1953, p. 18-25.

General geology: Kepferle and others, 1981, p. 294-295; Orton, 1874, p. 647.

SANDUSKY COUNTY

1. Small crystals of colorless calcite with celestite(?) in pockets of Lockport Dolomite. Also dolomite. Steetley

Resources, Inc., Ohio Lime Co. quarry, Millersville, secs. 7 and 8, Jackson Twp.; HELENA.

General geology: Janssens, 1974, p. 84; 1977, p. 22.

2. Crystals of calcite in pockets and fractures of Lockport Dolomite. Also celestite, fluorite, galena, and sphalerite. Charles Pfizer & Co., Inc., quarry NW of Gibsonburg, sec. 14, Madison Twp.; ELMORE.

Mineral occurrence: Strogonoff, 1966, p. 53.

General geology: Floyd, 1971, p. 167; Janssens, 1977, p. 3, 22; Stith, 1983, p. 11-13.

3. Crystals and aggregates of colorless, yellow, and brown calcite in cavities and fractures of Lockport Dolomite; may be associated with celestite. Also barite, dolomite, fluorite, galena, pyrite, and sphalerite. Steetley Resources, Inc., Ohio Lime Co. quarry, Woodville, W½ sec. 34, Woodville Twp.; ELMORE.

Mineral occurrence: Green, R., 1971, p. 281; Kahle and Floyd, 1968, p. 33; Strogonoff, 1966, p. 54.

General geology: Floyd, 1971, p. 167-169.

4. Crystals and granular aggregates of colorless to yellow calcite in cavities of Lockport Dolomite; may be associated with barite, celestite, and strontianite. Also dolomite, fluorite, galena, pyrite, and sphalerite. Martin Marietta Chemicals quarry (S part formerly Woodville Lime & Chemical Co. quarry), Woodville, E½ sec. 21 and W½ sec. 22, Woodville Twp.; ELMORE.

Mineral occurrence: Botoman and Stieglitz, 1978, p. 6; Carlson, 1986, p. 9-13.

General geology: Stout, 1941, p. 375; Summerson and others, 1963, p. 42.

5. Crystals and granular aggregates of colorless to yellow calcite in cavities of dolostones of *Detroit River Group* and *Columbus Limestone;* may be associated with fluorite. France Stone Co. quarry, Bellevue, N-central sec. 25, York Twp.; BELLEVUE.

Mineral occurrence: Farrington and Tillotson, 1908, p. 144-145; Nelson, 1967, p. 18-24; Winchell, 1873, p. 604-605.

General geology: Janssens, 1970b, p. 18-19; Stauffer, 1909, p. 114; Stout, 1941, p. 380; Summerson and others, 1957, p. 59.

SENECA COUNTY

1. Crystals of colorless to light-brownish-yellow calcite in cavities of Lockport Dolomite or Greenfield Dolomite. Also celestite, dolomite, fluorite, galena, sphalerite, strontianite, and sulfur. Old quarries at Tiffin, Clinton Twp.; TIFFIN SOUTH.

Mineral occurrence: Winchell, 1873, p. 616-618; also unpublished information from mineral collection at Heidelberg College.

General geology: Carman, 1927, p. 487; Janssens, 1977, p. 3.

2. Calcite with celestite in cavities of Greenfield Dolomite. Old quarry along E bank of Sandusky River at S edge of Tiffin, Clinton Twp.; TIFFIN SOUTH.

Mineral occurrence: Winchell, 1873, p. 618.

General geology: Carman, 1927, p. 487; Janssens, 1977, p. 3.

3. Crystals of calcite in cavities of Lockport Dolomite. Old quarry in E bank of Sandusky River about 2½ miles N of Tiffin, Clinton Twp.; TIFFIN NORTH.

Mineral occurrence: Cumings, 1930, p. 199-200.

General geology: Carman, 1927, p. 487; Janssens, 1977, p. 3.

4. Crystals of colorless calcite with celestite in cavities of Greenfield Dolomite. Old France Stone Co. quarry 1½ miles E of Bascom, central part of sec. 16, Hopewell Twp.; BASCOM.

General geology: Carman, 1927, p. 482; Stout, 1941, p. 353-354.

5. Crystals and granular aggregates of colorless to white calcite in cavities and fractures of *Lockport Dolomite* and *Greenfield Dolomite.* Also celestite, dolomite, fluorite, galena, marcasite, pyrite, sphalerite, and strontianite. Maple Grove Stone Co. quarry (formerly Basic Refractories), Maple Grove, sec. 11 and N½ sec. 14, Liberty Twp.; TIFFIN NORTH.

General geology: Floyd, 1971, p. 167, 173-174; Janssens, 1971, p. 35; 1974, p. 82, 84; 1977, p. 3, 22; Stout, 1941, p. 348-349.

6. Crystals of yellow calcite in cavities of Columbus Limestone. France Stone Co. Flat Rock quarry (formerly Northern Ohio Stone Co.), SW¼ sec. 11, Thompson Twp.; FIRESIDE, FLAT ROCK.

Mineral occurrence: Nelson, 1967, p. 74.

General geology: Janssens, 1970b, p. 3.

STARK COUNTY

1. Granular masses of brown calcite in veins of limestone concretions and granular masses of white calcite with pyrite and sphalerite in veins of ironstone concretions in shale beds of Putnam Hill limestone, Allegheny Group. East Ohio Limestone Co. quarry N of Cairo, sec. 21, Lake Twp.; HARTVILLE.

General geology: DeLong and White, 1963, p. 45-49, 180-181.

SUMMIT COUNTY

1. Granular masses of colorless calcite with chalcopyrite, kaolinite, pyrite, and sphalerite in veins of ironstone concretions from Meadville Shale Member, Cuyahoga Formation. Outcrop along small tributary that enters Cuyahoga River from N side about ¼ mile W of foot of dam at Cuyahoga Gorge Park, Cuyahoga Falls; AKRON WEST.

General geology: Kent State University, *in* Frank, 1969, p. 1.5-1.7; Szmuc, 1957, p. 159-161.

TUSCARAWAS COUNTY

1. Granular masses of calcite with pyrite, sphalerite, and wurtzite in veins of ironstone concretions from shales of Allegheny Group. Puskarich Mining, Inc., strip mine about 1 mile S of New Cumberland, SW¼ sec. 28, Warren Twp.; MINERAL CITY.

General geology: Lamborn, 1956, p. 140, 175.

UNION COUNTY

1. Crystals and coarsely granular aggregates of colorless and light-brown calcite with fluorite in cavities of Columbus Limestone. Also asphalt and marcasite. Union Aggregates Co. quarry 3½ miles S of Ostrander on E side of County Rd. 96, Mill Creek Twp.; SHAWNEE HILLS.

General geology: Janssens, 1970b, p. 3; Stout, 1941, p. 239.

2. Crystals and granular aggregates of colorless calcite in cavities of dolostones of Salina Group. Also pyrite. L. G. Rockhold & Sons, Inc., quarry ½ mile N of York Center on S side of Twp. Hwy. 212, York Twp.; YORK CENTER.

General geology: Stout, 1941, p. 238-239.

VAN WERT COUNTY

1. Crystals and coarse-grained aggregates of colorless and white calcite in cavities of Tymochtee Dolomite and dolostones of undifferentiated Salina Group. Also dolomite, fluorite, pyrite, and sphalerite. Ridge Township Quarry 2 miles W of Middle Point, NE¼ sec. 22, Ridge Twp.; MIDDLE POINT.

General geology: Janssens, 1971, p. 35.

2. Granular masses of white calcite in cavities of dolostones of undifferentiated Salina Group. Also asphalt, dolomite, fluorite, pyrite, and sphalerite. Stoneco quarry

(formerly Maumee Stone Co.), about 4 miles SW of Scott, sec. 8, Union Twp.; CONVOY.
General geology: Janssens, 1971, p. 35; 1977, p. 3, 29; Stout, 1941, p. 319-320.
3. Crystals and coarsely granular masses of white and colorless calcite in Tymochtee Dolomite and dolostones of undifferentiated Salina Group. Also asphalt, dolomite, fluorite, pyrite, and sphalerite. Suever Stone Co., Inc., quarry (formerly Delphos Quarries Co.), Delphos, sec. 25, Washington Twp.; DELPHOS.
Mineral occurrence: Botoman and Stieglitz, 1978, p. 6; Medici and Robinson, 1988, p. 128.
General geology: Janssens, 1971, p. 35; Stout, 1941, p. 313.

VINTON COUNTY
1. Calcite in cavities of Vanport limestone, Allegheny Group. Also galena, pyrite, quartz, and sphalerite. No specific localities given.
Mineral occurrence: Stout, 1927, p. 265-266.
General geology: Lamborn, 1951, p. 344-349.

WAYNE COUNTY
1. Calcite with barite, chalcopyrite, galena, pyrite, and sphalerite in veins of ironstone concretions from shales of lower Pottsville Group. Penn Central Railroad cut N of Marshallville, W-central sec. 33, Chippewa Twp.; DOYLESTOWN.
Mineral occurrence: Ver Steeg, 1940, p. 259.
General geology: Conrey, 1921, p. 92; Ver Steeg, 1948, p. 185.
2. Calcite with galena, pyrite, and sphalerite in veins of ironstone nodules from shales of Wooster Shale Member, Cuyahoga Formation. Also aragonite. Old quarry E of County Rd. 22 behind City of Wooster Service and Maintenance Facility, NE¼ sec. 5, Wooster Twp.; WOOSTER.
Mineral occurrence: Ver Steeg, 1940, p. 259.
General geology: Conrey, 1921, p. 62-63; Szmuc, 1957, p. 193-195.

WOOD COUNTY
1. Calcite in Tymochtee Dolomite. Also fluorite, gypsum, marcasite, pyrite, and sphalerite. France Stone Co. North Baltimore quarry, W½ sec. 26, Henry Twp.; NORTH BALTIMORE.
Mineral occurrence: Botoman and Stieglitz, 1978, p. 6.
General geology: Janssens, 1971, p. 35; 1977, p. 26; Kahle and Floyd, 1972, p. 46-48; Stout, 1941, p. 394-395.
2. Crystals of calcite with asphalt in cavities of Tymochtee Dolomite. Outcrop along E bank of Maumee River about 1 mile N of Miltonville Cemetery, Middleton Twp.; BOWLING GREEN NORTH, MAUMEE.
Mineral occurrence: Winchell, 1874, p. 375, map.
General geology: Carman, 1927, p. 482; Kahle and Floyd, 1971, p. 2075-2080.
3. Crystals and granular aggregates of colorless to honey-yellow calcite in caves, pockets, and fractures of dolostones of *Detroit River Group* and Dundee Formation; may be associated with barite, celestite, fluorite, or marcasite. Also asphalt, dolomite, glauconite, hexahydrite, pyrite, and sphalerite. France Stone Co. Custar quarry (formerly Pugh Quarry Co.) about 4 miles W of Weston, SW¼ sec. 6, Milton Twp.; MCCLURE.
Mineral occurrence: Bingaman and others, 1978, p. 18; Botoman and Stieglitz, 1978, p. 6; Feldmann and others, 1977, p. 35-37; Forsyth, 1966a, p. 204-205; Gettings, 1950, p. 601; Green, R., 1970a, p. 584; Janssens, 1970a, p. 7, 22; Kessen and others, 1981, p. 913-918; Nelson, 1967, p. 60, 65; Parr and Chang, 1979, p. 24-31; Roedder, 1979, p. 92; Strogonoff, 1966, p. 47-48.
General geology: Orton and Peppel, 1906, p. 133; Stout, 1941, p. 395-396.
4. Crystals of colorless to yellow calcite in cavities of *Lockport Dolomite* and *Greenfield Dolomite;* may be associated with dolomite and pyrite. Also barite, celestite, fluorite, hexahydrite, sphalerite, and strontianite. MacRitchie Materials, Inc., quarry (formerly Brough Stone Co.), West Millgrove, SE¼ sec. 4, Perry Twp.; FOSTORIA.
General geology: Janssens, 1971, p. 35; 1974, p. 82, 84; 1977, p. 22; Shaver, 1977, p. 1414; Stout, 1941, p. 392.
5. Crystals and granular aggregates of colorless to yellow calcite in cavities and fractures of *Lockport Dolomite* and *Greenfield Dolomite;* may be associated with barite, celestite, fluorite, pyrite, and sphalerite. Also aragonite, dolomite, galena, gypsum, marcasite, strontianite, and sulfur. Stoneco quarry (formerly Maumee Stone Co.), Lime City, SW¼ sec. 11, Perrysburg Twp.; ROSSFORD.
Mineral occurrence: Botoman and Stieglitz, 1978, p. 6; Green, R., 1970a, p. 584; Kahle and Floyd, 1972, p. 52; Strogonoff, 1966, p. 41, 43.
General geology: Janssens, 1971, p. 35; 1974, p. 82, 84; 1977, p. 22; Kahle and Floyd, 1968, p. 28-30.
6. Crystals and granular masses of colorless and white calcite in cavities of *Lockport Dolomite* and *Greenfield Dolomite*. Also celestite, dolomite, gypsum, sphalerite, and sulfur. Stoneco quarry (formerly Maumee Stone Co.) SE of Portage, sec. 7, Portage Twp., BOWLING GREEN SOUTH.
Mineral occurrence: Carlson, 1987c, p. 102-104.
General geology: Floyd, 1971, p. 188; Janssens, 1971, p. 35; 1974, p. 82, 84; 1977, p. 22.
7. Crystals of pale-brown calcite in cavities of Lockport Dolomite. Old France Stone Co. quarry, Luckey, NW¼ sec. 28, Troy Twp.; PEMBERVILLE.
Mineral occurrence: Gettings, 1952b, p. 493.
General geology: Stout, 1941, p. 390-391.

WYANDOT COUNTY
1. Calcite in cavities of Lockport Dolomite. Old Huffman quarry 2 miles N of Carey, NW¼ sec. 4, Crawford Twp.; CAREY.
Mineral occurrence: Winchell, 1873, p. 628-629.
General geology: Cumings, 1930, p. 200-201; Janssens, 1977, p. 3.
2. Scalenohedral crystals of colorless calcite in cavities of *Lockport Dolomite* and Greenfield Dolomite. Also celestite, dolomite, fluorite, gypsum, pyrite, sphalerite, and strontianite. National Lime & Stone Co. quarry, Carey, N½ sec. 15 and N½ sec. 16, Crawford Twp.; CAREY, MCCUTCHENVILLE.
General geology: Carlson, 1987c, p. 101-102; Cumings, 1930, p. 201-202; Hall and Alkire, 1956, p. 7, 31-33; Janssens, 1974, p. 82, 84; 1977, p. 22; Stout 1941, p. 294-295; Summerson and others, 1963, p. 39-40.
3. White and colorless calcite in cavities of Lockport Dolomite. Also dolomite and fluorite. Wyandot Dolomite, Inc., quarry N of Carey on N side of County Hwy. 16, sec. 9, Crawford Twp.; MCCUTCHENVILLE.
General geology: Cumings, 1930, p. 201-202; Hall and Alkire, 1956, p. 31-33; Janssens, 1977, p. 3.
4. Granular masses of white calcite in Tymochtee Dolomite and dolostones of undifferentiated Salina Group. Also celestite, gypsum, sphalerite, and sulfur. McCarthy Stone Quarry 3½ miles SE of upper Sandusky, N½ sec. 15, Pitt Twp.; NEVADA.
Mineral occurrence: Botoman and Stieglitz, 1978, p. 6.

General geology: Carlson, 1987c, p. 97-101; Janssens, 1977, p. 3, 29; Stout, 1941, p. 299.

CELESTITE (CELESTINE)
SrSO$_4$

Chemical class: Sulfate

Crystallization: Orthorhombic; dipyramidal; mmm

Habit: Generally well crystallized; commonly in open networks of tabular or bladed crystals; granular aggregates

Physical properties: Cleavage: {001} perfect pinacoidal and {210} good prismatic. H: 3-3½. G: 4.0. Luster: vitreous. Color: pale blue, white, colorless, pale yellow. Streak: white. May be fluorescent

Occurrence: Crystals and granular aggregates common in cavities and fractures of dolostones along the crest and flanks of the Findlay Arch in northwestern Ohio and rare in the vicinity of the Serpent Mound disturbance in southwestern Ohio

ADAMS COUNTY
1. Crystals of celestite in cavities in limestones of upper Bull Fork Formation. Outcrop along E side of Ohio Rte. 136, 2.9 miles N of Manchester, Spriggs Twp.; MANCHESTER ISLANDS.
   Mineral occurrence: Koucky, 1975, p. 12d, 50-51.

BROWN COUNTY
1. Celestite in fossil cavities in Bull Fork Formation. Road cut along Ohio Rte. 125 about ½ mile W of Georgetown, Pleasant Twp.; HIGGINSPORT.
   General geology: Outerbridge and others, 1973, map.

ERIE COUNTY
1. Bluish-white celestite in dolostones of *Detroit River Group* and Columbus and Delaware Limestones. Also calcite, fluorite, pyrite, and sphalerite. Sandusky Crushed Stone Co. quarry, Parkertown, just S of Portland Rd., Groton Twp., BELLEVUE.
   Mineral occurrence: Carlson, 1983, p. 425, 429-430; Nelson, 1967, p. 54-58.
   General geology: Janssens, 1970b, p. 10-12.

HANCOCK COUNTY
1. Bluish-white celestite in pockets and fractures of *Tymochtee Dolomite* and dolostones of undifferentiated Salina Group. Also asphalt, calcite, fluorite, gypsum, pyrite, and sphalerite. National Lime & Stone Co. quarry, Findlay, sec. 24 and NE¼ sec. 25, Liberty Twp.; FINDLAY.
   Mineral occurrence: Carlson, 1983, p. 25, 29-30; Strogonoff, 1966, p. 57.
   General geology: Janssens, 1971, p. 35; Stout, 1941, p. 342-343.
2. Small bladed crystals of colorless to white celestite with calcite and pyrite in cavities of Tymochtee Dolomite. Also barite and fluorite. Tarbox-McCall Stone Co. quarry, Findlay, W½ sec. 24, Liberty Twp.; FINDLAY.
   General geology: Janssens, 1977, p. 3.

LUCAS COUNTY
1. White celestite with calcite and strontianite in cavities of Silica Formation and *Tenmile Creek Dolomite*. Also barite, dolomite, pyrite, and sphalerite. W wall of France Stone Co. North quarry (formerly Medusa Portland Cement Co.), Sylvania, S-central sec. 7, Sylvania Twp.; SYLVANIA, BERKEY.
   Mineral occurrence: Carlson, 1983, p. 425, 429-430; Mychkovsky, 1978b, p. 18-20.
   General geology: Carman and others, 1962, p. 5-6; Ehlers, G. M., and others, 1951, p. 4.

2. Crystals of white, pale-blue, and pale-yellow celestite with calcite, pyrite, and sulfur in pockets and fractures and as replacements in nodules of gypsum in *Tymochtee Dolomite* and dolostones of undifferentiated Salina Group. Also asphalt, fluorite, gypsum, halite, and sphalerite. France Stone Co. quarry, Waterville, secs. 38 and 39, Waterville Twp.; BOWLING GREEN NORTH.
   Mineral occurrence: Carlson, 1983, p. 425, 429-430; Garske and Peacor, 1965, p. 205; Kahle and Floyd, 1968, p. 21-24; 1972, p. 65-68; Nelson, 1967, p. 81; Roedder, 1969, p. 797; Stout, 1941, p. 402-404; Strogonoff, 1966, p. 37-38.
   General geology: Janssens, 1977, p. 25-30; Kahle and Floyd, 1971, p. 2082-2086.
3. Crystals of sky-blue celestite with calcite in Greenfield Dolomite or Tymochtee Dolomite. Presque Isle on W side of Maumee River about 2 miles N of Waterville, Waterville and Monclova Twps.; MAUMEE (TOLEDO 15-minute).
   Mineral occurrence: Carlson, 1983, p. 425, 429-430; Silliman, 1824, p. 46.
   General geology: Gilbert, 1873, p. 574; Kahle and Floyd, 1971, p. 2075-2077.
4. Celestite with calcite in cavities in dolostones of Detroit River Group. Old Loeb's quarry 2 miles E of Whitehouse, Waterville Twp.; WHITEHOUSE.
   Mineral occurrence: Carlson, 1983, p. 425, 429-430; Dana, E. S., 1892, p. 1085; Gilbert, 1873, p. 576-577, 581, 583 (reported as strontianite); Sanford and Stone, 1914, p. 148.
   General geology: Ehlers, G. M., and others, 1951, p. 1.
5. Celestite in *Lockport Dolomite* and *Greenfield Dolomite*. Also asphalt, calcite, dolomite, fluorite, gypsum, pyrite, sphalerite, and sulfur. Stoneco quarry (formerly Maumee Stone Co.), Maumee, sec. 35, Waynesfield Twp.; MAUMEE.
   Mineral occurrence: Botoman and Stieglitz, 1978, p. 5; Carlson, 1983, p. 425, 429-430; Kahle, 1974, p. 34.
   General geology: Kahle, 1978, p. 63-115; Kahle and Floyd, 1972, p. 70-81; Summerson and others, 1963, p. 44-45; Textoris and Carozzi, 1966, p. 1375-1388.
6. White celestite in cavities of dolostones of undifferentiated Salina Group. Also calcite, fluorite, and gypsum. Outcrop on E side of West Sister Island in Lake Erie; METZGER MARSH.
   Mineral occurrence: Carlson, 1983, p. 425, 429-430; Gilbert, 1873, p. 589-590 (reported as strontianite); Sanford and Stone, 1914, p. 148.
   General geology: Herdendorf and Braidech, 1972, p. 9-12; Sparling, 1965, p. 95; 1970, p. 11.

MARION COUNTY
1. Tabular masses of white and colorless celestite in cavities of Lockport Dolomite and *Greenfield Dolomite*. Also calcite, dolomite, fluorite, marcasite, sphalerite, and strontianite. Tri-County Limestone Co. quarry (formerly Laubis Stone Co.) 2 miles SW of Marseilles, center sec. 19, Grand Twp.; MARSEILLES.
   General geology: Cumings, 1930, p. 202-203; Hall and Alkire, 1956, p. 5, 32-35; Stith, 1983, p. 15; Stout, 1941, p. 281-282.

OTTAWA COUNTY
1. White to pale-blue celestite in pockets, caves, and fractures of *Lockport Dolomite* and Greenfield Dolomite; may be associated with calcite, fluorite, and sphalerite. Also dolomite, galena, gypsum, and pyrite. Edward Kraemer & Sons, Inc., White Rock quarry, Clay Center, SE¼ sec. 9, NE¼ sec. 16, Allen Twp.; GENOA.

Mineral occurrence: Bernstein, 1979, p. 161; Botoman and Stieglitz, 1978, p. 5; Carman and others, 1962, p. 13-14; Carlson, 1983, p. 425, 429-430; Dana, E. S., 1932, p. 383; Floyd, 1971, p. 102-105, 167; Haden, 1977, p. 24-25; Howard, 1959, p. 128-130; Kessen and others, 1981, p. 913-918; Kraus and others, 1959, p. 340; Morrison, 1934, p. 15-16, 31-38; 1935, p. 782, 785-787; Mychkovsky, 1978b, p. 33, 54-57, 64; Orton, 1888c, p. 735 (reported as barite); Palache and others, 1951, p. 418; Robbins, 1983, p. 123; Roedder, 1967, p. 355; 1969, p. 796-810; 1979, p. 90-97; 1984, p. 321-322; Runkle, 1951, p. 4-5; Sparling, 1965, p. 171, 239-240; Stout, 1941, p. 415-418; Strogonoff, 1966, p. 10; White, J. S., 1977, p. 60-61.

General geology: Janssens, 1974, p. 82, 84; 1977, p. 22; Sparling, 1971, p. 19.

2. Celestite in Lockport Dolomite. Old quarry, sec. 2, Allen Twp.; GENOA.

Mineral occurrence: Carlson, 1983, p. 425, 429-430; Sparling, 1965, p. 172.

3. White celestite in cavities of *Lockport Dolomite* and Greenfield Dolomite; may be associated with calcite and fluorite. Also asphalt, dolomite, pyrite, sphalerite, and sulfur. Stoneco quarry (formerly Maumee Stone Co.), N of Rocky Ridge, sec. 23, Benton Twp.; OAK HARBOR.

Mineral occurrence: Botoman and Stieglitz, 1978, p. 6; Carlson, 1983, p. 425, 429-430; Mychkovsky, 1978b, p. 55, 64.

General geology: Forsyth, 1971, p. 14; Sparling, 1965, p. 172.

4. Celestite in dolostones of undifferentiated Salina Group and *Bass Islands Dolomite*. Also calcite, fluorite, and gypsum. Cliff exposure on NW edge of Catawba Island, Catawba Island Twp.; GYPSUM.

Mineral occurrence: Carlson, 1983, p. 425, 429-430; Treesh, 1970, p. 9.

General geology: Carman, 1927, p. 488-491; Janssens, 1977, p. 27-30; Sparling, 1970, p. 3, 19-21; 1971, p. 19-22.

5. Crystals of white celestite in pockets, caves, and fractures of Lockport Dolomite; may be associated with calcite. Also dolomite, fluorite, galena, marcasite, pyrite, and sphalerite. GenLime Group, L. P., quarry (formerly U.S. Gypsum Co.), Genoa, W½ sec. 3, Clay Twp.; GENOA.

Mineral occurrence: Carlson, 1983, p. 425, 429-430; 1986, p. 9-13; Fisher, H. H., 1977, p. 414; Floyd, 1971, p. 99-101, 167, 170; Forsyth, 1971, p. 15-16; Harness, 1942, p. 8; Mychkovsky, 1978b, p. 33; Orton, 1888c, p. 732-733 (reported as barite); Schreck and Arundale, 1959, p. 18, 39; Sparling, 1965, p. 171, 236-237; Stout, 1941, p. 413-414; Strogonoff, 1966, p. 16.

General geology: Janssens, 1977, p. 3, 22.

6. Celestite in dolostones of undifferentiated Salina Group. Also anhydrite and gypsum. Old U.S. Gypsum Co. pit near Gypsum, SE¼ sec. 10, Portage Twp.; VICKERY.

Mineral occurrence: Carlson, 1983, p. 425, 429-430; Stout, 1941, p. 420-421.

General geology: Janssens, 1977, p. 36-38; Jones, 1935, p. 493-501; Newberry, 1873a, p. 133-134; Orton, 1888b, p. 696-702.

7. Crystals of white to pale-blue celestite in cave of Bass Islands Dolomite. Also calcite. Crystal Cave near middle of South Bass Island, Put-in-Bay Twp.; PUT-IN-BAY.

Mineral occurrence: Botoman and Stieglitz, 1978, p. 6; Carlson, 1983, p. 425, 429-430; Courter, 1974, p. 664-672; Feldmann and others, 1977, p. 43-47; Frohman, 1971, p. 72-73; Kindt, 1952, p. 256; Kraus, 1905a, p. 286-289; 1905b, p. 167; Kraus and Hunt, 1906, p. 244; Kraus and others, 1959, p. 340; Mohr, 1931, p. 14; Mychkovsky, 1978b, p. 16, 22, 33; Palache and others, 1951, p. 418; Phalen, 1914, p. 524; Runkle, 1951, p. 3-4; Sanford and Stone, 1914, p. 148; Sparling, 1965, p. 100; 1970, p. 12; Strogonoff, 1966, p. 59; Thorndale, 1898, p. 350-352; White, G. W., 1926, p. 84; Wright, 1898, p. 502-503.

General geology: Janssens, 1977, p. 27-30; Sparling, 1971, p. 19-22.

8. Celestite crystals covered with layer of travertine in cave of Bass Islands Dolomite. Kindt's Cave about ¼ miles S of Crystal Cave, South Bass Island, Put-in-Bay Twp.; PUT-IN-BAY.

Mineral occurrence: Stansbery, 1965, p. 19.

General geology: Janssens, 1977, p. 27-30; Langlois, 1951, p. 116-117; Sparling, 1970, p. 12, 19-21; 1971, p. 19-22; White, G. W., 1926, p. 85.

9. Celestite with calcite and sulfur in Bass Islands Dolomite. South Bass Island, no specific location given, Put-in-Bay Twp.; PUT-IN-BAY.

Mineral occurrence: Dana, E. S., 1892, p. 907; Dana, J. D., 1868, p. 784; Newberry, 1873a, p. 106; 1874b, p. 202; 1875, p. 106.

General geology: Janssens, 1977, p. 27-30; Mohr, 1931, p. 28.

10. Small celestite crystals in dolostones of undifferentiated Salina Group and *Bass Islands Dolomite*. Also calcite and gypsum. Cliff exposure at South Point, South Bass Island, Put-in-Bay Twp.; PUT-IN-BAY.

Mineral occurrence: Mohr, 1931, p. 33-34; Treesh, 1970, p. 9.

General geology: Janssens, 1977, p. 27-30; Sparling, 1971, p. 19-22; Stout, 1941, p. 421-422.

11. White and pale-blue celestite in cavities and fractures of Bass Islands Dolomite. Also barite, calcite, fluorite, and pyrite. Fox Stone Products, Inc., quarry, N side of Langram Rd., S part of South Bass Island, Put-in-Bay Twp.; PUT-IN-BAY.

General geology: Janssens, 1977, p. 27-30; Sparling, 1971, p. 19-22.

12. White to blue celestite crystals in cavities of Bass Islands Dolomite. Outcrop on Green (Strontian) Island about 1 mile W of South Bass Island, Put-in-Bay Twp.; PUT-IN-BAY.

Mineral occurrence: Atwater, 1838, p. 61; Bigsby, 1822, p. 280-282; Carlson, 1983, p. 425, 429-430; Cleaveland, 1822, p. 145, 774; Dana, E. S., 1892, p. 907, 1085; Dana, E. S., and Ford, 1932, p. 751; Dana, J. D., 1868, p. 620, 784; Delafield, 1822, p. 279; Douglass, 1820, p. 241 (reported as barite); 1821, p. 363-364; Mohr, 1931, p. 40; Newberry, 1874b, p. 203; Runkle, 1951, p. 3; Sanford and Stone, 1914, p. 148; Troost, 1822, p. 300-302; Wright, 1898, p. 502.

General geology: Herdendorf and Braidech, 1972, p. 10; Janssens, 1977, p. 27-30; Sparling, 1970, p. 14; Verber and Stansbery, 1953, p. 358-362.

13. White celestite with fluorite in Bass Islands Dolomite. Rattlesnake Island about 1 mile W of Middle Bass Island, Put-in-Bay Twp.; PUT-IN-BAY.

Mineral occurrence: Carlson, 1983, p. 425, 429-430; Hamilton, 1953, p. 134.

General geology: Janssens, 1977, p. 27-30; Sparling, 1970, p. 3, 14.

14. Celestite in Bass Islands Dolomite. From a water well on North Bass Island, Put-in-Bay Twp.; PUT-IN-BAY.

Mineral occurrence: Carlson, 1983, p. 425, 429-430; Newberry, 1874b, p. 203.

General geology: Janssens, 1977, p. 27-30; Mohr, 1931, p. 28; Sparling, 1970, p. 3, 22.

SANDUSKY COUNTY

1. Celestite in Greenfield Dolomite. Exposure along Sandusky River at Ballville, NE¼ sec. 9, Ballville Twp.; FREMONT WEST.
   Mineral occurrence: Carlson, 1983, p. 425, 429-430; Stout, 1941, p. 377-379.
   General geology: Carman, 1927, p. 487.

2. Celestite in Greenfield Dolomite. Exposure along Sandusky River near bridge in central part of sec. 17, Ballville Twp.; FREMONT WEST.
   Mineral occurrence: Carlson, 1983, p. 425, 429-430; Stout, 1941, p. 376-378.
   General geology: Carman, 1927, p. 487.

3. Crystal molds of tabular celestite(?) in calcite in pockets of Lockport Dolomite. Also dolomite. Steetley Resources, Inc., Ohio Lime Co. quarry, Millersville, secs. 7 and 8, Jackson Twp.; HELENA.
   General geology: Janssens, 1974, p. 84; 1977, p. 22.

4. White celestite crystals in Lockport Dolomite. Also calcite, fluorite, galena, and sphalerite. Charles Pfizer & Co., Inc., quarry NW of Gibsonburg, sec. 14, Madison Twp.; ELMORE.
   Mineral occurrence: Botoman and Stieglitz, 1978, p. 6; Carlson, 1983, p. 425, 429-430; Green, R., 1970b, p. 677.
   General geology: Floyd, 1971, p. 167; Janssens, 1977, p. 3, 22; Stith, 1983, p. 11-13.

5. Celestite in cavities of *Lockport Dolomite* and *Greenfield Dolomite*. Also galena. Gottron Bros. Co. quarry, Fremont, secs. 32 and 33, Sandusky Twp.; FREMONT WEST.
   Mineral occurrence: Carlson, 1983, p. 425, 429-430; Stout, 1941, p. 368-369.
   General geology: Janssens, 1971, p. 35; 1974, p. 82, 84; 1977, p. 3, 22; Winchell, 1873, p. 601-602.

6. Crystals of white and pale-blue celestite with calcite in cavities of Lockport Dolomite. Also barite, dolomite, fluorite, galena, pyrite, and sphalerite. Steetley Resources, Inc., Ohio Lime Co. quarry, Woodville, W½ sec. 34, Woodville Twp.; ELMORE.
   Mineral occurrence: Botoman and Stieglitz, 1978, p. 6; Carlson, 1983, p. 425, 429-430; Gettings, 1954, p. 259; Green, R., 1970a, p. 585; 1971, p. 280; Kahle and Floyd, 1968, p. 33; Mychkovsky, 1978b, p. 32; Roedder, 1969, p. 797 (did not specify which Woodville quarry); Strogonoff, 1966, p. 54.
   General geology: Floyd, 1971, p. 167-169.

7. Crystals of white celestite with calcite and fluorite in pockets and caves of Lockport Dolomite. Also barite, dolomite, galena, pyrite, sphalerite, and strontianite. Martin Marietta Chemicals quarry (S part formerly Woodville Lime & Chemicals Co. quarry), Woodville, E½ sec. 21 and W½ sec. 22, Woodville Twp.; ELMORE.
   Mineral occurrence: Carlson, 1983, p. 425, 429-430; 1986, p. 9-13; Gettings, 1952a, p. 142; Mychkovsky, 1978b, p. 16-20, 32, 53-57, 64.
   General geology: Stout, 1941, p. 375; Summerson and others, 1963, p. 42.

SENECA COUNTY

1. Celestite in Greenfield Dolomite. Old quarry along E bank of Sandusky River at S edge of Tiffin, Clinton Twp.; TIFFIN SOUTH.
   Mineral occurrence: Carlson, 1983, p. 425, 429-430; Winchell, 1873, p. 618.
   General geology: Carman, 1927, p. 487; Janssens, 1977, p. 3.

2. Crystals of white to pale-blue celestite with fluorite in cavities of Lockport Dolomite or Greenfield Dolomite. Also calcite, galena, sphalerite, strontianite, and sulfur. Old quarries at Tiffin, Clinton Twp.; TIFFIN SOUTH.
   Mineral occurrence: Carlson, 1983, p. 425, 429-430; Palache and others, 1951, p. 35; also unpublished information from mineral collection at Heidelberg College.
   General geology: Carman, 1927, p. 487; Janssens, 1977, p. 3; Winchell, 1873, p. 616-618.

3. Crystals of pale-blue celestite with calcite in cavities of Greenfield Dolomite. Old France Stone Co. quarry 1½ miles E of Bascom, central part of sec. 16, Hopewell Twp.; BASCOM.
   Mineral occurrence: Carlson, 1983, p. 425, 429-430; Roedder, 1969, p. 797, 807; 1979, p. 91; Stout, 1941, p. 353-354.
   General geology: Carman, 1927, p. 482.

4. Crystals of white celestite with fluorite and strontianite in cavities and fractures of *Lockport Dolomite* and Greenfield Dolomite. Also calcite, dolomite, galena, marcasite, pyrite, and sphalerite. Maple Grove Stone Co. quarry (formerly Basic Refractories), Maple Grove, sec. 11 and N½ sec. 14, Liberty Twp.; TIFFIN NORTH.
   Mineral occurrence: Carlson, 1983, p. 425, 429-430.
   General geology: Floyd, 1971, p. 167, 173-174; Janssens, 1971, p. 35; 1974, p. 82, 84; 1977, p. 3, 22; Stout, 1941, p. 348-349.

WOOD COUNTY

1. Celestite in cavities of Lockport Dolomite. Old Wood County Stone and Construction Co. quarry just N of Portage, NE¼ sec. 1, Liberty Twp.; BOWLING GREEN SOUTH.
   Mineral occurrence: Carlson, 1983, p. 425, 429-430; Fisher, H. H., 1977, p. 414; Stout, 1941, p. 388.

2. Pale-blue celestite in cavities and fractures of dolostones of *Detroit River Group* and Dundee Formation; may be associated with calcite and marcasite. Also asphalt, barite, dolomite, fluorite, glauconite, hexahydrite, pyrite, and sphalerite. France Stone Co. Custar quarry (formerly Pugh Quarry Co.) about 4 miles W of Weston, SW¼ sec. 6, Milton Twp.; MCCLURE.
   Mineral occurrence: Bingaman and others, 1978, p. 18; Botoman and Stieglitz, 1978, p. 6; Carlson, 1983, p. 425, 429-430; Feldmann and others, 1977, p. 35-37; Fisher, H. H., 1977, p. 414; Green, R., 1970a, p. 584; Kessen and others, 1981, p. 913-918; Mychkovsky, 1978b, p. 33; Nelson, 1967, p. 65; Parr and Chang, 1980, p. 26-29; Robbins, 1983, p. 123.
   General geology: Forsyth, 1966a, p. 204-205; Janssens, 1970a, p. 7, 22; Orton and Peppel, 1906, p. 133; Stout, 1941, p. 395-396.

3. Crystals of white celestite in cavities of *Lockport Dolomite* and *Greenfield Dolomite*. Also barite, calcite, dolomite, fluorite, hexahydrite, pyrite, sphalerite, and strontianite. MacRitchie Materials, Inc., quarry (formerly Brough Stone Co.), West Millgrove, SE¼ sec. 4, Perry Twp.; FOSTORIA.
   Mineral occurrence: Carlson, 1983, p. 425, 429-430; Floyd, 1971, p. 99-100; Stout, 1941, p. 392-393.
   General geology: Janssens, 1971, p. 35; 1974, p. 82, 84; 1977, p. 22; Shaver, 1977, p. 1414.

4. Crystals of white and pale-blue celestite with calcite in caves and vugs of *Lockport Dolomite* and *Greenfield Dolomite*. Also aragonite, barite, dolomite, fluorite, galena, gypsum, marcasite, pyrite, sphalerite, strontianite, and sulfur. Stoneco quarry (formerly Maumee Stone Co.), Lime City, SW¼ sec. 11, Perrysburg Twp.; ROSSFORD.
   Mineral occurrence: Botoman and Stieglitz, 1978, p. 6; Carlson, 1983, p. 425, 429-430; Fisher, H. H., 1977, p. 414; Green, R., 1970a, p. 584; 1970b, p. 677; Haden, 1977, p. 24-25; Kahle and Floyd, 1968, p. 28-30; 1972,

p. 50-52; Mychkovsky, 1978b, p. 16-17, 32, 54-57; Robbins, 1983, p. 123; Roedder, 1969, p. 797; Strogonoff, 1966, p. 44; White, J. S., 1975, p. 38.
General geology: Janssens, 1971, p. 35; 1974, p. 82, 84; 1977, p. 22.

5. White to pale-blue celestite in pockets and caves and as replacements of gypsum in *Lockport Dolomite* and *Greenfield Dolomite*. Also calcite, dolomite, gypsum, sphalerite, and sulfur. Stoneco quarry (formerly Maumee Stone Co.) SE of Portage, sec. 7, Portage Twp.; BOWLING GREEN SOUTH.
Mineral occurrence: Carlson, 1983, p. 425, 429-430; 1987c, p. 96-104; Fisher, H. H., 1977, p. 414; Robbins, 1983, p. 123; Wilson, W. E., 1986, p. 147.
General geology: Floyd, 1971, p. 188; Janssens, 1971, p. 35; 1974, p. 82, 84; 1977, p. 22.

WYANDOT COUNTY
1. Crystals of white and sky-blue celestite in vugs of *Lockport Dolomite* and *Greenfield Dolomite*. Also calcite, dolomite, fluorite, gypsum, pyrite, sphalerite, and strontianite. National Lime & Stone Co. quarry, Carey, N½ sec. 15 and N½ sec. 16, Crawford Twp.; CAREY, MCCUTCHENVILLE.
Mineral occurrence: Botoman and Faure, 1976, p. 69; Botoman and Stieglitz, 1978, p. 6; Carlson, 1983, p. 425, 429-430; 1987c, p. 101-102; Stout, 1941, p. 294-295.
General geology: Cumings, 1930, p. 201-202; Hall and Alkire, 1956, p. 7, 31-33; Janssens, 1974, p. 82, 84; 1977, p. 22; Summerson and others, 1963, p. 39-40.

2. Crystals (replacements of gypsum) and granular masses of white celestite in cavities and fractures of Tymochtee Dolomite and dolostones of undifferentiated Salina Group. Also calcite, sphalerite, and sulfur. McCarthy Stone Quarry 3½ miles SE of Upper Sandusky, N½ sec. 15, Pitt Twp.; NEVADA.
Mineral occurrence: Carlson, 1987c, p. 97-101.
General geology: Janssens, 1977, p. 3, 29; Stout, 1941, p. 299.

CHALCEDONY
See QUARTZ

CHALCOPYRITE
CuFeS$_2$

Chemical class: Sulfide
Crystallization: Tetragonal; scalenohedral; $\overline{4}2m$
Habit: Crystals generally tetrahedral; commonly in finely crystalline granular aggregates
Physical properties: Cleavage: poorly developed, commonly indistinct. Fracture: uneven. H: 3½-4. G: 4.3. Luster: metallic. Color: brass yellow, may be iridescent. Streak: greenish black
Occurrence: Granular aggregates rare in veins of septarian ironstone concretions from black shales in eastern Ohio

COLUMBIANA COUNTY
1. Small masses of chalcopyrite in veins of ironstone concretions from shales above Lower Kittanning (No. 5) coal, Allegheny Group; may be associated with barite, kaolinite, and sphalerite. Also calcite, copiapite, gypsum, pyrite, and wurtzite. Metrel, Inc., quarry S of Negley, sec. 13, Middleton Twp.; EAST PALESTINE.
Mineral occurrence: Carlson, 1978, p. 248-249; Hollenbaugh, 1979, p. 9, 16-22; Hollenbaugh and Carlson, 1983, p. 697-703.
General geology: Stout and Lamborn, 1924, p. 111.

MAHONING COUNTY
1. Small granular masses of chalcopyrite in veins of ironstone concretions from shales below Lower Mercer limestone, Pottsville Group; may be associated with kaolinite. Also barite, calcite, pyrite, and sphalerite. Outcrop along West Branch Meander Creek just east of junction with Ohio Rte. 45 about ¾ mile S of Ellsworth, Ellsworth Twp.; CANFIELD.
Mineral occurrence: Carlson, 1978, p. 248-249.
General geology: Lamb, 1910, p. 114.

2. Chalcopyrite in veins of ironstone concretions from shales below Vanport(?) limestone, Allegheny Group; may be associated with barite, pyrite, and sphalerite. Keller mine S of Middletown Rd., NE¼ sec. 19, Smith Twp.; ALLIANCE.
Mineral occurrence: Carlson, 1978, p. 248-249.
General geology: DeLong and White, 1963, p. 42, 45; Lamb, 1910, p. 109.

PORTAGE COUNTY
1. Small granular masses of chalcopyrite with kaolinite and sphalerite in veins of ironstone concretions from shales of lower Pottsville Group. Also barite and calcite. Outcrop along SE shore of Michael J. Kirwan Reservoir at mouth of Silver Creek, just W of Alliance Rd., NE Edinburg Twp.; WINDHAM.
Mineral occurrence: Carlson, 1978, p. 248-249.
General geology: Winslow and White, 1966, p. 79.

SUMMIT COUNTY
1. Chalcopyrite with calcite, kaolinite, pyrite, and sphalerite in veins of ironstone concretions from Meadville Shale Member, Cuyahoga Formation. Outcrop along a small tributary that enters Cuyahoga River from N side about ¼ mile W of foot of dam at Cuyahoga Gorge Park, Cuyahoga Falls; AKRON WEST.
Mineral occurrence: Carlson, 1978, p. 248-249.
General geology: Kent State University, *in* Frank, 1969, p. 1.5-1.7; Szmuc, 1957, p. 159-161.

WAYNE COUNTY
1. Finely crystalline masses of chalcopyrite in veins of ironstone concretions from shales of lower Pottsville Group; may be associated with barite, calcite, galena, pyrite, and sphalerite. Penn Central Railroad cut N of Marshallville, W-central sec. 33, Chippewa Twp.; DOYLESTOWN.
Mineral occurrence: Carlson, 1978, p. 248-249.
General geology: Conrey, 1921, p. 92; Ver Steeg, 1948, p. 185.

CHERT
See QUARTZ

COESITE
SiO$_2$

Coesite, the high-pressure polymorph of silica (SiO$_2$), had been reported in shatter cones of the Lilley Dolomite in the Serpent Mound disturbance (Cohen A. J., and others, 1961, p. 1624; 1962, p. 1632; Frondel, 1962, p. 315). Later work, however, has not verified its presence (Reidel, 1972, p. 9; 1975, map; Reidel and Koucky, 1981, p. 394; Reidel and others, 1982, p. 1357).

COPIAPITE
Fe^{+2}Fe$_4^{+3}$(SO$_4$)$_6$(OH)$_2 \cdot$ 20H$_2$O

Chemical class: Sulfate
Crystallization: Triclinic; pinacoidal; $\overline{1}$

Habit: Commonly finely granular or scaly aggregates and crusts; globular masses; small tabular crystals

Physical properties: Cleavage: {010} perfect pinacoidal. H: 2½-3. G: 2.1. Luster: greasy to dull. Color: lemon yellow. Taste: astringent

Occurrence: Finely granular aggregates as an efflorescence associated with pyrite in coal and shale in central and eastern Ohio; much more common than the list below would suggest because it is commonly misidentified as sulfur

COLUMBIANA COUNTY
1. Efflorescence of copiapite with gypsum on Lower Kittanning (No. 5) coal, Allegheny Group. Also barite, calcite, chalcopyrite, kaolinite, pyrite, sphalerite, and wurtzite, Metrel, Inc., quarry S of Negley, sec. 13, Middleton Twp.; EAST PALESTINE.
General geology: Stout and Lamborn, 1924, p. 111.

MEIGS COUNTY
1. Efflorescence of copiapite with alunogen, botryogen, and pickeringite in shales above Redstone (Pomeroy) (No. 8A) coal, Monongahela Group. Old strip mine on E side of Twp. Hwy. 46 about 1 mile N of Langsville, Rutland Twp.; RUTLAND.
Mineral occurrence: Fisher, H. H., 1975, p. 416.
General geology: DeLong, 1955, p. 43-44.

PERRY COUNTY
1. Efflorescence of copiapite on melanterite from shale partings in Middle Kittanning (No. 6) coal, Allegheny Group. Also pyrite. Old Congo coal mine, Congo, SW¼ sec. 7, Monroe Twp.; NEW STRAITSVILLE.
Mineral occurrence: McCaughey, 1918, p. 162.
General geology: Flint, 1951, p. 82-83.

DIADOCHITE
$Fe_2(PO_4)(SO_4)(OH) \cdot 5H_2O$

Chemical class: Compound phosphate (phosphate-sulfate)
Crystallization: Triclinic; crystal class unknown
Habit: Very fine grained aggregate; colloform
Physical properties: Fracture: uneven. H: 3-4. G: 2.0-2.4. Luster: waxy to dull. Color: pale greenish yellow
Occurrence: Rare

COSHOCTON COUNTY
1. Disk-shaped nodules of diadochite in black shales (Columbiana shale) overlying Lower Kittanning (No. 5) coal, Allegheny Group. Former strip mine, now reclaimed, NW¼SE¼ sec. 5, Jackson Twp.; RANDLE.
Mineral occurrence: Hull, 1982, p. 6; Hull and Hansen, 1982, p. 31-32.
General geology: Lamborn, 1954, p. 155, 162-163.

DIAMOND
C

Chemical class: Native element
Crystallization: Isometric; hextetrahedral; $\bar{4}3m$
Habit: Crystals commonly octahedral
Physical properties: Cleavage: {111} perfect octahedral. H: 10. G: 3.5. Luster: adamantine. Color: colorless, white, yellow
Occurrence: Rare in glacial deposits such as outwash gravels and till; may be found when stream gravels are panned; characterized by a peculiar greasy appearance

CLERMONT COUNTY
1. A diamond in Illinoian glacial gravels. Sugar Camp Run about 2 miles N of its junction with East Fork Little Miami River near Perintown, Miami Twp.; GOSHEN.
Mineral occurrence: Hansen, 1985a, p. 1-2; Wuestner, 1938, p. 265.
General geology: Goldthwait and others, 1961, map.
2. A diamond in Illinoian glacial gravels. At Milford, Miami Twp.; MADEIRA.
Mineral occurrence: Blatchley, 1902, p. 41; Gunn, 1968, p. 333; Hansen, 1982, p. 1-2; 1985a, p. 1; Hobbs, 1899, p. 378; Vierthaler, 1961a, p. 26; 1961b, p. 214.
General geology: Goldthwait and others, 1961, map.

CUYAHOGA COUNTY
1. A diamond in Wisconsinan glacial gravels. Creek bed a few miles S of Cleveland.
Mineral occurrence: Blatchley, 1902, p. 46; Gunn, 1968, p. 302; Hansen, 1982, p. 2; 1985a, p. 1.
General geology: White, G. W., 1982, pl. 1.

HAMILTON COUNTY
1. A diamond in Illinoian glacial gravels reportedly found by a worker attending a boulder-crushing machine. Cincinnati.
Mineral occurrence: Gunn, 1968, p. 302; Kunz, 1892, p. 35; Hansen, 1982, p. 2; 1985a, p. 1.
General geology: Goldthwait and others, 1961, map.

MAHONING COUNTY
1. A diamond in Wisconsinan glacial gravels. Old gravel pit about 1 mile E of Salem on N side of Egypt Rd., NW¼ sec. 33, Green Twp.; SALEM.
Mineral occurrence: Hansen, 1985a, p. 2-3.
General geology: White, G. W., 1982, pl. 1.

SUMMIT COUNTY
1. A diamond in Wisconsinan glacial gravels. Borrow pit a few hundred feet S of Schrop Junior High School, Krumroy, W-central Springfield Twp.; AKRON EAST.
Mineral occurrence: Hansen, 1985a, p. 1.
General geology: White, G. W., 1953, pl. 6; 1982, pl. 1.

DOLOMITE-FERROAN DOLOMITE
$CaMg(CO_3)_2$-$Ca(Mg,Fe)(CO_3)_2$

Chemical class: Carbonate
Crystallization: Hexagonal (Trigonal); rhombohedral; $\bar{3}$
Habit: Generally well crystallized; commonly rhombohedral; saddle-shaped crystals with curved faces common; may be finely granular
Physical properties: Cleavage: {10$\bar{1}$1} perfect rhombohedral. H: 3½-4. G: 2.8. Luster: vitreous. Color: white, tan, brown, pink, gray; ferroan dolomite is greenish brown to dark brown and turns reddish brown to darker brown on weathered surfaces. Streak: white. Effervesces slowly in cold dilute hydrochloric acid. Both dolomite and ferroan dolomite may fluoresce in ultraviolet light
Chemistry: Most dolomite ($CaMg(CO_3)_2$) contains very little iron. In ferroan dolomite ($Ca(Mg,Fe)(CO_3)_2$) magnesium content exceeds iron; in ankerite ($Ca(Fe,Mg)(CO_3)_2$) iron exceeds magnesium
Occurrence: Small crystals, saddle type at some sites, and granular aggregates of dolomite in cavities and fractures of dolostones in western Ohio; rhombohedral crystals and granular aggregates of dolomite and ferroan dolomite in veins of limestone concretions of Ohio Shale

ADAMS COUNTY
1. Veins of finely crystalline tan dolomite with sphalerite in breccias of undifferentiated Peebles-Greenfield-Tymochtee Dolomites. Outcrop and small quarry 0.7 mile E of entrance to Serpent Mound State Memorial on Ohio Rte. 73 and 1.4 miles N on E side of Twp. Hwy. 116, Bratton Twp.; SINKING SPRING.
Mineral occurrence: Heyl and Brock, 1962, p. D95.
General geology: Koucky, 1975, p. 22; Koucky and Reidel, 1987, p. 431-436; Reidel, 1975, map; Reidel and Koucky, 1981, p. 391-403; Reidel and others, 1982, p. 1343-1377.
2. Crystals of dolomite with asphalt, barite, calcite, and quartz in veins of large limestone concretions from lower Ohio Shale. Also pyrite. Old quarry and cliff exposure on W side of Hackleshin Rd., 4 miles NE of Locust Grove, Franklin Twp.; JAYBIRD.
Mineral occurrence: Wuestner, 1938, p. 259-261.
General geology: Kepferle and others, 1981, p. 290-293; Lamborn, 1927, p. 712-714; Seyfried, 1953, p. 28.

ALLEN COUNTY
1. Small crystals of saddle-type white dolomite in cavities of Tymochtee Dolomite and dolostones of undifferentiated Salina Group. Also asphalt, calcite, fluorite, pyrite, and sphalerite. National Lime & Stone Co. quarry, Lima, sec. 29, Bath Twp.; LIMA.
Mineral occurrence: Kessen and others, 1981, p. 913-918.
General geology: Janssens, 1977, p. 3.
2. Small crystals of saddle-type white dolomite in cavities of Tymochtee Dolomite and dolostones of undifferentiated Salina Group. Also calcite, fluorite, pyrite, and sphalerite. Bluffton Stone Co. quarry, Bluffton, NW¼ sec. 12, Richland Twp.; BLUFFTON.
General geology: Janssens, 1977, p. 3; Stout, 1941, p. 310.

ERIE COUNTY
1. Crystalline aggregates of tan dolomite and brown ferroan dolomite with barite, calcite, and quartz in veins of large limestone concretions from lower Huron Shale Member, Ohio Shale. Also aragonite and sphalerite. Borrow pit at Huron just S of U.S. Rte. 6, 0.4 mile W of Rye Beach Rd. intersection, Huron Twp.; HURON.
General geology: Explorer, 1961, p. 5; Prosser, 1913, p. 324-341.
2. Crystals and granular aggregates of tan dolomite and brown ferroan dolomite (Mg:Fe ratio about 4:1) with barite, calcite, pyrite, and whewellite in veins of large limestone concretions from lower Huron Shale Member, Ohio Shale. Outcrops along Huron River about 1 mile W of Milan, Milan Twp.; KIMBALL.
Mineral occurrence: Hyde, C., and Landy, 1966, p. 228; Leavens, 1968, p. 456-457.
General geology: Prosser, 1913, p. 324-341.
3. Crystalline aggregates of tan dolomite and brown ferroan dolomite with barite, calcite, and quartz in veins of large limestone concretions from lower Huron Shale Member, Ohio Shale. Also pyrite. Outcrop just W of Milan on N side of Huron River and W side of U.S. Rte. 250 bridge, Milan Twp.; MILAN.
Mineral occurrence: Feldmann and others, 1977, p. 48-49.
General geology: Prosser, 1913, p. 327-328.

GREENE COUNTY
1. Small crystals of saddle-type white dolomite with marcasite and pyrite in cavities of Cedarville Dolomite. Also calcite and quartz. American Aggregates Corp. quarry 1 mile SE of Cedarville on N side of Turnbull Rd., Cedarville Twp.; CEDARVILLE.
General geology: Stith, 1983, p. 11-12, 14.

HARDIN COUNTY
1. Small rhombohedral crystals of gray dolomite in cavities of Lockport Dolomite. Also calcite and pyrite. Standard Slag Co. quarry, Forest, SW¼ sec. 19, Jackson Twp.; FOREST.
General geology: Cumings, 1930, p. 203; Janssens, 1974, p. 81-86; 1977, p. 3, 22; Stout, 1941, p. 270-272; Summerson and others, 1963, p. 38-39.
2. Small crystals of saddle-type white dolomite in cavities of Tymochtee Dolomite. Also asphalt, calcite, fluorite, pyrite, and sphalerite. Hardin Quarry Co., Inc., quarry, Blanchard, NW¼ sec. 6, Pleasant Twp.; FORAKER.
General geology: Janssens, 1977, p. 3; Stout, 1941, p. 274-276.

HURON COUNTY
1. Crystals and granular aggregates of tan dolomite and brown ferroan dolomite with barite, calcite, quartz, and sphalerite in veins of large limestone concretions from lower Huron Shale Member, Ohio Shale. Also aragonite and pyrite. Outcrop about 2 miles N of Monroeville at Lamereaux Rd. bridge on E side of West Branch Huron River, Ridgefield Twp.; KIMBALL.
Mineral occurrence: Bingaman and others, 1978, p. 16; Carlson, 1977, p. 24-25.
General geology: Broadhead and others, 1980, p. 10-15; Prosser, 1913, p. 324-341.

LOGAN COUNTY
1. Small crystals of saddle-type white dolomite with quartz in cavities of Columbus Limestone. Also calcite. Connolly Construction Co., Inc., quarry 1¼ miles W of East Liberty on N side of Ohio Rte 347 near intersection with U.S. Rte. 33, Perry Twp.; EAST LIBERTY.
General geology: Stout, 1941, p. 255-257.
2. Small crystals of saddle-type white dolomite in cavities of dolostones of undifferentiated Salina Group. Also asphalt, calcite, fluorite, pyrite, and sphalerite. C. E. Duff & Son, Inc., quarry, just E of Ohio Rte. 117 about 2 miles N of Huntsville, Richland Twp.; HUNTSVILLE.
Mineral occurrence: Fisher, H. H., 1976, p. 293; Richards and Chamberlain, 1987, p. 391-392.
General geology: Janssens, 1971, p. 35.
3. Crystals of saddle-type white dolomite in cavities of dolostones of undifferentiated Salina Group. Also asphalt, calcite, fluorite, and pyrite. Northwood Stone & Asphalt Co. quarry, ½ mile W of Northwood on S side of County Hwy. 105, just W of intersection with County Hwy. 106, Richland Twp.; RUSHSYLVANIA.
General geology: Summerson and others, 1963, p. 37; Stout, 1941, p. 245-247.

LUCAS COUNTY
1. Small crystals of saddle-type grayish-white dolomite in cavities of Silica Formation and *Tenmile Creek Dolomite*. Also barite, calcite, celestite, pyrite, sphalerite, and strontianite. W wall of France Stone Co. North quarry (formerly Medusa Portland Cement Co.), Sylvania, S-central sec. 7, Sylvania Twp.; SYLVANIA, BERKEY.
Mineral occurrence: Strogonoff, 1966, p. 28.
General geology: Carman and others, 1962, p. 5-6; Ehlers, G. M., and others, 1951, p. 4.
2. Small crystals of gray to tan dolomite in cavities of *Lockport Dolomite* and Greenfield Dolomite; may be associated with sphalerite. Also asphalt, calcite, celestite, fluorite, gypsum, pyrite, and sulfur. Stoneco quarry (formerly Maumee Stone Co.), sec. 35; Waynesfield Twp.; MAUMEE.
General geology: Kahle, 1974, p. 31-54; 1978, p. 63-115; Kahle and Floyd, 1972, p. 70-81; Summerson and others, 1963, p. 44-45; Textoris and Carozzi, 1966, p. 1375-1388.

MARION COUNTY
1. Tiny crystals of gray dolomite in cavities of *Lockport*

Dolomite and Greenfield Dolomite. Also calcite, celestite, fluorite, marcasite, sphalerite, and strontianite. Tri-County Limestone Co. quarry (formerly Laubis Stone Co.) 2 miles SW of Marseilles, center sec. 19, Grand Twp.; MARSEILLES.

General geology: Cumings, 1930, p. 202-203; Hall and Alkire, 1956, p. 5, 32-35; Stith, 1983, p. 15; Stout, 1941, p. 281-282.

MERCER COUNTY
1. Tiny crystals of buff dolomite in cavities of Lockport Dolomite. Also calcite. Rockford Stone Co. quarry 1½ miles NW of Rockford on N side of U.S. Rte. 33, Dublin Twp.; ROCKFORD.

General geology: Janssens, 1971, p. 35; Shaver, 1974, p. 97-102; Stout, 1941, p. 267-268.

2. Tiny crystals of gray dolomite in cavities of *Lockport Dolomite* and Greenfield Dolomite. Also asphalt, calcite, pyrite, quartz, and sphalerite. Stoneco quarry (formerly John W. Karch Stone Co.) 4 miles W of Celina, E½ sec. 8, Jefferson Twp.; ERASTUS.

General geology: Shaver, 1974, p. 95-97; Stout, 1941, p. 265-266.

MIAMI COUNTY
1. Large slightly pink dolomite crystals in *Brassfield Formation* and Dayton Formation. Also calcite, glauconite, and pyrite. Armco, Inc., quarry (formerly Piqua Stone Products Co.), Piqua, W½ sec. 29, Spring Creek Twp.; PIQUA EAST, TROY.

Mineral occurrence: Orton and Peppel, 1906, p. 146.

General geology: Stith, 1983, p. 11-12, 16; Stout, 1941, p. 187-190.

OTTAWA COUNTY
1. Small crystals of gray dolomite in cavities of *Lockport Dolomite* and Greenfield Dolomite; may be associated with celestite. Also calcite, fluorite, galena, gypsum, pyrite, and sphalerite. Edward Kraemer & Sons, Inc., White Rock quarry, Clay Center, SE¼ sec. 9 and NE¼ sec. 16, Allen Twp.; GENOA.

Mineral occurrence: Carman and others, 1962, p. 13-14; Strogonoff, 1966, p. 12.

General geology: Janssens, 1974, p. 82, 84; 1977, p. 22; Sparling, 1965, p. 239-240; 1971, p. 19; Stout, 1941, p. 415-418.

2. Small crystals of gray dolomite in cavities of *Lockport Dolomite* and Greenfield Dolomite. Also asphalt, calcite, celestite, fluorite, pyrite, sphalerite, and sulfur. Stoneco quarry (formerly Maumee Stone Co.), N of Rocky Ridge, sec. 23, Benton Twp.; OAK HARBOR.

General geology: Forsyth, 1971, p. 14; Sparling, 1965, p. 172.

3. Small crystals of light-gray to tan dolomite in cavities of Lockport Dolomite. Also calcite, celestite, fluorite, galena, marcasite, pyrite, and sphalerite. GenLime Group, L. P., quarry (formerly U.S. Gypsum Co.), Genoa, W½ sec. 3, Clay Twp.; GENOA.

Mineral occurrence: Carlson, 1986, p. 4-9; Strogonoff, 1966, p. 18.

General geology: Forsyth, 1971, p. 15-16; Janssens, 1977, p. 3, 22; Sparling, 1965, p. 236-237; Stout, 1941, p. 413-414.

PICKAWAY COUNTY
1. Small crystals and masses of sparry dolomite with marcasite and pyrite in Columbus Limestone. Also calcite. Melvin Stone Co. quarry (formerly F. H. Brewer Co.) about 1 mile E of Crownover Mill on N side of Williamsport-Crownover Mill Rd., N Perry Twp.; CLARKSBURG.

Mineral occurrence: Botoman and Stieglitz, 1978, p. 6, 9.
General geology: Stout, 1941, p. 140-141.

ROSS COUNTY
1. Granular masses of tan dolomite with barite, calcite, and quartz in veins of large limestone concretions from lower Huron Shale Member, Ohio Shale. Also halotrichite-pickeringite, melanterite, and pyrite. Cliff exposure at Copperas Mountain about 1 mile ESE of Seip Mound State Memorial on SE side of Paint Creek, Paxton Twp.; MORGANTOWN.

Mineral occurrence: Bingaman and others, 1978, p. 10; Carlson, 1987b, p. 428.

General geology: Briggs, 1838, p. 77-78; Kepferle and others, 1981, p. 294-295; Orton, 1874, p. 647; Seyfried, 1953, p. 18-25.

SANDUSKY COUNTY
1. Tiny crystals of buff dolomite in cavities of Lockport Dolomite. Also calcite and celestite(?). Steetley Resources, Inc., Ohio Lime Co. quarry, Millersville, secs. 7 and 8, Jackson Twp.; HELENA.

General geology: Janssens, 1974, p. 84; 1977, p. 22.

2. Small crystals of light-gray dolomite in cavities of Lockport Dolomite. Also barite, calcite, celestite, fluorite, galena, pyrite, sphalerite, and strontianite. Martin Marietta Chemicals quarry (S part formerly Woodville Lime & Chemical Co. quarry), Woodville, E½ sec. 21 and W½ sec. 22, Woodville Twp.; ELMORE.

Mineral occurrence: Carlson, 1986, p. 12-13.

General geology: Stout, 1941, p. 375; Summerson and others, 1963, p. 42.

3. Small crystals of rhombohedral light-gray dolomite in cavities of Lockport Dolomite. Also barite, calcite, celestite, fluorite, galena, pyrite, and sphalerite. Steetley Resources, Inc., Ohio Lime Co. quarry, Woodville, W½ sec. 34, Woodville Twp.; ELMORE.

General geology: Floyd, 1971, p. 167-169; Kahle and Floyd, 1968, p. 31-35.

SENECA COUNTY
1. Tiny crystals of buff dolomite with calcite in cavities of Lockport Dolomite or Greenfield Dolomite. Also celestite, fluorite, galena, sphalerite, strontianite, and sulfur. Old quarries at Tiffin, Clinton Twp.; TIFFIN SOUTH.

Mineral occurrence: unpublished information from mineral collection at Heidelberg College.

General geology: Carman, 1927, p. 487; Janssens, 1977, p. 3; Winchell, 1873, p. 616-618.

2. Small crystals of light-gray dolomite in cavities of *Lockport Dolomite* and Greenfield Dolomite. Also calcite, celestite, fluorite, galena, marcasite, pyrite, sphalerite, and strontianite. Maple Grove Stone Co. quarry (formerly Basic Refractories), Maple Grove, sec. 11 and N½ sec. 14, Liberty Twp.; TIFFIN NORTH.

General geology: Floyd, 1971, p. 167, 173-174; Janssens, 1971, p. 35; 1974, p. 82, 84; 1977, p. 3, 22; Stout, 1941, p. 348-349.

VAN WERT COUNTY
1. Tiny crystals of light-gray dolomite in cavities of Tymochtee Dolomite and dolostones of undifferentiated Salina Group. Also calcite, fluorite, pyrite, and sphalerite. Ridge Township Quarry 2 miles W of Middle Point, NE¼ sec. 22, Ridge Twp.; MIDDLE POINT.

General geology: Janssens, 1971, p. 35.

2. Tiny crystals of light-gray dolomite in cavities of dolostones of undifferentiated Salina Group. Also asphalt, calcite, fluorite, pyrite, and sphalerite. Stoneco quarry (formerly Maumee Stone Co.) about 4 miles SW of Scott, sec. 8, Union Twp.; CONVOY.

General geology: Janssens, 1971, p. 35; 1977, p. 3, 29; Stout, 1941, p. 319-320.

3. Crystals of saddle-type pink dolomite in Tymochtee

Dolomite and dolostones of undifferentiated Salina Group. Also asphalt, calcite, fluorite, pyrite, and sphalerite. Suever Stone Co., Inc., quarry (formerly Delphos Quarries Co.), Delphos, sec. 25, Washington Twp.; DELPHOS.
Mineral occurrence: Medici and Robinson, 1988, p. 128.
General geology: Janssens, 1971, p. 35; Stout, 1941, p. 313.

WOOD COUNTY

1. Crystals of saddle-type white and gray dolomite in cavities of dolostones of *Detroit River Group* and Dundee Formation. Also asphalt, barite, calcite, celestite, fluorite, glauconite, hexahydrite, marcasite, pyrite, and sphalerite. France Stone Co. Custar quarry (formerly Pugh Quarry Co.) about 4 miles W of Weston, SW¼ sec. 6, Milton Twp.; MCCLURE.
   Mineral occurrence: Feldmann and others, 1977, p. 35-37; Green, R., 1970a, p. 584; Kessen and others, 1981, p. 913-918; Nelson, 1967, p. 67; Parr and Chang, 1979, p. 31; Strogonoff, 1966, p. 51.
   General geology: Forsyth, 1966a, p. 204-205; Janssens, 1970a, p. 7, 22; Orton and Peppel, 1906, p. 133; Stout, 1941, p. 395-396.
2. Small crystals of tan and gray dolomite alone or with calcite or sphalerite in cavities of *Lockport Dolomite* and Greenfield Dolomite. Also barite, celestite, fluorite, hexahydrite, pyrite, and strontianite. MacRitchie Materials, Inc., quarry (formerly Brough Stone Co.), West Millgrove, SE¼ sec. 4, Perry Twp.; FOSTORIA.
   General geology: Janssens, 1971, p. 35; 1974, p. 82, 84; 1977, p. 22; Shaver, 1977, p. 1414; Stout, 1941, p. 392.
3. Small crystals of light-gray dolomite in cavities of *Lockport Dolomite* and Greenfield Dolomite. Also aragonite, barite, calcite, celestite, fluorite, galena, gypsum, marcasite, pyrite, sphalerite, strontianite, and sulfur. Stoneco quarry (formerly Maumee Stone Co.), Lime City, SW¼ sec. 11, Perrysburg Twp.; ROSSFORD.
   General geology: Janssens, 1971, p. 35; 1974, p. 82, 84; 1977, p. 22; Kahle and Floyd, 1968, p. 28-30; 1972, p. 50-52.
4. Small crystals of light-gray dolomite in cavities of *Lockport Dolomite* and Greenfield Dolomite. Also calcite, celestite, gypsum, sphalerite, and sulfur. Stoneco quarry (formerly Maumee Stone Co.) SE of Portage, sec. 7, Portage Twp.; BOWLING GREEN SOUTH.
   General geology: Floyd, 1971, p. 188; Janssens, 1971, p. 35; 1974, p. 82, 84; 1977, p. 22.

WYANDOT COUNTY

1. Small rhombs of brownish-yellow dolomite in cavities of *Lockport Dolomite* and Greenfield Dolomite. Also calcite, celestite, fluorite, gypsum, pyrite, sphalerite, and strontianite. National Lime & Stone Co. quarry, Carey, N½ sec. 15 and N½ sec. 16, Crawford Twp.; CAREY, MCCUTCHENVILLE.
   General geology: Carlson, 1987c, p. 101-102; Cumings, 1930, p. 201-202; Hall and Alkire, 1956, p. 7, 31-33; Janssens, 1974, p. 82, 84; 1977, p. 22; Stout, 1941, p. 294-295; Summerson and others, 1963, p. 39-40.
2. Small rhombs of buff to light-gray dolomite in cavities of Lockport Dolomite. Also calcite and fluorite. Wyandot Dolomite, Inc., quarry N of Carey on N side of County Hwy. 16, sec. 9, Crawford Twp.; MCCUTCHENVILLE.
   General geology: Cumings, 1930, p. 201-202; Hall and Alkire, 1956, p. 31-33; Janssens, 1977, p. 3.

EPSOMITE
MgSO$_4$ · 7H$_2$O

Chemical class: Sulfate
Crystallization: Orthorhombic; disphenoidal; 222
Habit: Commonly fibrous or acicular crusts; powdery; crystals commonly prismatic
Physical properties: Cleavage: {010} perfect pinacoidal. H: 2-2½. G: 1.7. Luster: vitreous to silky or dull. Color: white, colorless. Streak: white. Taste: bitter and salty
Occurrence: Fibrous crusts rare as efflorescence

SUMMIT COUNTY

1. Efflorescence of fibrous colorless epsomite crystals on Pleistocene glacial outwash deposits. SE side of Cuyahoga River just S of Peck Rd. ½ mile E of Cuyahoga St. junction, North Akron; AKRON WEST.
   General geology: White, G. W., 1953, pl. 6.

FLINT
See QUARTZ

FLUORITE
CaF$_2$

Chemical class: Halide
Crystallization: Isometric; hexoctahedral; m3m
Habit: Commonly well crystallized; cubic crystals common, trapezohedral modifications rare; granular aggregates
Physical properties: Cleavage: {111} perfect octahedral. H: 4. G: 3.2. Luster: vitreous. Color: colorless, yellow, light to dark brown, light to dark purple, pale green; color-zoned crystals with brown cores and colorless rims common. Streak: white. Brown and brownish-yellow fluorite generally fluorescent and phosphorescent
Occurrence: Crystals and granular aggregates common in cavities and fractures of dolostones along the crest and flanks of the Findlay Arch in northwestern Ohio and rare in the vicinity of the Serpent Mound disturbance in southwestern Ohio

ADAMS COUNTY

1. Fluorite with sphalerite and barite in fractures of Silurian dolostones and limestones. Unspecified locations within the Serpent Mound disturbance, Bratton and Franklin Twps.; SINKING SPRING.
   Mineral occurrence: Botoman and Stieglitz, 1978, p. 4-5; Heyl and Van Alstine, 1976, p. 79; Worl and others, 1974, p. 9.
   General geology: Koucky and Reidel, 1987, p. 431-436; Reidel, 1975, map; Reidel and Koucky, 1981, p. 391-403; Reidel and others, 1982, p. 1343-1377.
2. Fluorite in fractures and fossil cavities. Exposures along the Adams County monocline, no specific units or locations mentioned.
   Mineral occurrence: Gailbraith and others, *in* Koucky, 1975, p. 50-51.

ALLEN COUNTY

1. Yellow, brown, and purple fluorite in cavities of Tymochtee Dolomite and dolostones of undifferentiated Salina Group. Also asphalt, calcite, dolomite, pyrite, and sphalerite. National Lime & Stone Co. quarry, Lima, sec. 29, Bath Twp.; LIMA.
   Mineral occurrence: Botoman and Stieglitz, 1978, p. 5; Carlson, 1983, p. 425, 430; Kessen and others, 1981, p. 913-918.
   General geology: Janssens, 1977, p. 3.
2. Crystals of yellow, brown, colorless, and purple fluorite in cavities and fractures of Tymochtee Dolomite and dolostones of undifferentiated Salina Group. Also

calcite, dolomite, pyrite, and sphalerite. Bluffton Stone Co. quarry, Bluffton, NW¼ sec. 12, Richland Twp.; BLUFFTON.
Mineral occurrence: Carlson, 1983, p. 425, 430; Swemba, 1974, p. 5, 18, 22.
General geology: Janssens, 1977, p. 3; Stout, 1941, p. 310.

CRAWFORD COUNTY
1. Crystals of brown fluorite in cavities of *Columbus Limestone* and Delaware Limestone. Also asphalt and calcite. National Lime & Stone Co. quarry, Bucyrus (Spore), secs. 18 and 19, Holmes Twp.; OCEOLA.
General geology: Hall and Alkire, 1956, p. 3, 32-33, 35-36; Janssens, 1970b, p. 3; Stauffer, 1909, p. 109-110; Summerson and others, 1957, p. 59.

ERIE COUNTY
1. Brown and colorless fluorite with calcite in pockets of dolostones of *Detroit River Group* and Columbus and Delaware Limestones. Also celestite, pyrite, and sphalerite. Sandusky Crushed Stone Co. quarry, Parkertown, just S of Portland Rd.; Groton Twp.; BELLEVUE.
Mineral occurrence: Carlson, 1983, p. 425, 430; Nelson, 1967, p. 54.
General geology: Janssens, 1970b, p. 10-12.
2. Small crystals of brown fluorite in pockets of Columbus Limestone. Also calcite. Outcrop along N shore of Kelleys Island just W of N docks, Kelleys Island Twp.; KELLEYS ISLAND.
Mineral occurrence: Carlson, 1983, p. 425, 430.
General geology: Feldmann and Bjerstedt, 1987, p. 395-398; Feldmann and others, 1977, p. 46-47; Fisher, M., 1922, p. 39.
3. Brown and colorless fluorite in pockets of dolostones of Detroit River Group and *Columbus Limestone*. Also calcite. Wagner Quarries Co. Castalia quarry 1½ miles SW of Castalia along E side of Ohio Rte. 101, Margaretta Twp.; CASTALIA.
Mineral occurrence: Carlson, 1983, p. 425, 430; Nelson, 1967, p. 34, 37, 40.
General geology: Forsyth, 1971, p. 9-11; Janssens, 1970b, p. 14-16; Stout, 1941, p. 360-361.
4. Fluorite with calcite in cavities of Bass Islands Dolomite. Small cave about ½ mile S of Crystal Rock along Crystal Rd. near Crystal Cave, NW Margaretta Twp.; CASTALIA.
Mineral occurrence: Carlson, 1983, p. 425, 430.
General geology: Carman, 1927, p. 491; Janssens, 1977, p. 27-30; White, G. W., 1926, p. 86.

HANCOCK COUNTY
1. Brown and yellow fluorite in pockets and fractures of *Tymochtee Dolomite* and dolostones of undifferentiated Salina Group. Also asphalt, calcite, celestite, gypsum, pyrite, and sphalerite. National Lime & Stone Co. quarry, Findlay, sec. 24 and NE¼ sec. 25, Liberty Twp.; FINDLAY.
Mineral occurrence: Carlson, 1983, p. 425, 430; Strogonoff, 1966, p. 57.
General geology: Janssens, 1971, p. 35; Stout, 1941, p. 342-343.
2. Small crystals and large granular masses of brown fluorite with calcite and pyrite in cavities of Tymochtee Dolomite. Also barite and celestite. Tarbox-McCall Stone Co. quarry, Findlay, W½ sec. 24, Liberty Twp.; FINDLAY.
General geology: Janssens, 1977, p. 3.
3. Brown and yellow fluorite in cavities of Tymochtee Dolomite. Also calcite and pyrite. Pifer Stone Co. quarry, Williamstown, SE¼ sec. 24, Madison Twp.; DUNKIRK.
General geology: Janssens, 1977, p. 3; Stout, 1941, p. 338-340.

HARDIN COUNTY
1. Brown, yellow, and purple fluorite in Tymochtee Dolomite. Also asphalt, calcite, dolomite, pyrite, and sphalerite. Hardin Quarry Co. quarry, Blanchard, NW¼ sec. 6, Pleasant Twp.; FORAKER.
Mineral occurrence: Botoman and Stieglitz, 1978, p. 5; Carlson, 1983, p. 425, 430.
General geology: Janssens, 1977, p. 3; Stout, 1941, p. 274-276.

HURON COUNTY
1. Black to colorless fluorite crystals in rock cavities. No specific unit or locality given.
Mineral occurrence: Porter, 1823, p. 247; Silliman, 1822b, p. 255. (Author's note: at the time of the original description, Huron County included the area of Erie County.)

LOGAN COUNTY
1. Brown, yellow, colorless, and purple fluorite in pockets of dolostones of undifferentiated Salina Group. Also asphalt, calcite, dolomite, pyrite, and sphalerite. C. E. Duff & Son, Inc., quarry just E of Ohio Rte. 117 about 2 miles N of Huntsville, Richland Twp.; HUNTSVILLE.
Mineral occurrence: Carlson, 1983, p. 425, 430; Fisher, H. H., 1976, p. 293; Richards and Chamberlain, 1987, p. 391-392.
General geology: Janssens, 1971, p. 35.
2. Pale-yellow and colorless fluorite in cavities of dolostones of undifferentiated Salina Group. Also asphalt, calcite, dolomite, and pyrite. Northwood Stone & Asphalt Co. quarry ½ mile W of Northwood on S side of County Hwy. 105 just W of intersection with County Hwy. 106, Richland Twp.; RUSHSYLVANIA.
General geology: Summerson and others, 1963, p. 37; Stout, 1941, p. 245-247.

LUCAS COUNTY
1. Coatings of fine-grained purple fluorite in fractures of Sylvania Sandstone and dolostones of *Detroit River Group*. Also barite and calcite. France Stone Co. East quarry, Sylvania, W½ sec. 17, Sylvania Twp.; SYLVANIA.
Mineral occurrence: Carlson, 1983, p. 425, 430; Mychkovsky, 1978a, p. 279.
General geology: Ehlers, G. M., and others, 1951, p. 5-7; Strogonoff, 1966, p. 28-30.
2. Small cubes of brown fluorite in cavities, along joints, and as pseudomorphs after gypsum in *Tymochtee Dolomite* and dolostones of undifferentiated Salina Group. Also asphalt, calcite, celestite, halite, pyrite, sphalerite, and sulfur. France Stone Co. quarry, Waterville, secs. 38 and 39, Waterville Twp.; BOWLING GREEN NORTH.
Mineral occurrence: Carlson, 1983, p. 425, 430; Kahle and Floyd, 1972, p. 65-68; Nelson, 1967, p. 81.
General geology: Janssens, 1977, p. 25-30; Kahle and Floyd, 1968, p. 21-24; 1971, p. 2082-2086; Stout, 1941, p. 402-404.
3. Crystals of yellowish-brown or purple fluorite in cavities and breccias of *Lockport Dolomite* and *Greenfield Dolomite*. Also asphalt, calcite, celestite, dolomite, gypsum, pyrite, sphalerite, and sulfur. Stoneco quarry (formerly Maumee Stone Co.), Maumee, sec. 35, Waynesfield Twp.; MAUMEE.
Mineral occurrence: Botoman and Stieglitz, 1978, p. 5; Carlson, 1983, p. 425, 430; Kahle, 1974, p. 34; Kahle and Floyd, 1972, p. 77; Mychkovsky, 1978b, p. 20, 37-38; Strogonoff, 1966, p. 33-35.
General geology: Kahle, 1978, p. 63-115; Summerson and others, 1963, p. 44-45; Textoris and Carozzi, 1966, p. 1375-1388.

4. Brown fluorite in fractures of dolostones of undifferentiated Salina Group. Also calcite, celestite, and gypsum. Outcrop on N side of West Sister Island in Lake Erie; METZGER MARSH.

General geology: Gilbert, 1873, p. 589-590; Herdendorf and Braidech, 1972, p. 9-12; Sparling, 1965, p. 95; 1970, p. 11.

MARION COUNTY

1. Small crystals of yellow fluorite in cavities of *Lockport Dolomite* and Greenfield Dolomite. Also calcite, celestite, dolomite, marcasite, sphalerite, and strontianite. Tri-County Limestone Co. quarry (formerly Laubis Stone Co.) 2 miles SW of Marseilles, center sec. 19, Grand Twp.; MARSEILLES.

General geology: Cumings, 1930, p. 202-203; Hall and Alkire, 1956, p. 5, 32-35; Stith, 1983, p. 15; Stout, 1941, p. 281-282.

2. Granular aggregates of colorless and purple fluorite in cavities of *Columbus Limestone* and Delaware Limestone. Also calcite and pyrite. National Lime & Stone Co. quarry, Marion, secs. 2 and 3, Marion Twp., and sec. 34, Grand Prairie Twp.; MONNETT.

General geology: Hall and Alkire, 1956, p. 5, 32-35; Janssens, 1970b, p. 3.

OTTAWA COUNTY

1. Cubes or granular aggregates of brown and colorless fluorite in cavities of *Lockport Dolomite* and Greenfield Dolomite; may be associated with celestite or sphalerite. Also calcite, dolomite, galena, gypsum, and pyrite. Edward Kraemer & Sons, Inc., White Rock quarry, Clay Center, SE¼ sec. 9 and NE¼ sec. 16, Allen Twp.; GENOA.

Mineral occurrence: Allen, 1952, p. 917-923; Botoman and Stieglitz, 1978, p. 5, 8; Carlson, 1983, p. 425, 430; Carman and others, 1962, p. 13-14; Dana, E. S., 1932, p. 383; Gunnell, 1933, p. 145-146; Howard, 1959, p. 128-130; Kraus and others, 1959, p. 340; Morrison, 1934, p. 16-19; 1935, p. 782-784; Mychkovsky, 1978b, p. 22, 37; Palache and others, 1951, p. 35; Robbins, 1983, p. 72, 103; Roedder, 1967, p. 345-355; 1969, p. 807; 1979, p. 92; Sparling, 1965, p. 171, 239-240; Strogonoff, 1966, p. 12-13; Swemba, 1974, p. 5, 17, 22.

General geology: Janssens, 1974, p. 82, 84; 1977, p. 22; Sparling, 1971, p. 19; Stout, 1941, p. 415-418.

2. Brown and colorless fluorite with celestite in cavities of *Lockport Dolomite* and Greenfield Dolomite. Also asphalt, calcite, dolomite, pyrite, sphalerite, and sulfur. Stoneco quarry (formerly Maumee Stone Co.) N of Rocky Ridge, sec. 23, Benton Twp.; OAK HARBOR.

Mineral occurrence: Botoman and Stieglitz, 1978, p. 6; Carlson, 1983, p. 425, 430; Mychkovsky, 1978b, p. 37-38.

General geology: Forsyth, 1971, p. 14; Sparling, 1965, p. 172.

3. Yellow fluorite in dolostones of undifferentiated Salina Group and *Bass Islands Dolomite*. Also calcite, celestite, and gypsum. Cliff exposure on NW edge of Catawba Island, Catawba Island Twp.; GYPSUM.

Mineral occurrence: Mychkovsky, 1978b, p. 37-38.

General geology: Carman, 1927, p. 488-491; Janssens, 1977, p. 27-30; Sparling, 1970, p. 3, 19-21; 1971, p. 19-22.

4. Crystals of brown, brownish-yellow, and colorless fluorite with calcite in vugs of Lockport Dolomite. Also celestite, dolomite, galena, marcasite, pyrite, and sphalerite. GenLime Group, L. P., quarry (formerly U.S. Gypsum Co.), Genoa, W½ sec. 3, Clay Twp.; GENOA.

Mineral occurrence: Carlson, 1983, p. 425, 430; 1986, p. 4-9; Sparling, 1965, p. 171, 236-237; Strogonoff, 1966, p. 18.

General geology: Forsyth, 1971, p. 15; Janssens, 1977, p. 3, 22; Stout, 1941, p. 413-414.

5. Fluorite in Lockport Dolomite. Also sphalerite. Old Purtee quarry, Genoa, S½NE¼ sec. 4, Clay Twp.; GENOA.

Mineral occurrence: Botoman and Stieglitz, 1978, p. 6; Carlson, 1983, p. 425, 430; Green, R., 1970a, p. 585.

6. Brown fluorite in cavities and fractures of Bass Islands Dolomite. Also barite, calcite, celestite, and pyrite. Fox Stone Products, Inc., quarry, N side of Langram Rd., S part of South Bass Island, Put-in-Bay Twp.; PUT-IN-BAY.

General geology: Janssens, 1977, p. 27-30; Sparling, 1971, p. 19-22.

7. Small crystals of brown fluorite in Bass Islands Dolomite. South Bass Island, no specific locality given, Put-in-Bay Twp.; PUT-IN-BAY.

Mineral occurrence: Kindt, 1952, p. 256.

General geology: Janssens, 1977, p. 27-30; Mohr, 1931, p. 28.

8. Brown fluorite with celestite in Bass Islands Dolomite. Rattlesnake Island, about 1 mile W of Middle Bass Island, Put-in-Bay Twp.; PUT-IN-BAY.

Mineral occurrence: Carlson, 1983, p. 425, 430; Hamilton, 1953, p. 134; Newberry, 1874b, p. 203.

General geology: Janssens, 1977, p. 27-30; Sparling, 1970, p. 3, 14.

PAULDING COUNTY

1. Iridescent brown, colorless, and purple fluorite in cavities and fractures of dolostones of *Detroit River Group* and Dundee Formation; may be associated with calcite. Also asphalt, pyrite, quartz, and sphalerite. Stoneco Auglaize quarry (formerly Maumee Stone Co.), Junction, NW¼ sec. 32, Auglaize Twp.; JUNCTION.

Mineral occurrence: Botoman and Stieglitz, 1978, p. 6; Carlson, 1983, p. 425, 430; Feldmann and others, 1977, p. 32-33; Kessen and others, 1981, p. 913-918; Kyte, 1962, p. 27; Nelson, 1967, p. 43; Strogonoff, 1966, p. 61; Swemba, 1974, p. 5, 17, 22.

General geology: Janssens, 1970a, p. 21; Stauffer, 1909, p. 152-153; Stout, 1941, p. 324-325.

PUTNAM COUNTY

1. Fluorite in Tymochtee Dolomite and dolostones of undifferentiated Salina Group. Also calcite, pyrite, and sphalerite. Ottawa Stone Co., Inc., quarry, W½ sec. 27, Blanchard Twp.; LEIPSIC.

Mineral occurrence: Botoman and Stieglitz, 1978, p. 6; Carlson, 1983, p. 425, 430.

General geology: Janssens, 1971, p. 35; 1977, p. 29.

2. Brownish-yellow fluorite in Tymochtee Dolomite and dolostones of undifferentiated Salina Group. Also asphalt, calcite, pyrite, and sphalerite. Putnam Stone Co. quarry, NW¼ sec. 6, Riley Twp.; BLUFFTON.

Mineral occurrence: Botoman and Stieglitz, 1978, p. 6; Carlson, 1983, p. 425, 430.

General geology: Janssens, 1971, p. 35; 1977, p. 29.

3. Fluorite in Tymochtee Dolomite and dolostones of undifferentiated Salina Group. Also calcite and sphalerite. National Lime & Stone Co. quarry, Rimer, secs. 6, 7, and 8, Sugar Creek Twp.; KALIDA.

Mineral occurrence: Carlson, 1983, p. 425, 430; Chesterman, 1978, p. 428.

General geology: Janssens, 1971, p. 35; 1977, p. 29; Stith, 1983, p. 11-13; Stout, 1941, p. 327-328.

SANDUSKY COUNTY

1. Crystals of brown fluorite in cavities of Lockport Dolomite. Steetley Resources, Inc., quarry (formerly National Gypsum Co.) NE of Gibsonburg, sec. 13, Madison Twp.; ELMORE.

Mineral occurrence: Carlson, 1983, p. 425, 430; Mychkovsky, 1978b, p. 21, 22, 37.
General geology: Janssens, 1977, p. 3, 22; Stout, 1941, p. 372-373.

2. Crystals of iridescent brown and purple fluorite in pockets and fractures of Lockport Dolomite; may be associated with sphalerite. Also calcite, celestite, and galena. Charles Pfizer & Co., Inc., quarry NW of Gibsonburg, sec. 14, Madison Twp.; ELMORE.
Mineral occurrence: Botoman, 1975, p. 45-46; Botoman and Faure, 1976, p. 69; Botoman and Stieglitz, 1978, p. 6, 8; Carlson, 1983, p. 425, 430; Gettings, 1950, p. 601; Haden, 1977, p. 24-25; Strogonoff, 1966, p. 53; Swemba, 1974, p. 5, 18, 22.
General geology: Floyd, 1971, p. 167; Janssens, 1977, p. 3, 22; Stith, 1983, p. 11-13.

3. Crystals of brown and colorless fluorite with celestite in fractures and vugs of Lockport Dolomite. Also barite, calcite, dolomite, galena, pyrite, sphalerite, and strontianite. Martin Marietta Chemicals quarry (S part formerly Woodville Lime & Chemical Co. quarry), Woodville, E½ sec. 21 and W½ sec. 22, Woodville Twp.; ELMORE.
Mineral occurrence: Botoman and Stieglitz, 1978, p. 6; Carlson, 1983, p. 425, 430; 1986, p. 9-13; Gettings, 1952a, p. 142; Mychkovsky, 1978b, p. 37, 53, 57; Swemba, 1974, p. 5, 17, 22.
General geology: Stout, 1941, p. 375; Summerson and others, 1963, p. 42.

4. Brown fluorite in cavities of Lockport Dolomite. Also barite, calcite, celestite, dolomite, galena, pyrite, and sphalerite. Steetley Resources, Inc., Ohio Lime Co. quarry, Woodville, W½ sec. 34, Woodville Twp.; ELMORE.
Mineral occurrence: Botoman and Stieglitz, 1978, p. 6; Carlson, 1983, p. 425, 430; Gettings, 1954, p. 259; Haden, 1977, p. 24-25; Mychkovsky, 1978b, p. 37-38, 53, 56.
General geology: Floyd, 1971, p. 167-169; Kahle and Floyd, 1968, p. 31-33.

5. Iridescent brown, colorless, and purple fluorite in cavities of dolostones of *Detroit River Group* and Columbus Limestone; may be associated with calcite. France Stone Co. quarry, Bellevue, N-central sec. 25, York Twp.; BELLEVUE.
Mineral occurrence: Carlson, 1983, p. 425, 430; Haden, 1977, p. 24-25; Nelson, 1967, p. 24.
General geology: Janssens, 1970b, p. 18-19; Stauffer, 1909, p. 114; Stout, 1941, p. 380; Summerson and others, 1957, p. 59; Winchell, 1873, p. 604-605.

SENECA COUNTY
1. Crystals of iridescent brown and yellow fluorite with celestite in cavities of Lockport Dolomite or Greenfield Dolomite. Also calcite, dolomite, galena, sphalerite, strontianite, and sulfur. Old quarries at Tiffin, Clinton Twp.; TIFFIN SOUTH.
Mineral occurrence: Carlson, 1983, p. 425, 430; Dana, E. S., and Ford, 1932, p. 464; Palache and others, 1951, p. 35; also unpublished information from mineral collection at Heidelberg College.
General geology: Carman, 1927, p. 487; Janssens, 1977, p. 3; Winchell, 1873, p. 616-618.

2. Iridescent brown and colorless fluorite in *Lockport Dolomite* and Greenfield Dolomite; may be associated with celestite. Also calcite, dolomite, galena, marcasite, pyrite, sphalerite, and strontianite. Maple Grove Stone Co. quarry (formerly Basic Refractories), Maple Grove, sec. 11 and N½ sec. 14, Liberty Twp.; TIFFIN NORTH.
Mineral occurrence: Carlson, 1983, p. 425, 430.
General geology: Floyd, 1971, p. 167, 173-174; Janssens, 1971, p. 35; 1974, p. 82, 84; 1977, p. 3, 22; Stout, 1941, p. 348-349.

UNION COUNTY
1. Fine-grained purple fluorite with calcite in cavities of Columbus Limestone. Also asphalt and marcasite. Union Aggregates Co. quarry 3½ miles S of Ostrander on E side of County Rd. 96, Mill Creek Twp.; SHAWNEE HILLS.
General geology: Janssens, 1970b, p. 3; Stout, 1941, p. 239.

VAN WERT COUNTY
1. Brown and colorless fluorite in Tymochtee Dolomite and dolostones of undifferentiated Salina Group. Also calcite, dolomite, pyrite, and sphalerite. Ridge Township Quarry 2 miles W of Middle Point, NE¼ sec. 22, Ridge Twp.; MIDDLE POINT.
Mineral occurrence: Botoman and Stieglitz, 1978, p. 6; Carlson, 1983, p. 425, 430.
General geology: Janssens, 1971, p. 35; 1977, p. 3, 29.

2. Crystals and granular masses of colorless and yellowish-brown fluorite in cavities of dolostones of undifferentiated Salina Group. Also asphalt, calcite, dolomite, pyrite, and sphalerite. Stoneco quarry (formerly Maumee Stone Co.) about 4 miles SW of Scott, sec. 8, Union Twp.; CONVOY.
General geology: Janssens, 1971, p. 35; 1977, p. 3, 29; Stout, 1941, p. 319-320.

3. Brown, yellow, colorless, and purple fluorite in Tymochtee Dolomite and dolostones of undifferentiated Salina Group. Also asphalt, calcite, dolomite, pyrite, and sphalerite. Suever Stone Co., Inc., quarry (formerly Delphos Quarries Co.), Delphos, sec. 25, Washington Twp.; DELPHOS.
Mineral occurrence: Botoman and Stieglitz, 1978, p. 6; Carlson, 1983, p. 425, 430; Medici and Robinson, 1988, p. 128; Wilson, W. E., 1987, p. 361.
General geology: Janssens, 1971, p. 35; 1977, p. 3, 29; Stout, 1941, p. 313.

WOOD COUNTY
1. Fluorite in Tymochtee Dolomite. Also calcite, gypsum, marcasite, pyrite, and sphalerite. France Stone Co. North Baltimore quarry, W½ sec. 26, Henry Twp.; NORTH BALTIMORE.
Mineral occurrence: Botoman and Stieglitz, 1978, p. 6; Carlson, 1983, p. 425, 430.
General geology: Janssens, 1971, p. 35; 1977, p. 26; Kahle and Floyd, 1972, p. 46-48; Stout, 1941, p. 394-395.

2. Colorless and brown fluorite with calcite in cavities of dolostones of *Detroit River Group* and Dundee Formation. Also asphalt, barite, celestite, dolomite, glauconite, hexahydrite, marcasite, pyrite, and sphalerite. France Stone Co. Custar quarry (formerly Pugh Quarry Co.) about 4 miles W of Weston, SW¼ sec. 6, Milton Twp.; MCCLURE.
Mineral occurrence: Bingaman and others, 1978, p. 18; Botoman and Stieglitz, 1978, p. 6; Carlson, 1983, p. 425, 430; Feldmann and others, 1977, p. 32-33; Forsyth, 1966a, p. 204-205; Gettings, 1950, p. 601; Green, R., 1970a, p. 584; Kessen and others, 1981, p. 913-918; Mychkovsky, 1978b, p. 22, 56; Nelson, 1967, p. 67; Parr and Chang, 1979, p. 31; Robbins, 1983, p. 72; Strogonoff, 1966, p. 51; Swemba, 1974, p. 5, 17, 22.
General geology: Janssens, 1970a, p. 7, 22; Orton and Peppel, 1906, p. 133; Stout, 1941, p. 395-396.

3. Brown fluorite in cavities and fractures of *Lockport Dolomite* and Greenfield Dolomite. Also barite, calcite, celestite, dolomite, hexahydrite, pyrite, sphalerite, and strontianite. MacRitchie Materials, Inc., quarry

(formerly Brough Stone Co.), West Millgrove, SE¼ sec. 4, Perry Twp.; FOSTORIA.
Mineral occurrence: Carlson, 1983, p. 425, 430; Mychkovsky, 1978b, p. 22, 37.
General geology: Janssens, 1971, p. 35; 1974, p. 82, 84; 1977, p. 22; Shaver, 1977, p. 1414; Stout, 1941, p. 392.
4. Crystals of brown and colorless fluorite with calcite and celestite in vugs and fractures of *Lockport Dolomite* and *Greenfield Dolomite*. Also aragonite, barite, dolomite, galena, gypsum, marcasite, pyrite, sphalerite, strontianite, and sulfur. Stoneco quarry (formerly Maumee Stone Co.), Lime City, SW¼ sec. 11, Perrysburg Twp.; ROSSFORD.
Mineral occurrence: Botoman and Stieglitz, 1978, p. 6; Carlson, 1983, p. 425, 430; Green, R., 1970a, p. 584; Mychkovsky, 1978b, p. 23, 37; Strogonoff, 1966, p. 46; Wilson, W. E., 1987, p. 361.
General geology: Janssens, 1971, p. 35; 1974, p. 82, 84; 1977, p. 22; Kahle and Floyd, 1968, p. 28-30; 1972, p. 50-52.

WYANDOT COUNTY
1. Brown fluorite in cavities of *Lockport Dolomite* and Greenfield Dolomite. Also calcite, celestite, dolomite, gypsum, pyrite, sphalerite, and strontianite. National Lime & Stone Co. quarry, Carey, N½ sec. 15 and N½ sec. 16, Crawford Twp.; CAREY, MCCUTCHENVILLE.
General geology: Carlson, 1987c, p. 101-102; Cumings, 1930, p. 201-202; Hall and Alkire, 1956, p. 7, 31-33; Janssens, 1974, p. 82, 84; 1977, p. 22; Stout, 1941, p. 294-295; Summerson and others, 1963, p. 39-40.
2. Brown and yellow fluorite in cavities of Lockport Dolomite. Also calcite and dolomite. Wyandot Dolomite, Inc., quarry N of Carey on N side of County Hwy. 16, sec. 9, Crawford Twp.; MCCUTCHENVILLE.
General geology: Cumings, 1930, p. 201-202; Hall and Alkire, 1956, p. 31-33; Janssens, 1977, p. 3.

GALENA
PbS

Chemical class: Sulfide
Crystallization: Isometric; hexoctahedral; m3m
Habit: Commonly well crystallized; cubic crystals; granular aggregates
Physical properties: Cleavage: {001} perfect cubic. H: 2½. G: 7.5. Luster: metallic. Color: lead gray. Streak: lead gray
Occurrence: Crystals and granular aggregates in cavities and fractures of dolostones along the crest and flanks of the Findlay Arch in northwestern Ohio; rare in veins of ironstone concretions from black shales in eastern Ohio

COSHOCTON COUNTY
1. Galena as fossil replacements or in isolated crystals in Logan Formation. No specific locality given.
Mineral occurrence: Hodge, 1878, p. 565.
General geology: Lamborn, 1954, p. 29-30.

DELAWARE COUNTY
1. Galena in Berea Sandstone. Exposure along Big Walnut Creek near Sunbury, Berkshire Twp.; SUNBURY.
Mineral occurrence: Haden, 1977, p. 25, 28.
General geology: Westgate, 1926, p. 41-42.

GALLIA COUNTY
1. Galena on N side of Ohio River between Indian Wheeling and Campaign Creeks near Gallipolis.
Mineral occurrence: Cleaveland, 1822, p. 632.

LICKING AND MUSKINGUM COUNTIES
1. Galena on S side of Licking Creek between Newark and Zanesville.
Mineral occurrence: Cleaveland, 1822, p. 632.

OTTAWA COUNTY
1. Crystals and granular aggregates of galena in cavities of *Lockport Dolomite* and Greenfield Dolomite; may be associated with calcite. Also celestite, dolomite, fluorite, gypsum, pyrite, and sphalerite. Edward Kraemer & Sons, Inc., White Rock quarry, Clay Center, SE¼ sec. 9 and NE¼ sec. 16, Allen Twp.; GENOA.
Mineral occurrence: Botoman, 1975, p. 46; Botoman and Faure, 1976, p. 69; Botoman and Stieglitz, 1978, p. 5, 8; Carlson, 1983, p. 427, 430; Haden, 1977, p. 25, 28; Mychkovsky, 1978b, p. 27-28; Strogonoff, 1966, p. 15.
General geology: Carman and others, 1962, p. 13-14; Janssens, 1974, p. 82, 84; 1977, p. 22; Sparling, 1965, p. 239-240; 1971, p. 19; Stout, 1941, p. 415-418.
2. Small galena crystals in cavities and fractures of Lockport Dolomite. Also calcite, celestite, dolomite, fluorite, marcasite, pyrite, and sphalerite. GenLime Group, L. P., quarry (formerly U.S. Gypsum Co.), Genoa, W½ sec. 3, Clay Twp.; GENOA.
Mineral occurrence: Carlson, 1983, p. 427, 430; 1986, p. 4-9.
General geology: Forsyth, 1971, p. 15-16; Janssens, 1977, p. 3, 22; Sparling, 1965, p. 236-237; Stout, 1941, p. 413-414.

SANDUSKY COUNTY
1. Galena crystals with fluorite in veins of Lockport Dolomite. Also calcite, celestite, and sphalerite. Charles Pfizer & Co., Inc., quarry NW of Gibsonburg, sec. 14, Madison Twp.; ELMORE.
Mineral occurrence: Botoman, 1975, p. 46; Botoman and Faure, 1976, p. 69; Botoman and Stieglitz, 1978, p. 6, 8; Carlson, 1983, p. 427, 430; Haden, 1977, p. 25, 28.
General geology: Floyd, 1971, p. 167; Janssens, 1977, p. 3, 22; Stith, 1983, p. 11-13.
2. Galena in *Lockport Dolomite* and Greenfield Dolomite. Also celestite. Gottron Bros. Co. quarry, Fremont, secs. 32 and 33, Sandusky Twp.; FREMONT WEST.
Mineral occurrence: Winchell, 1873, p. 601-602.
General geology: Janssens, 1971, p. 35; 1974, p. 82, 84; 1977, p. 3, 22; Stout, 1941, p. 368-369.
3. Galena crystals in cavities of Lockport Dolomite. Also barite, calcite, celestite, dolomite, fluorite, pyrite, sphalerite, and strontianite. Martin Marietta Chemicals quarry (S part formerly Woodville Lime & Chemical Co. quarry), Woodville, E½ sec. 21 and W½ sec. 22, Woodville Twp.; ELMORE.
Mineral occurrence: Carlson, 1983, p. 427, 430; 1986, p. 9-13.
General geology: Stout, 1941, p. 375; Summerson and others, 1963, p. 42.
4. Galena in Lockport Dolomite. Also barite, calcite, celestite, dolomite, fluorite, pyrite, and sphalerite. Steetley Resources, Inc., Ohio Lime Co. quarry, Woodville, W½ sec. 34, Woodville Twp.; ELMORE.
Mineral occurrence: Botoman, 1975, p. 46; Botoman and Stieglitz, 1978, p. 6, 8; Carlson, 1983, p. 427, 430.
General geology: Floyd, 1971, p. 167-169; Kahle and Floyd, 1968, p. 31-35.

SENECA COUNTY
1. Granular masses of galena in Lockport Dolomite or Greenfield Dolomite. Also calcite, celestite, dolomite, fluorite, sphalerite, strontianite, and sulfur. Old quarries at Tiffin, Clinton Twp.; TIFFIN SOUTH.
Mineral occurrence: Carlson, 1983, p. 427, 430; Winchell, 1873, p. 616-617; also unpublished information from mineral collection at Heidelberg College.
General geology: Carman, 1927, p. 487; Janssens, 1977, p. 3.

2. Granular masses of galena in *Lockport Dolomite* and Greenfield Dolomite. Also calcite, celestite, dolomite, fluorite, marcasite, pyrite, sphalerite, and strontianite. Maple Grove Stone Co. quarry (formerly Basic Refractories), Maple Grove, sec. 11 and N½ sec. 14, Liberty Twp.; TIFFIN NORTH.
   Mineral occurrence: Carlson, 1983, p. 427, 430.
   General geology: Floyd, 1971, p. 167, 173-174; Janssens, 1971, p. 35; 1974, p. 82, 84; 1977, p. 3, 22; Stout, 1941, p. 348-349.

VINTON COUNTY
1. Small crystals of galena in Vanport limestone, Allegheny Group. Also calcite, pyrite, quartz, and sphalerite. No specific localities given.
   Mineral occurrence: Stout, 1927, p. 265-266.
   General geology: Lamborn, 1951, p. 344-349.

WAYNE COUNTY
1. Galena with barite, calcite, chalcopyrite, pyrite, and sphalerite in veins of septarian ironstone concretions from shales of lower Pottsville Group. Penn Central Railroad cut N of Marshallville, W-central sec. 33, Chippewa Twp.; DOYLESTOWN.
   Mineral occurrence: Ver Steeg, 1942, p. 223.
   General geology: Conrey, 1921, p. 92; Ver Steeg, 1948, p. 185.
2. Galena crystals in shale, as fossil fillings, and with calcite, pyrite, and sphalerite in veins of ironstone nodules from shales of Wooster Shale Member, Cuyahoga Formation. Also aragonite. Old quarry E of County Rd. 22 behind City of Wooster Service and Maintenance Facility, NE¼ sec. 5, Wooster Twp.; WOOSTER.
   Mineral occurrence: Ver Steeg, 1940, p. 259.
   General geology: Conrey, 1921, p. 62-63; Szmuc, 1957, p. 193-195.

WOOD COUNTY
1. Galena in *Lockport Dolomite* and Greenfield Dolomite. Also aragonite, barite, calcite, celestite, dolomite, fluorite, gypsum, marcasite, pyrite, sphalerite, strontianite, and sulfur. Stoneco quarry (formerly Maumee Stone Co.), Lime City, SW¼ sec. 11, Perrysburg Twp.; ROSSFORD.
   Mineral occurrence: Botoman and Stieglitz, 1978, p. 6; Carlson, 1983, p. 427, 430; Haden, 1977, p. 25, 28.
   General geology: Janssens, 1971, p. 35; 1974, p. 82, 84; 1977, p. 22; Kahle and Floyd, 1968, p. 28-30; 1972, p. 50-52.

GLAUCONITE
K(Fe,Mg,Al)$_2$Si$_4$O$_{10}$(OH)$_2$

Chemical class: Silicate
Crystallization: Monoclinic; domatic or prismatic; m or 2/m
Habit: Almost always massive; granules or scales
Physical properties: Cleavage: {001} perfect pinacoidal. H: 2. G: 2.9. Luster: dull. Color: green to greenish black. Streak: green
Occurrence: Common in Ohio's marine sedimentary rocks, but rarely concentrated in relatively pure masses; forms green films along bedding planes of dolostones and limestones of western Ohio

MIAMI COUNTY
1. Partings of bright-green glauconite in *Brassfield Formation* and Dayton Formation. Also calcite, dolomite, and pyrite. Armco, Inc., quarry (formerly Piqua Stone Products Co.), Piqua, W½ sec. 29, Spring Creek Twp.; PIQUA EAST, TROY.
   General geology: Stith, 1983, p. 11-12, 16; Stout, 1941, p. 187-190.

WOOD COUNTY
1. Platy films of relatively pure bright-green glauconite in dolostones of *Detroit River Group* and Dundee Formation. Also asphalt, barite, calcite, celestite, dolomite, fluorite, hexahydrite, marcasite, pyrite, and sphalerite. France Stone Co. Custar quarry (formerly Pugh Quarry Co.) about 4 miles W of Weston, SW¼ sec. 6, Milton Twp.; MCCLURE.
   General geology: Forsyth, 1966a, p. 204-205; Janssens, 1970a, p. 7, 22; Orton and Peppel, 1906, p. 133; Stout, 1941, p. 395-396.

GOLD
Au

Chemical class: Native element
Crystallization: Isometric; hexoctahedral; m3m
Habit: Crystals generally octahedral; also massive, dendritic; commonly in scales when released from rock or sediment
Physical properties: Fracture: irregular. H: 2½-3. G: 19.3. Luster: metallic. Color: gold yellow. Streak: gold yellow
Occurrence: Small amounts in glacial deposits, especially outwash gravels and till of Illinoian age; probably present in any glaciated county in Ohio, although sites along the glacial boundary appear to be most favorable

BROWN COUNTY
1. Gold in Illinoian glacial gravels near the glacial boundary. No specific localities given.
   Mineral occurrence: Hansen, 1985b, p. 3; Wright, 1890, p. 104-105.
   General geology: Goldthwait and others, 1961, map.

CARROLL COUNTY
1. Gold in glacial gravels. Sandy Creek, no specific localities given, Brown Twp.; MALVERN, MINERVA.
   Mineral occurrence: Bingaman and others, 1978, p. 8; Hansen, 1985b, p. 3, 6.
   General geology: Goldthwait and others, 1961, map; White, G. W., 1982, pl. 1.

CLERMONT COUNTY
1. Gold in Illinoian glacial gravels. East Fork Little Miami River near Batavia, Batavia Twp.; BATAVIA.
   Mineral occurrence: Hansen, 1985b, p. 3-5; Reidel and Koucky, 1981, p. 396; Roudebush, 1880, p. 20-21.
   General geology: Goldthwait and others, 1961, map; Orton, 1873, p. 436.
2. Gold in Illinoian glacial gravels. Stonelick Creek and Brushy Fork of Stonelick Creek about 1 mile N of Owensville, Stonelick Twp.; GOSHEN.
   Mineral occurrence: Caster and others, 1970, p. 15-16; Hansen, 1985b, p. 5; Maslowski, 1986, p. 20-22; Wuestner, 1938, p. 264.
   General geology: Goldthwait and others, 1961, map.
3. Gold in Illinoian glacial gravels. Stonelick Creek near Newtonsville, Wayne Twp.; NEWTONSVILLE.
   Mineral occurrence: Bingaman and others, 1978, p. 8.
   General geology: Goldthwait and others, 1961, map.
4. Gold in Illinoian glacial gravels. Deep gullies and old mine workings about 1 mile SW of Williamsburg, Williamsburg Twp.; WILLIAMSBURG.
   Mineral occurrence: Hansen, 1985b, p. 3-5; Newberry, 1874a, p. 71; Orton, 1873, p. 441; Wuestner, 1938, p. 263-264.
   General geology: Goldthwait and others, 1961, map.
5. Gold in Illinoian glacial gravels near the glacial boundary. No specific localities given.
   Mineral occurrence: Wright, 1890, p. 104-105.
   General geology: Goldthwait and others, 1961, map.

KNOX COUNTY
1. Gold in Illinoian glacial gravels. Northern Knox County near Bellville (Richland County), no specific localities given.
   Mineral occurrence: Hansen, 1985b, p. 3; Newberry, 1874a, p. 70; Wright, 1890, p. 104-105.
   General geology: Goldthwait and others, 1961, map.

LICKING COUNTY
1. Gold in Illinoian glacial gravels. Gully on a hillside about 1 mile N of Brownsville, Bowling Green Twp.; GLENFORD.
   Mineral occurrence: Andrews, 1871, p. 138-139; Hansen, 1985b, p. 3; Newberry, 1874a, p. 70; Smith, C. M., 1885, p. 859.
   General geology: Forsyth, 1966b, map; Goldthwait and others, 1961, map.
2. Gold in Illinoian glacial gravels. Gullies cutting glacial terraces about 1½ miles SE of Newark, Newark Twp.; NEWARK.
   Mineral occurrence: Andrews, 1871, p. 139; Hansen, 1985b, p. 3; Newberry, 1874a, p. 70.
   General geology: Forsyth, 1966b, map; Goldthwait and others, 1961, map.
3. Gold in Illinoian glacial gravels near the glacial boundary. No specific localities given.
   Mineral occurrence: Wright, 1890, p. 104-105.
   General geology: Forsyth, 1966b, map; Goldthwait and others, 1961, map.

MAHONING COUNTY
1. Gold in Wisconsinan glacial gravels. Middle Fork Little Beaver Creek about 1 mile E of Salem, Green Twp.; SALEM.
   Mineral occurrence: Hansen, 1985b, p. 3.
   General geology: Goldthwait and others, 1961, map; White, G. W., 1982, pl. 1.

RICHLAND COUNTY
1. Gold in Illinoian glacial gravels. Clear Fork Mohican River and its tributaries including Deadman's Run and Steltz's Run N of Bellville, Wildcat Hollow SE of Gatton Rock, and Gold Run near Butler, Jefferson and Worthington Twps.; BUTLER, LUCAS, MANSFIELD SOUTH.
   Mineral occurrence: Baughman, 1904, p. 84; Hansen, 1985b, p. 3-5; Read, 1878a, p. 314-315; Totten, 1973, p. 49.
   General geology: Goldthwait and others, 1961, map.

ROSS COUNTY
1. Gold in glacial gravels. Buckskin Creek S of Humboldt, junction of Paint and Paxton Twps.; SOUTH SALEM, BAINBRIDGE.
   Mineral occurrence: Hansen, 1985b, p. 3.
   General geology: Goldthwait and others, 1961, map; Quinn and Goldthwait, 1985, pl. 1.
2. Gold in glacial gravels. Paint Creek and its tributaries in Bainbridge-Chillicothe area, Paint, Paxton, Twin, and Union Twps.
   Mineral occurrence: Bingaman and others, 1978, p. 8; Hansen, 1985b, p. 3.
   General geology: Goldthwait and others, 1961, map; Quinn and Goldthwait, 1985, pl. 1.

SENECA COUNTY
1. Gold in Wisconsinan glacial gravels. Honey Creek, no specific localities given, Eden and Bloom Twps.; TIFFIN SOUTH, BLOOMVILLE.
   Mineral occurrence: Bingaman and others, 1978, p. 8; Hansen, 1985b, p. 3.
   General geology: Goldthwait and others, 1961, map.

WARREN COUNTY
1. Gold in glacial gravels. No specific localities given.
   Mineral occurrence: Hansen, 1985b, p. 3; Newberry, 1874a, p. 71; Orton, 1873, p. 441.
   General geology: Goldthwait and others, 1961, map.

GYPSUM (SELENITE)
$CaSO_4 \cdot 2H_2O$

Chemical class: Sulfate
Crystallization: Monoclinic; prismatic; 2/m
Habit: Commonly well crystallized, prismatic or tabular; may form rosettes; also commonly massive
Physical properties: Cleavage: {010} perfect pinacoidal, {100} distinct pinacoidal, and {011} distinct prismatic. H: 2. G: 2.3. Luster: vitreous to silky if well crystallized, dull if massive. Color: white, gray, colorless. Streak: white. May be fluorescent
Varieties: Coarsely crystalline transparent gypsum is known as selenite
Occurrence: Massive beds, nodules, crystals, and molds of crystals of evaporite origin in bedded dolostones in north-central Ohio; selenite crystals in glacial lake beds of bluish-gray silts and clays in northeastern Ohio; finely granular gypsum common as efflorescence on shales and sandstones

ATHENS COUNTY
1. Selenite rosettes in black shale partings of the Lower Kittanning (No. 5) coal, Allegheny Group. Also melanterite and pyrite. Exposures along Twp. Hwy. 276 and in abandoned mines, SW¼ sec. 24 and NW¼ sec. 23, York Twp.; NELSONVILLE (ATHENS 15-minute).
   Mineral occurrence: Sturgeon and associates, 1958, p. 558-559.

COLUMBIANA COUNTY
1. Gypsum as an efflorescence with copiapite on Lower Kittanning (No. 5) coal, Allegheny Group. Also barite, calcite, chalcopyrite, kaolinite, pyrite, sphalerite, and wurtzite. Metrel, Inc., quarry S of Negley, sec. 13, Middleton Twp.; EAST PALESTINE.
   General geology: Stout and Lamborn, 1924, p. 111.

CUYAHOGA COUNTY
1. Selenite crystals in glacial lake beds of gray to brown silt and clay. General Sand Products, Inc., gravel pit W of intersection of Riverview and Snowville Rds., E Brecksville Twp.; NORTHFIELD.
   Mineral occurrence: Wittine, 1970, p. 63.
   General geology: White, G. W., 1953, p. 23.
2. Gypsum as an efflorescence on *Cleveland Shale Member, Ohio Shale* and *Berea Sandstone*. Outcrops on N side of Chippewa Creek S of Ohio Rte. 82 bridge, Brecksville Reservation, E Brecksville Twp.; NORTHFIELD.
   Mineral occurrence: Connors, 1974, p. 37.
   General geology: Kent State University, *in* Frank, 1969, p. 1.4-1.9.
3. Efflorescence of white gypsum with hexahydrite on Berea Sandstone. Outcrop on S side of Chippewa Creek just S of Ohio Rte. 82 bridge, Brecksville Reservation, E Brecksville Twp.; NORTHFIELD.
   Mineral occurrence: Connors, 1974, p. 37.
   General geology: Kent State University, *in* Frank, 1969, p. 1.4-1.9.
4. Selenite crystals in lake beds of blue clay. Cliff exposures along shore of Lake Erie at Euclid, Euclid Twp.; EAST CLEVELAND.
   Mineral occurrence: Anonymous, 1936, p. 462; Greene, 1937, p. 273.
   General geology: Cushing and others, 1931, p. 81, 104-105; Newberry, 1873b, p. 174-177.

DELAWARE COUNTY
1. Flattened crystals of gypsum on parting planes of Ohio Shale. No specific localities given.
   Mineral occurrence: Westgate, 1926, p. 63.

ERIE COUNTY
1. Massive gypsum beds in dolostones of undifferentiated Salina Group. Abandoned mine 2½ miles NW of Castalia, Margaretta Twp.; CASTALIA.
   Mineral occurrence: Bownocker, 1920, p. 220, 223; Janssens, 1977, p. 36-38; Lintner, 1944, p. 24; Withington, 1962, p. 10.

HANCOCK COUNTY
1. Molds of gypsum crystals in *Tymochtee Dolomite* and dolostones of undifferentiated Salina Group. Also asphalt, calcite, celestite, fluorite, pyrite, and sphalerite. National Lime & Stone Co. quarry, Findlay, sec. 24 and NE¼ sec. 25, Liberty Twp.; FINDLAY.
   General geology: Janssens, 1971, p. 35; Stout, 1941, p. 342-343.

HURON COUNTY
1. Efflorescence of gypsum with halotrichite-pickeringite on Huron Shale Member, Ohio Shale. Also barite and pyrite. Cliff exposure about 2 miles N of Monroeville and ¼ mile SW of Lamereaux Rd. bridge on W side of West Branch Huron River, Ridgefield Twp.; KIMBALL.
   General geology: Prosser, 1913, p. 324-341.

LAKE COUNTY
1. Selenite crystals in glacial deposits. Outcrops near Kirtland, Kirtland Twp.; CHESTERLAND.
   Mineral occurrence: Anonymous, 1936, p. 462; Greene, 1937, p. 273.

LUCAS COUNTY
1. Massive gypsum in dolostones of Detroit River Group. Old excavation on Tenmile Creek just S of Sylvania, Sylvania Twp.; SYLVANIA.
   Mineral occurrence: Bownocker, 1920, p. 218; Gilbert, 1873, p. 583; Janssens, 1977, p. 37; Orton, 1888b, p. 697; Withington, 1962, p. 10.
   General geology: Ehlers, G. M., and others, 1951, p. 1-17.
2. Massive gypsum nodules with celestite and pseudomorphs of calcite, celestite, and fluorite after gypsum in Tymochtee Dolomite and dolostones of undifferentiated Salina Group. Also asphalt, halite, pyrite, sphalerite, and sulfur. France Stone Co. quarry, Waterville, secs. 38 and 39, Waterville Twp.; BOWLING GREEN NORTH.
   Mineral occurrence: Carman, 1948, p. 2, 11; Kahle and Floyd, 1968, p. 21-24; 1971, p. 2082-2086; 1972, p. 65-68; Nelson, 1967, p. 81; Stout, 1941, p. 402-404; Strogonoff, 1966, p. 37.
   General geology: Janssens, 1977, p. 25-30.
3. Large pseudomorphs of calcite after gypsum in Tymochtee Dolomite. Exposure on Granger Island in Maumee River, E edge of Waterville, Waterville Twp.; BOWLING GREEN NORTH.
   Mineral occurrence: Kahle and Floyd, 1971, p. 2080-2081.
4. Molds of gypsum crystals in Lockport Dolomite and *Greenfield Dolomite*. Also asphalt, calcite, celestite, dolomite, fluorite, pyrite, sphalerite, and sulfur. Stoneco quarry (formerly Maumee Stone Co.), Maumee, sec. 35, Waynesfield Twp.; MAUMEE.
   Mineral occurrence: Kahle, 1974, p. 34, 49; Kahle and Floyd, 1972, p. 71; Summerson, 1966, p. 221-224; Textoris and Carozzi, 1966, p. 1384-1385.
   General geology: Kahle, 1978, p. 63-115; Summerson and others, 1963, p. 44-45.
5. Massive gypsum beds in dolostones of undifferentiated Salina Group. Also calcite, celestite, and fluorite. Outcrop on West Sister Island in Lake Erie, METZGER MARSH.
   Mineral occurrence: Gilbert, 1873, p. 589-590; Sanford and Stone, 1914, p. 148; Sparling, 1965, p. 95; 1970, p. 11.
   General geology: Herdendorf and Braidech, 1972, p. 9-12.

MAHONING COUNTY
1. Selenite crystals in lake beds of bluish-gray silt or clay. Outcrop on Meander Creek near W border of Canfield; CANFIELD.
   Mineral occurrence: Anonymous, 1936, p. 462; Dana, E. S., 1892, p. 936, 1085; Dana, J. D., 1858, p. 379, 495; 1868, p. 639, 784; Greene, 1937, p. 273; Hildreth, 1837, p. 34.
2. Selenite crystals in lake beds of bluish-gray clay. Outcrop on S bank of West Branch Meander Creek about 1/3 mile E of junction with Ohio Rte. 45, S of Ellsworth, Ellsworth Twp.; CANFIELD.
   Mineral occurrence: Anonymous, 1936, p. 462; Cleaveland, 1822, p. 776; Dana, E. S., 1892, p. 936, 1085; Dana, E. S., and Ford, 1932, p. 759; Greene, 1937, p. 272-273; Lamb, 1910, p. 114; Newberry, 1878, p. 810; Palache and others, 1951, p. 485; Robinson, 1825, p. 235; Silliman, 1821, p. 51-52.
3. Selenite crystals in lake beds of bluish-gray silt or clay. Outcrops near E shore of Lake Milton S of Pointview Ave., Milton Twp.; LAKE MILTON.
   Mineral occurrence: Whittlesey, 1838, p. 68.
4. Selenite crystals in lake beds of bluish-gray clay. Outcrops near Poland.
   Mineral occurrence: Cleaveland, 1816, p. 144; 1822, p. 211; Comstock, 1837, p. 81; Dana, J. D., 1858, p. 379, 495; 1868, p. 639, 784; Robinson, 1825, p. 235.

OTTAWA COUNTY
1. White gypsum crystals in pockets of *Lockport Dolomite* and Greenfield Dolomite. Also calcite, celestite, dolomite, fluorite, galena, pyrite, and sphalerite. Edward Kraemer & Sons, Inc., White Rock quarry, Clay Center, SE¼ sec. 9 and NE¼ sec. 16, Allen Twp.; GENOA.
   Mineral occurrence: Botoman and Stieglitz, 1978, p. 5; Morrison, 1934, p. 21; 1935, p. 784.
   General geology: Carman and others, 1962, p. 13-14; Janssens, 1974, p. 82, 84; 1977, p. 22; Sparling, 1965, p. 239-240; 1971, p. 19; Stout, 1941, p. 415-418.
2. Gypsum molds in dolostones of *undifferentiated Salina Group* and *Bass Islands Dolomite*. Also calcite, celestite, and fluorite. Cliff exposure on NW edge of Catawba Island, Catawba Island Twp.; GYPSUM.
   Mineral occurrence: Treesh, 1970, p. 9.
   General geology: Carman, 1927, p. 488-491; Janssens, 1977, p. 27-30; Sparling, 1970, p. 3, 19-21; 1971, p. 19-22.
3. Nodules and beds of finely crystalline gypsum in dolostones of undifferentiated Salina Group; may be associated with anhydrite. Also celestite. Old quarries and underground workings of U.S. Gypsum Co., SE¼ sec. 10 and SW½ sec. 11, Portage Twp.; VICKERY.
   Mineral occurrence: Atwater, 1838, p. 61-62; Bownocker, 1920, p. 222; Janssens, 1977, p. 36-38; Jones, 1935, p. 493-501; Lintner, 1944, p. 14; Newberry, 1873a, p. 133-134; 1874b, p. 194; Orton, 1888b, p. 696-702; Peppel, 1904, p. 38; Silliman, 1822a, p. 39; 1824, p. 48; Stout, 1941, p. 420-421; Withington, 1962, p. 10.
4. Massive gypsum nodules and beds and molds of gypsum crystals in dolostones of undifferentiated Salina Group; may be associated with anhydrite. Also pyrite. Celotex Corp. quarry, W½ sec. 10, Portage Twp.; VICKERY.
   Mineral occurrence: Bownocker, 1920, p. 222; Feldmann and others, 1977, p. 38-42; Forsyth, 1971, p. 13-14;

Janssens, 1977, p. 36-38; Lintner, 1944, p. 10-11; Sparling, 1965, p. 174-175, 253-254; 1970, p. 11; 1971, p. 21; Strogonoff, 1966, p. 21; Withington, 1962, p. 10.
5. Massive gypsum beds in dolostones of undifferentiated Salina Group. Old slope mine about ½ mile NW of Gypsum, Portage Twp.; GYPSUM.
    Mineral occurrence: Bownocker, 1920, p. 222; Lintner, 1944, p. 24; Withington, 1962, p. 10.
    General geology: Janssens, 1977, p. 36-38.
6. Gypsum molds in dolostones of *undifferentiated Salina Group* and *Bass Islands Dolomite*. Also calcite and celestite. Cliff exposure at South Point, South Bass Island, Put-in-Bay Twp.; PUT-IN-BAY.
    Mineral occurrence: Treesh, 1970, p. 9.
    General geology: Janssens, 1977, p. 27-30; Mohr, 1931, p. 33-34; Stout, 1941, p. 421-422.

PIKE COUNTY
1. Selenite crystals in shales of Cuyahoga Formation. Outcrop along Ohio Rte. 772 ½ mile S of Nipgen, NE Benton Twp.; MORGANTOWN.
    Mineral occurrence: Hyde, J. E., and Marple, 1953, p. 167.

PORTAGE COUNTY
1. Gypsum as an efflorescence on Sharon conglomerate, Pottsville Group. Outcrop below waterfall on tributary of Aurora Branch of Chagrin River near intersection of Ohio Rte. 306 and Crackel Rd., Aurora Twp.; AURORA.
    Mineral occurrence: Connors, 1974, p. 38.
2. Selenite crystals in glacial lake beds of gray silt and clay. Outcrops on NE bank of Michael J. Kirwan Reservoir S of Ohio Rte. 5, Charlestown Twp.; RAVENNA.
    Mineral occurrence: Birkheimer, 1938, p. 331; Gettings, 1955, p. 485.
    General geology: Winslow and White, 1966, p. 6-7, 44.
3. Gypsum as an efflorescence on Connoquenessing sandstone, Pottsville Group. Outcrop on small N-flowing tributary of Eagle Creek crossed by Hankee Rd. just E of Asbury Rd., Freedom Twp.; MANTUA.
    Mineral occurrence: Connors, 1974, p. 38.

ROSS COUNTY
1. Selenite crystals in yellow clay of Cuyahoga Formation. Outcrop at Bainbridge, Paxton Twp.; BAINBRIDGE.
    Mineral occurrence: Hyde, J. E., and Marple, 1953, p. 167.

SUMMIT COUNTY
1. Selenite crystals in glacial lake beds of brown silt and clay. Outcrop 100 yds W of Revere Rd. at S end of a pond 0.2 mile S of intersection of Revere and Bath Rds., E-central Bath Twp.; PENINSULA.
    Mineral occurrence: Wittine, 1970, p. 56.
    General geology: White, G. W., 1953, p. 23.
2. Selenite crystals in glacial lake beds of buff silt and clay. Cliff exposure on Revere Rd. 0.1 mile S of intersection of Bath and Revere Rds., central Bath Twp.; PENINSULA.
    Mineral occurrence: Metzler, 1967, p. 46-47.
    General geology: White, G. W., 1953, p. 23.
3. Selenite crystals in glacial lake beds of gray silt and clay. Outcrop along W bank of Furnace Run 300 yds N of intersection of Everett and Oak Hill Rds., SW Boston Twp.; PENINSULA.
    Mineral occurrence: Wittine, 1970, p. 60.
    General geology: White, G. W., 1953, p. 23.
4. Selenite crystals in glacial lake beds of gray to brown silt and clay. Exposure along drainage ditch on N side of I-271 overpass 200 ft W of Riverview Rd., NW Boston Twp.; NORTHFIELD.
    Mineral occurrence: Wittine, 1970, p. 61.
    General geology: White, G. W., 1953, p. 23.
5. Selenite crystals in glacial lake beds of gray silt and clay. Outcrop along Haskell Run a short distance W of dam S of Ohio Rte. 303 and N of Ritchie Ledges at N end of Virginia Kendall Park, Boston Twp.; PENINSULA.
    General geology: White, G. W., 1953, p. 23.
6. Efflorescence of white gypsum with potash alum and thenardite on Sharon conglomerate, Pottsville Group. King's Creek Cave on N side of Cuyahoga River about 1/5 mile W of Mary Campbell Cave, Cuyahoga Gorge Park, Cuyahoga Falls; AKRON WEST.
    Mineral occurrence: Connors, 1974, p. 37.
    General geology: Kent State University, *in* Frank, 1969, p. 1.4-1.7.
7. Efflorescence of white gypsum on Sharpsville Siltstone Member, Cuyahoga Formation. Exposure at river level on N side of Cuyahoga River just W of dam at Cuyahoga Gorge Park, Cuyahoga Falls; AKRON WEST.
    Mineral occurrence: Connors, 1974, p. 37.
    General geology: Kent State University, *in* Frank, 1969, p. 1.4-1.7.
8. Selenite crystals in glacial lake beds of gray silt and clay. Cliff exposure on E bank of Yellow Creek just N of intersection of Bath and Yellow Creek Rds., W Northampton Twp.; PENINSULA.
    Mineral occurrence: Metzler, 1967, p. 45-46; Miller, 1970, p. 157, 160.
    General geology: White, G. W., 1953, p. 23.
9. Selenite crystals in glacial lake beds of gray silt and clay. Outcrop on hill E of Akron-Peninsula Rd. 1.3 miles N of intersection of Ira and Akron-Peninsula Rds., NW Northampton Twp.; PENINSULA.
    Mineral occurrence: Wittine, 1970, p. 55.
    General geology: White, G. W., 1953, p. 23.
10. Selenite crystals in glacial lake beds of buff silt and clay. Outcrop on tributary of Furnace Run ½ mile W of intersection of Everett and Oak Hill Rds., SE Richfield Twp.; PENINSULA.
    Mineral occurrence: Metzler, 1967, p. 44.
    General geology: White, G. W., 1953, p. 23.
11. Efflorescence of white gypsum with potash alum on Sharon conglomerate, Pottsville Group. Outcrop on E side of hill 1 mile W of Aurora Pond, NE Twinsburg Twp.; TWINSBURG.
    Mineral occurrence: Connors, 1974, p. 38.

VINTON COUNTY
1. Selenite crystals in shale beds of Putnam Hill limestone, Allegheny Group. Abandoned strip mine of Vinton Coal Co., SE¼ sec. 7, Elk Twp.; ALLENSVILLE.
    General geology: Lamborn, 1951, p. 342.

WASHINGTON COUNTY
1. Selenite crystals in shales and veins of gypsum in sandstones of Washington Formation. Also hematite. Old Cisler and Son's Brick Plant clay pit, Marietta, E½ sec. 36, Marietta Twp.; MARIETTA (MARIETTA 15-minute).
    Mineral occurrence: Stauffer and Schroyer, 1920, p. 15, 125.
    General geology: Lamborn and others, 1938, p. 218-219.

WOOD COUNTY
1. Nodules of finely crystalline gypsum in Tymochtee Dolomite. Also calcite, fluorite, marcasite, pyrite, and sphalerite. France Stone Co. North Baltimore quarry, W½ sec. 26, Henry Twp.; NORTH BALTIMORE.
    Mineral occurrence: Botoman and Stieglitz, 1978, p. 6; Janssens, 1977, p. 26; Kahle and Floyd, 1972, p. 46-48.
    General geology: Janssens, 1971, p. 35; Stout, 1941, p. 394-395.

2. Molds of gypsum and/or anhydrite crystals in Lockport Dolomite and *Greenfield Dolomite*. Also aragonite, barite, calcite, celestite, dolomite, fluorite, galena, marcasite, pyrite, sphalerite, strontianite, and sulfur. Stoneco quarry (formerly Maumee Stone Co.), Lime City, SW¼ sec. 11, Perrysburg Twp.; ROSSFORD.
Mineral occurrence: Kahle and Floyd, 1968, p. 28; 1972, p. 52.
General geology: Janssens, 1971, p. 35; 1974, p. 82, 84; 1977, p. 22.
3. Crystals and beds of gypsum replaced by celestite in Lockport Dolomite and *Greenfield Dolomite*. Also calcite, dolomite, sphalerite, and sulfur. Stoneco quarry (formerly Maumee Stone Co.) SE of Portage, sec. 7, Portage Twp.; BOWLING GREEN SOUTH.
Mineral occurrence: Carlson, 1987c, p. 96-104.
General geology: Floyd, 1971, p. 188; Janssens, 1971, p. 35; 1974, p. 82, 84; 1977, p. 22.

WYANDOT COUNTY
1. Nodules of gypsum (replaced by celestite) in Lockport Dolomite and *Greenfield Dolomite*. Also calcite, dolomite, fluorite, pyrite, sphalerite, and strontianite. National Lime & Stone Co. quarry, Carey, N½ sec. 15 and N½ sec. 16, Crawford Twp.; CAREY, MCCUTCHENVILLE.
Mineral occurrence: Carlson, 1987c, p. 101-102.
General geology: Cumings, 1930, p. 201-202; Hall and Alkire, 1956, p. 7, 31-33; Janssens, 1974, p. 82, 84; 1977, p. 22; Stout, 1941, p. 294-295; Summerson and others, 1963, p. 39-40.
2. Gypsum crystals (replaced by celestite) in *Tymochtee Dolomite* and dolostones of undifferentiated Salina Group. Also calcite, sphalerite, and sulfur. McCarthy Stone Quarry 3½ miles SE of Upper Sandusky, N½ sec. 15, Pitt Twp.; NEVADA.
Mineral occurrence: Botoman and Stieglitz, 1978, p. 6; Carlson, 1987c, p. 97-101.
General geology: Janssens, 1977, p. 3, 29; Stout, 1941, p. 299.

HALITE
NaCl

Chemical class: Halide
Crystallization: Isometric; hexoctahedral; m3m
Habit: Commonly well crystallized; cubic crystals; granular aggregates; may be massive
Physical properties: Cleavage: {001} perfect cubic. H: 2½. G: 2.2. Luster: vitreous. Color: white or colorless. Streak: white. Taste: salty
Occurrence: In granular beds of evaporite origin with bedded dolostone and anhydrite in northeastern Ohio; molds of crystals of evaporite origin in dolostones in northwestern Ohio

CUYAHOGA COUNTY
1. Granular halite in beds of Salina Group; may be associated with anhydrite. AKZO Salt, Inc., mine (formerly International Salt Co.), Whiskey Island just S of mouth of Cuyahoga River along shore of Lake Erie, Cleveland; CLEVELAND SOUTH.
Mineral occurrence: Clifford, 1973, p. 16-17; Hall, 1963, p. 27; Heimlich and others, 1974, p. 5-17; Jacoby, 1970, p. 447.

LAKE COUNTY
1. Granular halite in beds of Salina Group; may be associated with anhydrite. Morton Salt Co. mine on W side of Grand River, Fairport Harbor, Painesville Twp.; MENTOR.
Mineral occurrence: Clifford, 1973, p. 16-17; Hall, 1963, p. 27.

LUCAS COUNTY
1. Hopper-shaped molds of halite in dolostones of Detroit River Group. Exposures in vicinity of Sylvania, Sylvania Twp.; SYLVANIA.
Mineral occurrence: Gilbert, 1873, p. 583; Janssens, 1977, p. 37.
2. Molds of halite crystals in *Tymochtee Dolomite* and dolostones of undifferentiated Salina Group. Also asphalt, calcite, celestite, fluorite, gypsum, pyrite, sphalerite, and sulfur. France Stone Co. quarry, Waterville, secs. 38 and 39, Waterville Twp.; BOWLING GREEN NORTH.
Mineral occurrence: Kahle and Floyd, 1971, p. 2087; 1972, p. 44, 65-68.
General geology: Janssens, 1977, p. 25-30; Kahle and Floyd, 1968, p. 21-24; Stout, 1941, p. 402-404.

OTTAWA COUNTY
1. Hopper-shaped casts of halite in Tymochtee Dolomite or Bass Islands Dolomite. South Bass Island, no specific localities given, Put-in-Bay Twp.; PUT-IN-BAY.
Mineral occurrence: Kraus, 1905a, p. 288.

WYANDOT COUNTY
1. Halite molds in Tymochtee Dolomite. Outcrop along Tymochtee Creek near junction of U.S. Rte. 23 and Twp. Rd. 103J, secs. 27 and 34, Crawford Twp.; MCCUTCHENVILLE.
Mineral occurrence: Kahle and Floyd, 1971, p. 2087; 1972, p. 44.
General geology: Winchell, 1873, p. 633.

HALOTRICHITE-PICKERINGITE SERIES
(Fe,Mg)Al$_2$(SO$_4$)$_4 \cdot$ 22H$_2$O-(Mg,Fe)Al$_2$(SO$_4$)$_4 \cdot$ 22H$_2$O

Chemical class: Sulfate
Crystallization: Monoclinic; sphenoidal; 2
Habit: Commonly in fibrous aggregates; prismatic crystals
Physical properties: Cleavage: {010} poor pinacoidal. H: 1½. G: 1.9. Luster: vitreous to silky. Color: generally white; may be stained pale yellow or pale red. Streak: white. Taste: astringent
Chemistry: Members of the halotrichite-pickeringite series have similar physical properties but contain varying amounts of iron and magnesium. In halotrichite, (Fe,Mg)Al$_2$(SO$_4$)$_4 \cdot$ 22H$_2$O, iron content exceeds magnesium; in pickeringite, (Mg,Fe)Al$_2$(SO$_4$)$_4 \cdot$ 22H$_2$O, magnesium exceeds iron. In the absence of chemical data, specimens are identified generally as members of the halotrichite-pickeringite series
Occurrence: Fibrous efflorescence commonly associated with pyrite in shale or coal in central and eastern Ohio; much more common than the list below indicates; numerous and vague notations to "alum" in the Ohio geological literature most likely refer to members of this series

CUYAHOGA COUNTY
1. Efflorescence of white pickeringite (4.47% MgO, 1.17% Fe$_2$O$_3$) on Cleveland Shale Member, Ohio Shale. Exposure along E valley wall of Rocky River ½ mile S of mouth of Abrams Creek, Middleburg Twp.; LAKEWOOD.
Mineral occurrence: Collins, R. F., 1924, p. 2, 3.

ERIE COUNTY
1. Fibrous efflorescence of white halotrichite-pickeringite on Cleveland Shale Member, Ohio Shale. Exposure

along E bank of Vermilion River at Garfield Rd. bridge, Florence Twp.; KIPTON.

General geology: Herdendorf, 1963, map.

HURON COUNTY

1. Fibrous efflorescence of white halotrichite-pickeringite with gypsum on Huron Shale Member, Ohio Shale. Also barite and pyrite. Cliff exposure about 2 miles N of Monroeville and ¼ mile SW of Lamereaux Rd. bridge on W side of West Branch Huron River, Ridgefield Twp.; KIMBALL.

General geology: Broadhead and others, 1980, p. 10-15; Prosser, 1913, p. 324-341.

LORAIN COUNTY

1. Fibrous efflorescence of white pickeringite (4.80% MgO, 2.64% Fe_2O_3) on Cleveland Shale Member, Ohio Shale. Also barite, calcite, pyrite, and quartz. Cliff exposures along Vermilion River at Mill Hollow-Bacon Woods Park, Brownhelm Twp.; VERMILION EAST.

Mineral occurrence: Collins, R. F., 1924, p. 2, 4.

General geology: Broadhead and others, 1980, p. 23-30; Herdendorf, 1963, map; Prosser, 1913, p. 348.

MEIGS COUNTY

1. Efflorescence of pickeringite with alunogen, botryogen, and copiapite in shale above Redstone (Pomeroy) (No. 8A) coal, Monongahela Group. Old strip mine on E side of Twp. Hwy. 46 about 1 mile N of Langsville, Rutland Twp.; RUTLAND.

Mineral occurrence: Fisher, H. H., 1975, p. 416.

General geology: DeLong, 1955, p. 43-44.

ROSS COUNTY

1. Fibrous efflorescence of white halotrichite-pickeringite with melanterite on Huron Shale Member, Ohio Shale. Also barite, calcite, dolomite, pyrite, and quartz. Cliff exposure along SE side of Paint Creek at Copperas Mountain about 1 mile ESE of Seip Mound State Memorial, Paxton Twp.; MORGANTOWN.

Mineral occurrence: Briggs, 1838, p. 77-78; Carlson, 1987b, p. 428; Dana, J. D., 1858, p. 385, 495; 1868, p. 646, 784; Dana, E. S., 1892, p. 942, 1085; Wuestner, 1938, p. 261; (reported as alum in some references).

General geology: Kepferle and others, 1981, p. 294-295; Orton, 1874, p. 647; Seyfried, 1953, p. 18-25.

STARK COUNTY

1. Fibrous efflorescence of white halotrichite-pickeringite on sandstone above Lower Freeport (No. 6A) coal, Allegheny Group. Penn Central Railroad cut W of Ohio Rte. 183 intersection, sec. 25, Paris Twp.; HOMEWORTH.

General geology: DeLong and White, 1963, pl. 1.

VINTON COUNTY

1. Efflorescence of white magnesian halotrichite (2.7% MgO, 5.9% FeO) with melanterite and rozenite on pyrite and spall rock from mining operations in Middle Kittanning (No. 6) coal, Allegheny Group. Abandoned coal mines along upper reaches of Sandy Run, NE Brown Twp.; MINERAL.

Mineral occurrence: Brant and Foster, 1959, p. 187-188; Ehlers, E. G., and Stiles, 1965, p. 1457-1458.

HEMATITE
Fe_2O_3

Chemical class: Oxide

Crystallization: Hexagonal (Trigonal); ditrigonal scalenohedral; $\bar{3}m$

Habit: May be well crystallized; crystals commonly tabular; generally finely crystalline and massive; may be oolitic or concretionary

Physical properties: Fracture: uneven. H: 5½-6½. G: 5.0. Luster: metallic if well crystallized and pure or dull if poorly crystallized and impure. Color: brownish red to dark gray. Streak: red

Occurrence: Concretions and nodules in red shales of Conemaugh and Monongahela Groups and Washington Formation in southeastern Ohio; nodules locally form placer deposits in stream beds; thin layers of oolitic hematite in Brassfield Formation of southwestern Ohio

ADAMS COUNTY

1. Oolitic hematite in Brassfield Formation. Outcrop on hill on W side of Ohio Rte. 41 S of Sinking Spring, just S of Highland Co. line, Bratton Twp.; SINKING SPRING.

Mineral occurrence: Dana, E. S., 1892, p. 1085; Orton, 1871b, p. 269; 1884b, p. 372; Sanford and Stone, 1914, p. 149; Wuestner, 1938, p. 263.

2. Oolitic hematite in Brassfield Formation. Also calcite and sphalerite. Exposure on S side of Ohio Rte. 73, 1.5 miles W of Louden, Bratton Twp.; SINKING SPRING. OGS section no. 14350.

Mineral occurrence: Koucky, 1975, p. 14-15.

General geology: Hopkins, 1954, p. 88.

3. Oolitic hematite in Brassfield Formation. Road cut on W side of Ohio Rte. 41 just S of bridge over Ohio Brush Creek 1 mile SW of Jacksonville, Oliver Twp.; PEEBLES.

Mineral occurrence: Rexroad and others, 1965, p. 11; Schmidt and others, 1961, p. 281-282; Stout, 1941, p. 49-51; 1944, p. 11-13; Summerson and others, 1963, p. 16-17.

4. Oolitic hematite in Brassfield Formation. Also calcite. Outcrop along Lick Creek 3½ miles S of Dunkinsville, Tiffin Twp.; WEST UNION.

Mineral occurrence: Hopkins, 1954, p. 90.

ATHENS COUNTY

1. Siderite-hematite concretions in gray shales of Skelley limestone, Conemaugh Group. Exposure along ravine on E side of Margaret Creek, SE¼SE¼ sec. 33, Alexander Twp.; ALBANY.

Mineral occurrence: Sturgeon and associates, 1958, p. 297.

2. Hematite nodules in red shales of Lower and Upper Pittsburgh units, Monongahela Group. Exposure up stream in NE corner of Alexander Twp., into SE corner of Athens Twp., and into W½SW¼ sec. 31, Canaan Twp.; ATHENS.

Mineral occurrence: Sturgeon and associates, 1958, p. 307.

3. Joint fillings and nodules of hematite in red and gray shales of Duquesne coal and Gaysport limestone, Conemaugh Group. Exposures along Ohio Rte. 550 and hillside, E½ sec. 20, Ames Twp.; JACKSONVILLE.

Mineral occurrence: Smith, G. E., 1951, p. 125-126; Sturgeon and associates, 1958, p. 144, 332.

4. Septarian nodules of hematite in red shales of Duquesne coal, Conemaugh Group. Exposures in bed of South Fork Dutch Creek and hillside along Twp. Hwy. 218, NE¼SW¼ and SE¼NW¼ sec. 25, Ames Twp.; JACKSONVILLE.

Mineral occurrence: Smith, G. E., 1951, p. 101; Sturgeon and associates, 1958, p. 144, 325.

5. Masses of hematite in red shales of Birmingham shale, Conemaugh Group. Exposures along NE side of County Hwy. 37 and hillside, NW¼NE¼ sec. 17, Ames Twp.; AMESVILLE.

Mineral occurrence: Smith, G. E., 1951, p. 134-135; Sturgeon and associates, 1958, p. 335.

6. Hematite nodules in shales of Upper Conemaugh Group. Loose nodules abundant at head of Bryson Run, sec. 36, Ames Twp.; JACKSONVILLE.
   Mineral occurrence: Stout, 1945, p. 147.
7. Hematite nodules in gray to tan shales of Gaysport limestone, Conemaugh Group. Exposure along NE side of Ohio Rte. 329 and uphill toward old house, NE¼NW¼ sec. 11, Ames Twp.; AMESVILLE.
   Mineral occurrence: Smith, G. E., 1951, p. 138; Sturgeon and associates, 1958, p. 336.
8. Hematite nodules in red shales of Upper Conemaugh Group. Exposures along slopes above Hyde Fork of Federal Creek, N Ames Twp.; AMESVILLE.
   Mineral occurrence: Condit, 1912, p. 118-119.
9. Hematite nodules in gray siltstones of Upper Pittsburgh sandstone, Monongahela Group. Exposures from Long Run through a strip mine, SE¼NW¼ sec. 25, Canaan Twp.; ATHENS.
   Mineral occurrence: Sturgeon and associates, 1958, p. 405-406.
10. Hematite masses in red and green shales of Fishpot limestone, Monongahela Group. Exposure up a dead-end road about 100 yds NW of intersection of U.S. Rte. 33 and Twp. Hwy. 86, beginning in SW¼SW¼ sec. 36, Lodi Twp., and extending up hill into Alexander Twp.; ATHENS.
    Mineral occurrence: Sturgeon and associates, 1958, p. 304-305, 463-464.
11. Hematite nodules in red clays above Mahoning sandstone, Conemaugh Group. Outcrop in vicinity of Hamley Run along N boundary of sec. 12, Waterloo Twp.; NELSONVILLE.
    Mineral occurrence: Condit, 1912, p. 121.

CLINTON COUNTY
1. Oolitic hematite in the Brassfield Formation. Outcrop on Todd Fork 200 yds upstream from Center Rd. bridge about 3 miles NW of Wilmington, Union Twp.; WILMINGTON.
   Mineral occurrence: Foerste, 1891, p. 29; Hopkins, 1954, p. 83; Sanford and Stone, 1914, p. 149; Stout, 1941, p. 33, 123; 1944, p. 11.

COLUMBIANA COUNTY
1. Hematite nodules in red shales between Ames and Cambridge limestones, Conemaugh Group. Exposures SE of West Point near right-angle bend in Torma Rd., sec. 15, Madison Twp.; WEST POINT.
   Mineral occurrence: Condit, 1912, p. 35-36, 220-221; Stout, 1944, p. 211.

GALLIA COUNTY
1. Hematite nodules in red clays above Cambridge limestone, Conemaugh Group. Outcrop along Steele Rd. on hill S of Northup, sec. 13, Green Twp.; RODNEY.
   Mineral occurrence: Condit, 1912, p. 86; Stout, 1944, p. 219.
2. Hematite nodules in red clays above Ames limestone, Conemaugh Group. Exposures along Bethel Rd., sec. 2, Springfield Twp.; GALLIPOLIS.
   Mineral occurrence: Condit, 1912, p. 81.

HIGHLAND COUNTY
1. Oolitic hematite in Brassfield Formation. Also calcite and sphalerite. Outcrop along tributary of Little West Fork Ohio Brush Creek near intersection of Pondlick and Richardson Rds. about 2¼ miles SE of Sugar Tree Ridge, central Concord Twp.; SUGAR TREE RIDGE. OGS section no. 9732.
   Mineral occurrence: Hopkins, 1954, p. 87.
   General geology: Rogers, J. K., 1936, p. 95.
2. Hematite layer in upper Brassfield Formation. Exposure along creek bank at bridge ¼ mile N of old Wildwood School about 1 mile SW of Belfast, Jackson Twp.; BELFAST (HILLSBORO 15-minute).
   Mineral occurrence: Rogers, J. K., 1936, p. 93.
3. Oolitic hematite in Brassfield Formation. Outcrop along N bank of Rocky Fork W of bridge on Ohio Rte. 73, 2 miles SE of Hillsboro, Liberty Twp.; HILLSBORO.
   Mineral occurrence: Hopkins, 1954, p. 86; Rogers, J. K., 1936, p. 91-92; Summerson and others, 1963, p. 14.
4. Oolitic hematite in Brassfield Formation. Sharp's quarry just E of Turtle Creek about 2 miles ENE of Lynchburg, Union Twp.; MARTINSVILLE.
   Mineral occurrence: Hopkins, 1954, p. 84.
   General geology: Rogers, J. K., 1936, p. 96-97.
5. Oolitic hematite in Brassfield Formation. Outcrop along small westerly tributary of Ohio Brush Creek 1¼ miles E of Folsom, Washington Twp.; BELFAST.
   Mineral occurrence: Rogers, J. K., 1936, p. 93-94; Stout, 1941, p. 76-77.
6. Oolitic hematite in Brassfield Formation. Exposure along Twp. Hwy. 228 and in stream bed of large northerly tributary of Ohio Brush Creek near their intersection about 1½ miles NE of Folsom, Washington Twp.; BELFAST.
   Mineral occurrence: Rogers, J. K., 1936, p. 94.

LAWRENCE COUNTY
1. Six-inch layer of earthy red hematite at base of sandstone underlying Brush Creek limestone, Conemaugh Group. Old quarry along Ohio Rte. 141, N½ sec. 19, Mason Twp.; WATERLOO.
   Mineral occurrence: Condit, 1912, p. 67.
2. Hematite nodules as placer deposit from beds in upper Conemaugh Group. Bed of Paddy Creek, S Rome Twp.; BARBOURSVILLE.
   Mineral occurrence: Stout, 1944, p. 220.
   General geology: Condit, 1912, p. 74.
3. Hematite nodules in red and gray clays above Cambridge limestone, Conemaugh Group. Outcrop along hill road at W end of Waterloo, sec. 25, Symmes Twp.; WATERLOO.
   Mineral occurrence: Condit, 1912, p. 64-65.

MEIGS COUNTY
1. Hematite nodules in gray and red shales above Waynesburg sandstone, Washington Formation. Exposures in stream and on Ohio Rte. 681 just W of Reedsville, Olive Twp.; POND CREEK, PORTLAND.
   Mineral occurrence: Stauffer and Schroyer, 1920, p. 137-138.
2. Hematite nodules in red clays above Cambridge limestone and Ames limestone, Conemaugh Group. Exposure along abandoned road SE of Hanesville, NE¼ sec. 1, Salem Twp.; RUTLAND.
   Mineral occurrence: Condit, 1912, p. 102; Stout, 1944, p. 218-219.
3. Hematite nodules in red clays above Ames limestone, Conemaugh Group. Exposures along hillside a little over 1 mile W of Pagetown, Scipio Twp.; ALBANY.
   Mineral occurrence: Condit, 1912, p. 102-103.
4. Hematite nodules in red and gray shales above Waynesburg sandstone, Washington Formation. Exposures along S bank of Jennie Walls Run and up Mt. Moriah Rd. about 1½ miles SE of Racine, SE Sutton Twp.; NEW HAVEN.
   Mineral occurrence: Stauffer and Schroyer, 1920, p. 138-139.

MORGAN COUNTY
1. Hematite nodules in red shales above Ames limestone, Conemaugh Group. Outcrop E of McConnelsville, SW¼ sec. 12, Morgan Twp.; MCCONNELSVILLE.
   Mineral occurrence: Stout, 1944, p. 217.
2. Hematite nodules in shales of upper Conemaugh Group. Loose nodules abundant along bed of East Branch

Sunday Creek near Ringgold, Union Twp.; CORNING, RINGGOLD.

Mineral occurrence: Stout, 1944, p. 218; 1945, p. 147.

MUSKINGUM COUNTY
1. Hematite nodules in red shales of Conemaugh Group. Exposure in SE quadrant of Ohio Rte. 83 and I-70 interchange 1 mile S of New Concord, Union Twp.; NEW CONCORD.

General geology: Frye, 1976, p. 3.

NOBLE COUNTY
1. Hematite concretions in red shales above Skelley limestone, Conemaugh Group. Exposure S of Senecaville along Ohio Rte. 285, sec. 6, Wayne Twp.; SENECAVILLE.

Mineral occurrence: Condit, 1912, p. 159; Stout, 1944, p. 216.

PERRY COUNTY
1. Hematite nodules in red and green shales above and below Brush Creek limestone, Conemaugh Group. Exposure along Twp. Hwy. 423 just S of Sayre, Bearfield Twp.; DEAVERTOWN.

Mineral occurrence: Condit, 1912, p. 126.

2. Hematite nodules in shales above Brush Creek limestone, Conemaugh Group. Placer deposit in stream bed of Black Fork ½ mile E of Sayre and S of Ohio Rte. 37, NW¼ sec. 23, Bearfield Twp.; DEAVERTOWN.

Mineral occurrence: Flint, 1951, p. 129; Stout, 1945, p. 147.

3. Hematite nodules in shales above Brush Creek limestone, Conemaugh Group. Placer deposit in stream bed E of Ohio Rte. 555, SE¼ sec. 12, Bearfield Twp.; DEAVERTOWN.

Mineral occurrence: Flint, 1951, p. 129.

4. Hematite nodules in red shales overlying Ames limestone, Conemaugh Group. Exposures in Bearfield, Monroe, and Pleasant Twps.

Mineral occurrence: Stout, 1944, p. 218.

PREBLE COUNTY
1. Oolitic hematite in Brassfield Formation. Also pyrite and sphalerite. Old Marble Cliff quarry, Lewisburg, SW¼ sec. 21, Harrison Twp.; LEWISBURG.

Mineral occurrence: Horvath and Sparling, 1967, p. 2-3; Shaver and others, 1961, p. 31-32; Stout, 1941, p. 170.

SCIOTO COUNTY
1. Hematite nodules. Outcrops, no specific localities given.
Mineral occurrence: Mills, 1917, p. 373.

WASHINGTON COUNTY
1. Hematite nodules in red and gray shales at several horizons above Waynesburg coal, Washington Formation. Exposures along County Hwy. 42 W from Stanleyville, Fearing Twp.; MARIETTA.

Mineral occurrence: Stauffer and Schroyer, 1920, p. 121-122.

2. Hematite nodules in red shale above Marietta sandstone, Washington Formation. Also gypsum. Old Cisler and Son's Brick Plant clay pit, Marietta, E½ sec. 36, Marietta Twp.; MARIETTA (MARIETTA 15-minute).

Mineral occurrence: Stauffer and Schroyer, 1920, p. 125-126.

General geology: Lamborn and others, 1938, p. 218-219.

3. Hematite nodules in red shales above Washington coal, Washington Formation. Exposure along Ohio Rte. 351 0.4 mile N of intersection with Ohio Rte. 26 near Waterworks Hill, E side of Marietta, Marietta Twp.; MARIETTA.

Mineral occurrence: Cross and others, 1950, p. 1, 32.

HEMIMORPHITE
$Zn_4(Si_2O_7)(OH)_2 \cdot H_2O$

Chemical class: Silicate
Crystallization: Orthorhombic; rhombic-pyramidal; mm2
Habit: Commonly massive; colloform; crystals thin and tabular
Physical properties: Cleavage: {110} perfect prismatic. H: 4½-5. G: 3.4. Luster: vitreous. Color: generally white or colorless; also yellow, brown. Streak: white
Occurrence: Associated with smithsonite and hydrozincite as a weathering product of sphalerite in Serpent Mound area

ADAMS COUNTY
1. Tiny crystals of white hemimorphite with smithsonite as thin, porous, yellowish-white crusts coating sphalerite in undifferentiated Peebles-Greenfield-Tymochtee Dolomites. Also hydrozincite. Exposure on small hill 0.1 mile W of Ohio Rte. 41 and 1.8 miles N of intersection with Ohio Rte. 73, Franklin Twp.; SINKING SPRING.

General geology: Koucky and Reidel, 1987, p. 431-436; Reidel and Koucky, 1981, p. 391-403; Reidel and others, 1982, p. 1343-1377.

HEXAHYDRITE
$MgSO_4 \cdot 6H_2O$

Chemical class: Sulfate
Crystallization: Monoclinic; prismatic; 2/m
Habit: Commonly acicular or fibrous; powdery; crystals may be tabular
Physical properties: Cleavage: {100} perfect pinacoidal. H: 2. G: 1.7. Luster: generally silky to dull. Color: white. Streak: white. Taste: bitter and salty
Occurrence: Common as efflorescence, especially on dolostones in western Ohio

ADAMS COUNTY
1. Efflorescence of white hexahydrite on Peebles Dolomite. Exposure in Bratton Twp.
Mineral occurrence: Foster, W. R., and Hoover, 1963, p. 152-153.

2. Efflorescence of white hexahydrite on Brassfield Formation. Exposure in Monroe Twp.
Mineral occurrence: Foster, W. R., and Hoover, 1963, p. 152-153.

CUYAHOGA COUNTY
1. Efflorescence of white hexahydrite with gypsum on Berea Sandstone. Outcrop on S side of Chippewa Creek just S of Ohio Rte. 82 bridge, Brecksville Reservation, E Brecksville Twp.; NORTHFIELD.

Mineral occurrence: Connors, 1974, p. 37.
General geology: Kent State University, in Frank, 1969, p. 1.4-1.9.

HANCOCK COUNTY
1. Efflorescence of white hexahydrite on Greenfield Dolomite. Exposure at Findlay, Liberty Twp.
Mineral occurrence: Foster, W. R., and Hoover, 1963, p. 152-153.

HIGHLAND COUNTY
1. Efflorescence of white hexahydrite on Bisher Dolomite. Exposure in Brush Creek Twp.
Mineral occurrence: Foster, W. R., and Hoover, 1963, p. 152-153.

OTTAWA COUNTY
1. Efflorescence of white hexahydrite on Bass Islands Dolo-

mite. Cliff exposure at South Bass Island State Park, Put-in-Bay Twp.; PUT-IN-BAY.

General geology: Forsyth, 1971, p. 7-9; Janssens, 1977, p. 27-30.

SANDUSKY COUNTY
1. Efflorescence of white hexahydrite on Lockport Dolomite. Exposure at Gibsonburg, Madison Twp.

Mineral occurrence: Foster, W. R., and Hoover, 1963, p. 152-153.

WOOD COUNTY
1. Efflorescence of white hexahydrite on dolostones of Detroit River Group and *Dundee Formation*. Also asphalt, barite, calcite, celestite, dolomite, fluorite, glauconite, marcasite, pyrite, and sphalerite. France Stone Co. Custar quarry (formerly Pugh Quarry Co.) about 4 miles W of Weston, SW¼ sec. 6, Milton Twp.; MCCLURE.

Mineral occurrence: Foster, W. R., and Hoover, 1963, p. 152-153.

General geology: Forsyth, 1966a, p. 202-206; Janssens, 1970a, p. 7, 22; Orton and Peppel, 1906, p. 133; Stout, 1941, p. 395-396.

2. Efflorescence of white hexahydrite on Lockport Dolomite and *Greenfield Dolomite*. Also barite, calcite, celestite, dolomite, fluorite, pyrite, sphalerite, and strontianite. MacRitchie Materials, Inc., quarry (formerly Brough Stone Co.), West Millgrove, SE¼ sec. 4, Perry Twp.; FOSTORIA.

Mineral occurrence: Foster, W. R., and Hoover, 1963, p. 152-153, 155.

General geology: Janssens, 1971, p. 35; 1974, p. 82, 84; 1977, p. 22; Shaver, 1977, p. 1414; Stout, 1941, p. 392-393.

WYANDOT COUNTY
1. Efflorescence of white hexahydrite on Tymochtee Dolomite. Exposure in Crane Twp.

Mineral occurrence: Foster, W. R., and Hoover, 1963, p. 152-153.

2. Efflorescence of white hexahydrite on *Lockport Dolomite* and *Greenfield Dolomite*. Exposure at Carey, Crawford Twp.

Mineral occurrence: Foster, W. R., and Hoover, 1963, p. 152-153.

HYDROZINCITE
Zn$_5$(CO$_3$)$_2$(OH)$_6$

Chemical class: Carbonate
Crystallization: Monoclinic; prismatic; 2/m
Habit: Commonly massive
Physical properties: Cleavage: {100} perfect pinacoidal. H: 2-2½. G: 4.0. Luster: dull. Color: commonly white. Streak: white. Almost always fluoresces bluish white in ultraviolet light
Occurrence: Associated with smithsonite and hemimorphite as a weathering product of sphalerite in Serpent Mound area

ADAMS COUNTY
1. Masses of white hydrozincite with smithsonite, sphalerite, and sulfur in cavities and fractures of undifferentiated Peebles-Greenfield-Tymochtee Dolomites. Also calcite and dolomite. Outcrop and small quarry 0.7 mile E of entrance to Serpent Mound Memorial on Ohio Rte. 73 and 1.4 miles N on E side of Twp. Hwy. 116, Bratton Twp.; SINKING SPRING.

Mineral occurrence: Heyl and Brock, 1962, p. D95; Koucky, 1975, p. 22; Reidel and Koucky, 1981, p. 391-403; Wedow and Heyl, 1968, p. 454, 464.

General geology: Koucky and Reidel, 1987, p. 431-436; Reidel, 1975, map; Reidel and Koucky, 1981, p. 391-403; Reidel and others, 1982, p. 1343-1377.

2. Hydrozincite with smithsonite and sphalerite in Peebles Dolomite. Outcrop in gully behind museum at Serpent Mound State Memorial, Bratton Twp.; SINKING SPRING.

Mineral occurrence: Koucky, 1975, p. 16.

General geology: Koucky and Reidel, 1987, p. 431-436; Reidel, 1975, map; Reidel and Koucky, 1981, p. 391-403; Reidel and others, 1982, p. 1343-1377.

3. Finely crystalline masses of white hydrozincite with smithsonite and sphalerite in cavities of brecciated Tymochtee Dolomite. Hillside exposure 1.0 mile E of entrance to Serpent Mound State Memorial on Ohio Rte. 73 and 0.4 mile S on E side of Wallace Rd., Bratton Twp.; SINKING SPRING.

Mineral occurrence: Koucky and Reidel, 1987, p. 432-435; Reidel and Koucky, 1981, p. 397-398.

General geology: Reidel and others, 1982, p. 1343-1377.

4. Hydrozincite with asphalt, calcite, smithsonite, and sphalerite in breccias of Silurian dolostone and limestone. Numerous exposures within Serpent Mound disturbance (in addition to Adams County sites 1, 2, 3, and 5 given here), Bratton and Franklin Twps.; SINKING SPRING.

Mineral occurrence: Reidel, 1972, p. 98.

General geology: Koucky and Reidel, 1987, p. 431-436; Reidel, 1975, map; Reidel and Koucky, 1981, p. 391-403; Reidel and others, 1982, p. 1343-1377.

5. White hydrozincite with hemimorphite, smithsonite, and sphalerite in fractures and cavities of undifferentiated Peebles-Greenfield-Tymochtee Dolomites. Exposure on small hill 0.1 mile W of Ohio Rte. 41 and 1.8 miles N of intersection with Ohio Rte. 73, Franklin Twp.; SINKING SPRING.

General geology: Koucky, 1975, p. 27-28; Koucky and Reidel, 1987, p. 431-436; Reidel, 1975, map; Reidel and Koucky, 1981, p. 391-403; Reidel and others, 1982, p. 1343-1377.

MANGANESE OXIDES
(PYROLUSITE, ETC.)

Chemical class: Oxide
Crystallization: Varied
Habit: Commonly massive; dendritic; acicular; may be porous
Physical properties: H: 2-6. G: 4.0-5.1. Luster: metallic to dull. Color: dark gray to brownish black. Streak: brown to black
Occurrence: Fine-grained deposits as coatings on bedding and joint planes and as bog ore in association with peat

ADAMS COUNTY
1. Sheets of unidentified manganese oxide along bedding planes in Bisher Dolomite near intersection of two faults. Also calcite and pyrite. Outcrop on W side of Ohio Rte. 41 about 1 mile N of Locust Grove, Franklin Twp.; SINKING SPRING.

Mineral occurrence: Galbraith, 1968, p. 25, 32-33.

General geology: Reidel, 1975, map.

COSHOCTON COUNTY
1. Dendritic coatings of unidentified black manganese oxides on fractures of flint bed in Upper Mercer limestone, Pottsville Group. Also quartz. Road cut along County Hwy. 82, 0.6 mile W of junction with Twp. Hwy. 59, Jefferson Twp.; WARSAW.

General geology: Lamborn, 1954, p. 93; Morningstar, 1922, p. 107-108; Stout and Schoenlaub, 1945, p. 56.

GEAUGA COUNTY
1. Deposit of bog manganese in swampy ground. Old J. R. Smith farm, lot 4, SW Auburn Twp.; AURORA.
   Mineral occurrence: Read, 1871, p. 470; Stout, 1940, p. 42.

HAMILTON COUNTY
1. Masses of manganese bog ore in glacial deposits. Field just N of Boomer Rd. and 2 miles W of North Bend Rd., sec. 17, Green Twp.; CINCINNATI WEST.
   Mineral occurrence: Wuestner, 1938, p. 266.

LICKING COUNTY
1. Dendrites of unidentified black manganese oxide on fractures of flint bed in Vanport limestone, Allegheny Group. Also quartz. Road cut about ¼ mile N of Flint Ridge State Memorial on Ohio Rte. 668, Hopewell Twp.; GLENFORD.
   General geology: Carlson, 1987a, p. 415-418; DeLong, 1972, map; Mills, 1921, p. 90-161.

MARCASITE
FeS_2

Chemical class: Sulfide
Crystallization: Orthorhombic; dipyramidal; mmm
Habit: Commonly well crystallized; tabular or prismatic forms most common; twinned crystals form spear-shaped intergrowths; granular; also commonly finely crystalline and massive; stalactitic, radiating
Physical properties: Fracture: uneven. H: 6-6½. G: 4.9. Luster: metallic. Color: pale bronze yellow; tin white on fresh fractures; may be iridescent. Streak: grayish black
Occurrence: Rare as small crystals and granular aggregates in cavities and fractures of dolostones of western Ohio; nodules and aggregates of crystals uncommon in black shales and coal seams of central and eastern Ohio. Marcasite, in comparison to pyrite, is relatively rare in Ohio and is less common than the geologic literature would indicate. X-ray identification of marcasite has been made by the author for occurrences at several localities and is indicated within the location description. Most other "marcasite" localities are listed under pyrite

DELAWARE COUNTY
1. Concretions and twinned crystals of marcasite in Olentangy Shale. Also pyrite. Cliff exposure along E bank of Olentangy River ¼ mile S of Penn Central Railroad bridge and opposite sewage disposal plant at Delaware, Delaware Twp.; DELAWARE.
   Mineral occurrence: Van Horn and Van Horn, 1933, p. 292; Westgate, 1926, p. 33-34, 56.
   General geology: Janssens, 1969, p. 1.7-1.8; Stauffer, 1909, p. 88-89.
2. Clusters of twinned crystals of marcasite in Olentangy Shale. Also melanterite and pyrite. Exposures of shale banks, no specific localities given.
   Mineral occurrence: Westgate, 1926, p. 56, 63.

GREENE COUNTY
1. Large tabular crystals of marcasite with dolomite and pyrite in cavities of Cedarville Dolomite. Also calcite and quartz. American Aggregates Corp. quarry 1 mile SE of Cedarville on N side of Turnbull Rd., Cedarville Twp.; CEDARVILLE. Identified by x-ray.

General geology: Stith, 1983, p. 11-12, 14.

MARION COUNTY
1. Small crystals of marcasite in cavities of *Lockport Dolomite* and Greenfield Dolomite. Also calcite, celestite, dolomite, fluorite, sphalerite, and strontianite. Tri-County Limestone Co. quarry (formerly Laubis Stone Co.) 2 miles SW of Marseilles, center sec. 19, Grand Twp.; MARSEILLES. Identified by x-ray.
   General geology: Cumings, 1930, p. 202-203; Hall and Alkire, 1956, p. 5, 32-35; Stith, 1983, p. 15; Stout, 1941, p. 281-282.

OTTAWA COUNTY
1. Thin coatings of finely crystalline marcasite in Lockport Dolomite. Also calcite, celestite, dolomite, fluorite, galena, pyrite, and sphalerite. GenLime Group, L. P., quarry (formerly U.S. Gypsum Co.), Genoa, W½ sec. 3, Clay Twp.; GENOA. Identified by x-ray.
   General geology: Carlson, 1986, p. 4-9; Forsyth, 1971, p. 15-16; Janssens, 1977, p. 3, 22; Sparling, 1965, p. 236-237; Stout, 1941, p. 413-414.

PICKAWAY COUNTY
1. Marcasite and pyrite with dolomite in Columbus Limestone. Also calcite. Melvin Stone Co. quarry (formerly F. H. Brewer Co.) about 1 mile E of Crownover Mill on N side of Williamsport-Crownover Mill Rd., N Perry Twp.; CLARKSBURG.
   Mineral occurrence: Botoman and Stieglitz, 1978, p. 6, 9.
   General geology: Stout, 1941, p. 140-141.

SENECA COUNTY
1. Thin crusts of finely crystalline marcasite in fractures of *Lockport Dolomite* and Greenfield Dolomite. Also calcite, celestite, dolomite, fluorite, galena, pyrite, sphalerite, and strontianite. Maple Grove Stone Co. quarry (formerly Basic Refractories), Maple Grove, sec. 11 and N½ sec. 14, Liberty Twp.; TIFFIN NORTH. Identified by x-ray.
   General geology: Floyd, 1971, p. 167, 173-174; Janssens, 1971, p. 35; 1974, p. 82, 84; 1977, p. 3, 22; Stout, 1941, p. 348-349.

UNION COUNTY
1. Crystals and thin crusts of finely crystalline marcasite in cavities of Columbus Limestone. Also asphalt, calcite, and fluorite. Union Aggregates Co. quarry 3½ miles S of Ostrander on E side of County Rd. 96, Mill Creek Twp.; SHAWNEE HILLS. Identified by x-ray.
   General geology: Janssens, 1970b, p. 3; Stout, 1941, p. 239.

WOOD COUNTY
1. Marcasite in Tymochtee Dolomite. Also calcite, fluorite, gypsum, pyrite, and sphalerite. France Stone Co. North Baltimore quarry, W½ sec. 26, Henry Twp.; NORTH BALTIMORE.
   Mineral occurrence: Botoman and Stieglitz, 1978, p. 6.
   General geology: Janssens, 1971, p. 35; 1977, p. 26; Kahle and Floyd, 1972, p. 46-48; Stout, 1941, p. 394-395.
2. Small equant crystals and acicular, radiating masses of iridescent marcasite in cavities and fractures of dolostones of *Detroit River Group* and Dundee Formation; may be associated with calcite, celestite, fluorite, and sphalerite. Also asphalt, barite, dolomite, glauconite, hexahydrite, and pyrite. France Stone Co. Custar quarry (formerly Pugh Quarry Co.) about 4 miles W of Weston, SW¼ sec. 6, Milton Twp.; MCCLURE. Identified by x-ray.
   Mineral occurrence: Bingaman and others, 1978, p. 18; Botoman and Faure, 1976, p. 69; Botoman and

Stieglitz, 1978, p. 6; Feldmann and others, 1977, p. 35-37; Forsyth, 1966a, p. 204-205; Green, R., 1970a, p. 584; Janssens, 1970a, p. 7, 22; Nelson, 1967, p. 71; Parr and Chang, 1977, p. 213-222; Strogonoff, 1966, p. 61.

General geology: Orton and Peppel, 1906, p. 133; Stout, 1941, p. 395-396.

3. Tiny balls of marcasite on dolomite crystals in *Lockport Dolomite* and Greenfield Dolomite. Also aragonite, barite, calcite, celestite, fluorite, galena, gypsum, pyrite, sphalerite, strontianite, and sulfur. Stoneco quarry (formerly Maumee Stone Co.), Lime City, SW¼ sec. 11, Perrysburg Twp.; ROSSFORD. Identified by x-ray.

Mineral occurrence: Haden, 1977, p. 25, 28.

General geology: Janssens, 1971, p. 35; 1974, p. 82, 84; 1977, p. 22; Kahle and Floyd, 1968, p. 28-30; 1972, p. 50-52.

MELANTERITE (COPPERAS)
FeSO$_4$ · 7H$_2$O

Chemical class: Sulfate
Crystallization: Monoclinic; prismatic; 2/m
Habit: Commonly in fibrous, acicular, or powdery aggregates and crusts; equant to prismatic crystals
Physical properties: Cleavage: {001} perfect pinacoidal. H: 2. G: 1.9. Luster: vitreous to silky if well crystallized or dull if powdery. Color: commonly pale greenish white or bluish white; crystals may be transparent with pale-greenish tint. Streak: white. Taste: astringent. Melanterite is unstable and dehydrates readily to rozenite and szomolnokite
Occurrence: Finely crystalline aggregates as efflorescence on or associated with pyrite in coal and shale in central and eastern Ohio

ADAMS COUNTY
1. Efflorescence of melanterite with alum on lower Ohio Shale. Also barite, calcite, and pyrite. Outcrop at Blue Creek near Ohio Rte. 125, Jefferson Twp.; BLUE CREEK.

Mineral occurrence: Locke, 1838, p. 260-261.

General geology: Seyfried, 1953, p. 13, 26.

2. Considerable quantities of melanterite in crevices of Ohio Shale. Also pyrite. E branches of [Ohio] Brush Creek, no specific localities given.

Mineral occurrence: Hildreth, 1834, p. 249-250.

ATHENS COUNTY
1. Efflorescence of melanterite on gray shale in Upper Freeport (No. 7) coal, Allegheny Group. Exposure in strip mine, N½ sec. 36, Dover Twp.; NELSONVILLE.

Mineral occurrence: Sturgeon and associates, 1958, p. 447-449.

2. Efflorescence of melanterite on Middle Kittanning (No. 6) coal, Allegheny Group. Murray Coal Co. mine no. 5, Murray City, NW¼NW¼ sec. 33, Trimble Twp.; NEW STRAITSVILLE.

Mineral occurrence: Sturgeon and associates, 1958, p. 513.

3. Efflorescence of melanterite on Upper Freeport (No. 7) coal, Allegheny Group. Mine near W edge of Hollister on S side of Mud Fork Creek, sec. 21, Trimble Twp.; CORNING.

Mineral occurrence: Sturgeon and associates, 1958, p. 514.

4. Efflorescence of melanterite on Upper Freeport (No. 7) coal, Allegheny Group. Exposure along W side of Ohio Rte. 691, SW¼SW¼ sec. 12, Waterloo Twp.; THE PLAINS.

Mineral occurrence: Sturgeon and associates, 1958, p. 546; Sturgeon and Smith, 1954, p. 5.

5. Efflorescence of melanterite on Lower Freeport (No. 6A) coal, Allegheny Group. Exposure in strip mine E of Carbondale on N side of road, NE¼NE¼ sec. 30, Waterloo Twp.; UNION FURNACE.

Mineral occurrence: Sturgeon and associates, 1958, p. 524.

6. Efflorescence of melanterite on Middle Kittanning (No. 6) coal, Allegheny Group. Baltimore and Ohio Railroad cut at W portal of Kings Tunnel No. 4, sec. 32, Waterloo Twp.; MINERAL.

Mineral occurrence: Sturgeon and associates, 1958, p. 533.

7. Efflorescence of melanterite on Middle Kittanning (No. 6) coal, Allegheny Group. Abandoned mine in ravine, E½SW¼ sec. 33, Waterloo Twp.; MINERAL.

Mineral occurrence: Sturgeon and associates, 1958, p. 536.

8. Efflorescence of melanterite on Lower Kittanning (No. 5) coal, Allegheny Group. Also gypsum and pyrite. Exposures along Twp. Hwy. 276 and in abandoned mines, SW¼ sec. 24 and NW¼ sec. 23, York Twp.; NELSONVILLE (ATHENS 15-minute).

Mineral occurrence: Sturgeon and associates, 1958, p. 558-559.

9. Efflorescence of melanterite on Middle Kittanning (No. 6) coal, Allegheny Group. Exposure along road cut and in strip mine on N side of Ohio Rte. 216 W of Monday Creek, NE¼SE¼ sec. 18, York Twp.; NELSONVILLE.

Mineral occurrence: Sturgeon and associates, 1958, p. 562-563.

10. Efflorescence of melanterite on Lower Freeport (No. 6A) coal, Allegheny Group. Exposure in a strip mine N of Buchtel-Nelsonville Rd., NW¼NE¼ sec. 18, York Twp.; NELSONVILLE.

Mineral occurrence: Sturgeon and associates, 1958, p. 565.

11. Efflorescence of melanterite on Middle Kittanning (No. 6) coal, Allegheny Group. Abandoned strip mine on E side of Dorr Run valley, NE¼ sec. 30, York Twp.; NELSONVILLE.

Mineral occurrence: Denton and others, 1961, p. 201; Sturgeon and associates, 1958, p. 587-588.

CARROLL COUNTY
1. Efflorescence of melanterite with rozenite and szomolnokite on Lower Kittanning (No. 5) coal and Middle Kittanning (No. 6) coal, Allegheny Group. Also barite, pyrite, sphalerite, and wurtzite. James Bros. Coal Co. strip mine about 3 miles SE of Mineral City, N½ sec. 25, Rose Twp.; MINERAL CITY.

General geology: Lamborn, 1942, p. 10, 13.

COLUMBIANA COUNTY
1. Efflorescence of melanterite on Lower Kittanning (No. 5) coal, Allegheny Group. Also pyrite. Exposure along W side of Ohio Rte. 7 just S of Wellsville and 0.5 mile N of county line, NW¼SW¼ sec. 9, Yellow Creek Twp.; WELLSVILLE.

Mineral occurrence: Denton and others, 1961, p. 153, 188; Hollenbaugh, 1979, p. 9, 16-17.

CUYAHOGA COUNTY
1. Efflorescence of melanterite with alumlike compounds on Chagrin Shale Member, Ohio Shale. Also pyrite. Railroad cut between Cedar Ave. and Mayfield Rd., Cleveland Heights, EAST CLEVELAND.
   Mineral occurrence: Van Horn, 1910, p. 772.
DELAWARE COUNTY
1. Efflorescence of melanterite on *Olentangy Shale* and *Ohio Shale*. Also marcasite and pyrite. Exposures of shale banks, no specific localities given.
   Mineral occurrence: Westgate, 1926, p. 56, 63.
HIGHLAND COUNTY
1. Noticeable amounts of melanterite as weathering product of pyrite in Ohio Shale. Exposures along E margin of county, no specific localities given.
   Mineral occurrence: Rogers, J. K., 1936, p. 84-85.
LORAIN COUNTY
1. Efflorescence of melanterite with rozenite on gray Bedford Shale. Cliff exposure on W bank of Black River near junction of West and East Branches, S end of Cascade Park, Elyria, Elyria Twp.; GRAFTON.
   General geology: Newberry, 1874b, p. 211-212.
2. Efflorescence of melanterite in upper Huron or lower Cleveland Shale Members, Ohio Shale. Cliff E of old Lake Breeze House grounds on Lake Erie shore, Sheffield Twp.; AVON (OBERLIN 15-minute).
   Mineral occurrence: Prosser, 1913, p. 352.
PERRY COUNTY
1. Fibrous light-green melanterite with copiapite between shale partings in Middle Kittanning (No. 6) coal, Allegheny Group. Also pyrite. Old Congo coal mine, Congo, SW¼ sec. 7, Monroe Twp.; NEW STRAITSVILLE.
   Mineral occurrence: McCaughey, 1918, p. 162.
   General geology: Flint, 1951, p. 82-83.
ROSS COUNTY
1. Efflorescence of melanterite with halotrichite-pickeringite on Huron Shale Member, Ohio Shale. Also barite, calcite, dolomite, pyrite, and quartz. Cliff exposure along SE side of Paint Creek at Copperas Mountain about 1 mile ESE of Seip Mound State Memorial, Paxton Twp.; MORGANTOWN.
   Mineral occurrence: Bingaman and others, 1978, p. 10; Briggs, 1838, p. 77-78; Carlson, 1987b, p. 428; Dana, E. S., 1892, p. 942, 1085; Dana, J. D., 1858, p. 385, 495; 1868, p. 646, 784; Knille and Gibbs, 1942, p. 318-320; Wuestner, 1938, p. 261.
   General geology: Kepferle and others, 1981, p. 294-295; Orton, 1874, p. 647; Seyfried, 1953, p. 18-25.
VINTON COUNTY
1. Fibrous pale-green melanterite with halotrichite and rozenite on pyrite from Middle Kittanning (No. 6) coal, Allegheny Group. Abandoned coal mines along upper reaches of Sandy Run, NE Brown Twp.; MINERAL.
   Mineral occurrence: Ehlers, E. G., and Stiles, 1965, p. 1457-1458.
   General geology: Brant and Foster, 1959, p. 187-188.

OPAL
$SiO_2 \cdot nH_2O$

Chemical class: Silicate
Crystallization: Amorphous
Habit: Massive; may be botryoidal
Physical properties: Fracture: conchoidal. H: 5½-6½. G: 2.0-2.2. Luster: vitreous to greasy. Color: white, yellow, red, blue, green, gray; may be opalescent with a rich play of colors.
Streak: white
Occurrence: Small masses rare in association with fossil fish fragments in bone beds of the Delaware Limestone in central Ohio
FRANKLIN COUNTY
1. Opalescent white to gray opal replacing fish fragments from bone beds of Columbus Limestone and *Delaware Limestone*. American Aggregates Corp. Marble Cliff quarry (formerly Marble Cliff Quarries Co. Scioto quarry) W of Scioto River about ½ mile S of Griggs Dam, SE Norwich Twp.; NORTHWEST COLUMBUS.
   Mineral occurrence: Wells, 1944a, p. 10; 1944b, p. 281.
   General geology: Stauffer and others, 1911, p. 113-115; Stout, 1941, p. 215-216.

POTASH ALUM
$KAl(SO_4)_2 \cdot 12H_2O$

Chemical class: Sulfate
Crystallization: Isometric; diploidal; m3
Habit: Commonly finely granular, powdery crusts; octahedral crystals
Physical properties: Fracture: conchoidal. H: 2-2½. G: 1.8. Luster: vitreous to dull. Color: white, colorless. Streak: white. Taste: sweetish and astringent
Occurrence: Finely granular efflorescence rare in sandstone and shale. Most of the numerous reports of alum in the Ohio geological literature refer instead to members of the halotrichite-pickeringite series
SCIOTO COUNTY
1. Potash alum along bedding planes of Berea Sandstone; may be kalinite. Railroad cut ¼ mile W of McDermott on N side of Scioto Brush Creek, Rush Twp.; WEST PORTSMOUTH.
   Mineral occurrence: Calvert and others, 1968, p. 26-27.
SUMMIT COUNTY
1. Efflorescence of white potash alum with thenardite and gypsum on Sharon conglomerate, Pottsville Group. King's Creek Cave on N side of Cuyahoga River about 1/5 mile W of Mary Campbell Cave, Cuyahoga Gorge Park, Cuyahoga Falls; AKRON WEST.
   Mineral occurrence: Connors, 1974, p. 37.
   General geology: Kent State University, *in* Frank, 1969, p. 1.4-1.7.
2. Efflorescence of white potash alum with gypsum on Sharon conglomerate, Pottsville Group. Outcrop on E side of hill 1 mile W of Aurora Pond, NE Twinsburg Twp.; TWINSBURG.
   Mineral occurrence: Connors, 1974, p. 38.

PYRITE
FeS_2

Chemical class: Sulfide
Crystallization: Isometric; diploidal; m3
Habit: Commonly well crystallized; cubic and octahedral forms most common; also trapezohedral, diploidal, pyritohedral; granular; also finely crystalline and massive, radiating, acicular
Physical properties: Fracture: uneven to conchoidal. H: 6-6½. G: 5.0. Luster: metallic. Color: pale brass yellow; may be iridescent. Streak: greenish black
Occurrence: Small crystals and finely granular coatings in cavities and fractures of dolostones in western Ohio; nodules common in

shales and less common in dolostones, especially those of Devonian age, in eastern and northwestern Ohio, respectively; nodules, lenses, and bands common in many of the coal beds of eastern Ohio; small crystals and finely granular aggregates common in septarian ironstone nodules in eastern Ohio. X-ray identification of pyrite has been made by the author for several localities and is indicated within the location description

ADAMS COUNTY
1. Nodular masses of pyrite in Lilley Dolomite, Peebles Dolomite, Greenfield Dolomite, Tymochtee Dolomite, and *Ohio Shale*. Also calcite and sphalerite. Davon, Inc., Plum Run quarry about 1 mile S on Twp. Hwy. 126 from its intersection with Ohio Rte. 74 at Bacon Flat, Franklin-Meigs Twp. boundary; JAYBIRD.
   Mineral occurrence: Schmidt and others, 1961, p. 285-288; Summerson and others, 1963, p. 18-23.
   General geology: Rexroad and others, 1965, p. 29; Stith, 1983, p. 11-12, 15.
2. Pyrite with barite, calcite, and quartz in veins of large limestone concretions and as nodules in Ohio Shale. Abandoned Norfolk and Western Railroad cut at Beaver Pond, Franklin Twp.; JAYBIRD.
   Mineral occurrence: Hoskins and Blickle, 1940, p. 474; Seyfried, 1953, p. 13, 30.
3. Nodules of pyrite in Ohio Shale. Norfolk and Western Railroad cut at junction of Ohio Rtes. 73 and 74, Franklin Twp.; JAYBIRD.
   Mineral occurrence: Seyfried, 1953, p. 13, 28.
4. Nodules of pyrite in Ohio Shale. Road cut along Ohio Rte. 73, 1.6 miles E of bridge over Scioto Brush Creek, E Franklin Twp.; JAYBIRD.
   Mineral occurrence: Seyfried, 1953, p. 13, 25.
5. Masses of pyrite in Bisher Dolomite near intersection of two faults. Also calcite and manganese oxides. Outcrop on W side of Ohio Rte. 41 about 1 mile N of Locust Grove, Franklin Twp.; SINKING SPRING.
   Mineral occurrence: Galbraith, 1968, p. 25, 32-33.
   General geology: Reidel, 1975, map.
6. Pyrite nodules in lower Ohio Shale. Also asphalt, barite, calcite, dolomite, and quartz. Old quarry and cliff exposure on W side of Hackleshin Rd. 4 miles NE of Locust Grove, Franklin Twp.; JAYBIRD.
   Mineral occurrence: Wuestner, 1938, p. 259-261.
   General geology: Kepferle and others, 1981, p. 290-293; Lamborn, 1927, p. 712-714; Seyfried, 1953, p. 28.
7. Pyrite and its weathering products in undifferentiated Peebles-Greenfield-Tymochtee Dolomites. Serpent Mound disturbance, no specific localities given.
   Mineral occurrence: Botoman and Stieglitz, 1978, p. 4-5; Reidel, 1972, p. 72, 80.
   General geology: Koucky and Reidel, 1987, p. 431-436; Reidel and Koucky, 1981, p. 391-403; Reidel and others, 1982, p. 1343-1377.
8. Pyrite nodules in lower Olentangy Shale. Outcrop near head of tributary to Ohio River on N side of U.S. Rte. 52, 5/8 mile NW of Long Lick Run, Green Twp.; BUENA VISTA.
   Mineral occurrence: Lamborn, 1927, p. 715; 1929, p. 37-38.
9. Pyrite concretions in lower Ohio Shale. Also barite, calcite, and melanterite. Outcrop at Blue Creek near Ohio Rte. 125, Jefferson Twp.; BLUE CREEK.
   Mineral occurrence: Locke, 1838, p. 260-261, map; Seyfried, 1953, p. 13, 26.
10. Pyrite concretions in Ohio Shale. Also melanterite. Outcrops along E branches of [Ohio] Brush Creek, no specific localities given.
    Mineral occurrence: Hildreth, 1834, p. 249-250.

ALLEN COUNTY
1. Thin crusts of fine-grained pyrite in cavities and fractures of Tymochtee Dolomite and dolostones of undifferentiated Salina Group. Also asphalt, calcite, dolomite, fluorite, and sphalerite. National Lime & Stone Co. quarry, Lima, sec. 29, Bath Twp.; LIMA. Identified by x-ray.
   Mineral occurrence: Botoman and Stieglitz, 1978, p. 5.
   General geology: Janssens, 1977, p. 3.
2. Pyrite in Tymochtee Dolomite. Also calcite and sphalerite. National Lime & Stone Co. quarry (formerly Western Ohio Stone Co.), Lima, W½ sec. 29, Bath Twp.; LIMA.
   Mineral occurrence: Botoman and Stieglitz, 1978, p. 5.
   General geology: Janssens, 1977, p. 3; Stout, 1941, p. 305.
3. Fine- to medium-grained pyrite in cavities and fractures of *Tymochtee Dolomite* and dolostones of undifferentiated Salina Group. Also calcite, dolomite, fluorite, and sphalerite. Bluffton Stone Co. quarry, Bluffton, NW¼ sec. 12, Richland Twp.; BLUFFTON. Identified by x-ray.
   General geology: Janssens, 1977, p. 3; Stout, 1941, p. 310.

ASHTABULA COUNTY
1. Nodules of pyrite and marcasite in Chagrin Shale Member, Ohio Shale. Outcrops along banks of Ashtabula River, Ashtabula and Plymouth Twps.; ASHTABULA SOUTH, GAGEVILLE.
   Mineral occurrence: Prosser, 1912, p. 449.

ATHENS COUNTY
1. Masses of pyrite in Pittsburgh (No. 8) coal, Monongahela Group. Exposure along a stream SE of Pleasanton, N-central sec. 3, Alexander Twp.; SHADE.
   Mineral occurrence: Sturgeon and associates, 1958, p. 305-306.
2. Lenses of pyrite in Pittsburgh (No. 8) coal, Monongahela Group. Old Black Diamond mine, N-central sec. 28, Bern Twp.; AMESVILLE.
   Mineral occurrence: Bownocker and Dean, 1929, p. 231; Bownocker and others, 1908, p. 72-73; Sturgeon and associates, 1958, p. 380; Tucker, 1919, p. 203, 214.
3. Nodules of pyrite in Pittsburgh (No. 8) coal, Monongahela Group. Old Federal Coal Co. mine, Broadwell, S-central sec. 13, Bern Twp.; STEWART.
   Mineral occurrence: Bownocker and Dean, 1929, p. 233; Bownocker and others, 1908, p. 75.
4. Large masses of pyrite in Pittsburgh (No. 8) coal, Monongahela Group. Exposure in abandoned strip mine, sec. 36, Bern Twp.; AMESVILLE.
   Mineral occurrence: Sturgeon and associates, 1958, p. 376.
5. Masses of pyrite in Middle Kittanning (No. 6) coal, Allegheny Group. New York Coal Co. Chauncy mine no. 25, secs. 14 and 15, Dover Twp.; JACKSONVILLE.
   Mineral occurrence: Sturgeon and associates, 1958, p. 437.
6. Lenses of pyrite in Middle Kittanning (No. 6) coal, Allegheny Group. Drydock Coal Co. mine, NW¼SE¼ sec. 23, Dover Twp.; JACKSONVILLE.
   Mineral occurrence: Sturgeon and associates, 1958, p. 444.
7. Lenses of pyrite in Upper Freeport (No. 7) coal, Allegheny Group. Old New York Coal Co. mine no. 36, near junction of Buchtel, Dover, and Trimble Twps.; NELSONVILLE.
   Mineral occurrence: Tucker, 1919, p. 205, 214.

8. Lenses of pyrite in Upper Freeport (No. 7) coal, Allegheny Group. McClelland mine, SE¼ sec. 21, Trimble Twp.; JACKSONVILLE.
Mineral occurrence: Dean, 1949, p. 7.
9. Lenses of pyrite in Middle Kittanning (No. 6) coal, Allegheny Group. Goldbrick mine, NW¼NW¼ sec. 22, Waterloo Twp.; MINERAL.
Mineral occurrence: Sturgeon and associates, 1958, p. 527-528.
10. Lenses of pyrite in Upper Freeport (No. 7) coal, Allegheny Group. Old Nixon Edington mine, Nelsonville, York Twp.; NELSONVILLE.
Mineral occurrence: Tucker, 1919, p. 205, 214.
11. Balls and lenses of pyrite in Lower Kittanning (No. 5) coal, Allegheny Group. Also gypsum and melanterite. Exposures along Twp. Hwy. 276 and in abandoned mines, SW¼ sec. 24 and NW¼ sec. 23, York Twp.; NELSONVILLE (ATHENS 15-minute).
Mineral occurrence: Sturgeon and associates, 1958, p. 558-559.
12. Masses of pyrite in Upper Freeport (No. 7) coal, Allegheny Group. Strip mine ½ mile S of Buchtel, SW¼SE¼ sec. 6, York Twp.; NELSONVILLE.
Mineral occurrence: Sturgeon and associates, 1958, p. 563-564.
13. Thick layers of pyrite in Upper Freeport (No. 7) coal, Allegheny Group. Strip mine, NW¼ sec. 9, York Twp.; NELSONVILLE.
Mineral occurrence: Sturgeon and associates, 1958, p. 570-571.
14. Lenses of pyrite in Upper Freeport (No. 7) coal, Allegheny Group. Wharton Coal Co. strip mine, N side of U.S. Rte. 33, NW¼NE¼ sec. 2, SW¼SE¼ sec. 3, York Twp.; NELSONVILLE.
Mineral occurrence: Sturgeon and associates, 1958, p. 580-581.
15. Colloform pyrite along a fault in Middle Kittanning (No. 6) coal or Upper Freeport (No. 7) coal, Allegheny Group. Old New York Coal Co. mine no. 38 at Buchtel, York? Twp.; NELSONVILLE.
Mineral occurrence: Tucker, 1919, p. 200, 205.

AUGLAIZE COUNTY
1. Thin crusts of finely crystalline pyrite in Lockport Dolomite and Greenfield Dolomite. Also calcite, quartz, and sphalerite. National Lime & Stone Co. Buckland quarry, E½ sec. 10, Moulton Twp.; MOULTON. Identified by x-ray.
General geology: Janssens, 1971, p. 35; 1974, p. 82, 84; Shaver, 1974, p. 89-95.

BELMONT COUNTY
1. Lenses and nodules of pyrite in Pittsburgh (No. 8) coal, Monongahela Group. Old Blaine No. 5 mine, Blaine, Colerain Twp.; LANSING.
Mineral occurrence: Tucker, 1919, p. 204, 216.
2. Lenses and nodules of pyrite in Pittsburgh (No. 8) coal, Monongahela Group. Old Fairview mine near Barton, Colerain Twp.; LANSING.
Mineral occurrence: Tucker, 1919, p. 204, 216.
3. Lenses and nodules of pyrite in Pittsburgh (No. 8) coal, Monongahela Group. Old Crescent No. 3 mine near Crescent, Colerain Twp.; LANSING.
Mineral occurrence: Tucker, 1919, p. 204, 216.
4. Lenses of pyrite in Pittsburgh (No. 8) coal, Monongahela Group. Old mines near Maynard, Colerain Twp.; HARRISVILLE, ST. CLAIRSVILLE.
Mineral occurrence: Brown, 1888, p. 608; Tucker, 1919, p. 204, 216.
5. Nodules of pyrite in Meigs Creek (No. 9) coal, Monongahela Group. Old Flushing Coal Co. mine, Flushing, E-central sec. 26, Flushing Twp.; FLUSHING.
Mineral occurrence: Bownocker and Dean, 1929, p. 250; Bownocker and others, 1908, p. 128-129.
6. Lenses of pyrite in Pittsburgh (No. 8) coal, Monongahela Group. Old F. W. McCartney bank (small mine) ½ mile W of Hendrysburg, NE¼ sec. 20, Kirkwood Twp.; FAIRVIEW.
Mineral occurrence: Bownocker and Dean, 1929, p. 211; Bownocker and others, 1908, p. 24; Brown, 1888, p. 612.
7. Lenses of pyrite in Pittsburgh (No. 8) coal, Monongahela Group. Old mines between Dilles Bottom and mouth of Pipe Creek, Mead Twp.; BUSINESSBURG.
Mineral occurrence: Bownocker, 1917, p. 64-65; Bownocker and others, 1908, p. 28-29; Tucker, 1919, p. 203, 216.
8. Lenses of pyrite in Pittsburgh (No. 8) coal, Monongahela Group. Old mines near Bellaire, Mead and Pultney Twps.; BUSINESSBURG, LANSING, MOUNDSVILLE, WHEELING.
Mineral occurrence: Tucker, 1919, p. 203, 216.
9. Lenses and nodules of pyrite in Pittsburgh (No. 8) coal, Monongahela Group. Old mines near Lansing, Pease Twp.; LANSING.
Mineral occurrence: Tucker, 1919, p. 204, 216.
10. Lenses and nodules of pyrite in Pittsburgh (No. 8) coal, Monongahela Group. Old mines N of Martins Ferry, Pease Twp.; TILTONSVILLE, WHEELING.
Mineral occurrence: Tucker, 1919, p. 204, 216.
11. Lenses and nodules of pyrite in Pittsburgh (No. 8) coal, Monongahela Group. Old mines near Neffs, Pultney Twp.; LANSING.
Mineral occurrence: Bownocker and Dean, 1929, p. 212-213; Bownocker and others, 1908, p. 22; Tucker, 1919, p. 203-204, 216.
12. Lenses and nodules of pyrite in Pittsburgh (No. 8) coal, Monongahela Group. Old mines near Stewartsville, Richland Twp.; LANSING.
Mineral occurrence: Tucker, 1919, p. 203, 216.
13. Lenses of pyrite in Pittsburgh (No. 8) coal, Monongahela Group. Old Clarkson No. 1 mine near St. Clairsville, Richland Twp.; ST. CLAIRSVILLE.
Mineral occurrence: Tucker, 1919, p. 204, 216.
14. Lenses of pyrite in Pittsburgh (No. 8) coal, Monongahela Group. Old Delora No. 1 mine, Glencoe, NE¼ sec. 5, Smith Twp.; ST. CLAIRSVILLE.
Mineral occurrence: Bownocker and Dean, 1929, p. 216; Bownocker and others, 1908, p. 27-28; Tucker, 1919, p. 203, 216.
15. Lenses of pyrite in Pittsburgh (No. 8) coal, Monongahela Group. Old Elinor mine near Warnock, Smith Twp.; ST. CLAIRSVILLE.
Mineral occurrence: Tucker, 1919, p. 203, 216.
16. Disks of pyrite in Pittsburgh (No. 8) coal, Monongahela Group. Strip mine, SW¼NE¼ sec. 27, Warren Twp.; BARNESVILLE.
Mineral occurrence: Berryhill, 1963, p. 20.
17. Lenses of pyrite in Pittsburgh (No. 8) coal, Monongahela Group. Old Captina Coal Co. mine, Armstrongs Mills, NW¼ sec. 10, Washington Twp.; ARMSTRONGS MILLS.
Mineral occurrence: Bownocker, 1917, p. 65; Bownocker and Dean, 1929, p. 222; Bownocker and others, 1908, p. 33-34.
18. Lenses and bands of pyrite in Pittsburgh (No. 8) coal, Monongahela Group. Also szomolnokite. North American Coal Co., G-North sec., Powhatan No. 1 mine, sec. 14, Washington Twp.; CAMERON. Identified by x-ray.
General geology: Berryhill, 1963, p. 19-21.

19. Small crystals of pyrite with barite and kaolinite in veins of limestone concretions from shales of Sewickley sandstone, Monongahela Group. Outcrop about ¼ mile E of Ohio Rte. 9 and 2 miles N of Baltimore and Ohio Railroad crossing in Fairpoint, sec. 20, Wheeling Twp.; HARRISVILLE. Identified by x-ray.

General geology: Berryhill, 1963, p. 32-33.

20. Thick band of pyrite in Pittsburgh (No. 8) coal, Monongahela Group. Old Dorsey farm, SW¼ sec. 14, York Twp.; POWHATAN POINT.

Mineral occurrence: Bownocker and others, 1908, p. 33; Brown, 1888, p. 620.

CARROLL COUNTY

1. Pyrite as concretions in Lower Kittanning (No. 5) coal, Allegheny Group, and with barite, sphalerite, and wurtzite in veins of ironstone concretions from shales above both Lower Kittanning (No. 5) coal and Middle Kittanning (No. 6) coal, Allegheny Group. Also melanterite, rozenite, and szomolnokite. James Bros. Coal Co. strip mine about 3 miles SE of Mineral City, N½ sec. 25, Rose Twp.; MINERAL CITY. Identified by x-ray.

General geology: Lamborn, 1942, p. 10, 13.

2. Nodules of pyrite in Middle Kittanning (No. 6) coal, Allegheny Group. Old John Moody bank on Indian Fork of Conotton Creek about 1 mile S of Carrollton, Union Twp.; CARROLLTON.

Mineral occurrence: Stevenson, 1878, p. 187.

COLUMBIANA COUNTY

1. Lenses of pyrite in Lower Kittanning (No. 5) coal, Allegheny Group, and stalactitic and finely crystalline iridescent pyrite in veins of ironstone concretions from shales above Lower Kittanning (No. 5) coal; may be associated with barite, calcite, kaolinite, sphalerite, and wurtzite. Also chalcopyrite, copiapite, and gypsum. Metrel, Inc. quarry S of Negley, sec. 13, Middleton Twp.; EAST PALESTINE. Identified by x-ray.

Mineral occurrence: Hollenbaugh, 1979, p. 9, 16-22; Hollenbaugh and Carlson, 1983, p. 697-703.

General geology: Stout and Lamborn, 1924, p. 111, 123.

2. Lenses and balls of pyrite in Lower Mercer (No. 3) coal, Pottsville Group. Old shaft mines near Leetonia, Salem Twp.; LISBON, SALEM.

Mineral occurrence: Tucker, 1919, p. 208, 216.

General geology: Stout and Lamborn, 1924, p. 104.

3. Lenses and nodules of pyrite in Middle Kittanning (No. 6) coal, Allegheny Group. Old shaft mines near Salineville, Washington Twp.; GAVERS, SALINEVILLE.

Mineral occurrence: Tucker, 1919, p. 207, 216.

4. Lenses of pyrite in Upper Freeport (No. 7) coal, Allegheny Group. Also melanterite. Exposure along W side of Ohio Rte. 7 just S of Wellsville and ½ mile N of Columbiana-Jefferson County line, NW¼SW¼ sec. 9, Yellow Creek Twp.; WELLSVILLE.

Mineral occurrence: Denton and others, 1961, p. 153, 188; Hollenbaugh, 1979, p. 9, 16-17.

COSHOCTON COUNTY

1. Pyrite balls in Lower Kittanning (No. 5) coal, Allegheny Group. Old Sharples mine, S-central sec. 7, Bedford Twp.; WARSAW.

Mineral occurrence: Meyers, 1929, p. 74-75.

CUYAHOGA COUNTY

1. Nodules of pyrite in Cleveland Shale Member, Ohio Shale. Outcrop along S bank of Tinkers Creek near a picnic area in NE part of Bedford Reservation, Bedford, Bedford Twp.; SHAKER HEIGHTS. Identified by x-ray.

General geology: Prosser, 1912, p. 84-85.

2. Concretions of pyrite in Chagrin Shale Member, Ohio Shale. Also melanterite. Railroad cut between Cedar Ave. and Mayfield Rd., Cleveland Heights; EAST CLEVELAND.

Mineral occurrence: Van Horn, 1910, p. 771.

3. Nodules of pyrite with barite and sphalerite in Chagrin Shale Member, Ohio Shale. Cliff exposure along N side of Chippewa Creek about ½ mile downstream from Ohio Rte. 82 bridge, Brecksville Reservation, E Brecksville Twp.; NORTHFIELD. Identified by x-ray.

General geology: Kent State University, *in* Frank, 1969, p. 1.4-1.9; Prosser, 1912, p. 119.

4. Nodules and spheres of pyrite in Cleveland Shale Member, Ohio Shale. Outcrop along Euclid Creek, Euclid; EAST CLEVELAND.

Mineral occurrence: Anonymous, 1936, p. 462.

General geology: Cushing and others, 1931, p. 36-37.

5. Large masses of pyrite in clastic dikes in Bedford Shale. Outcrop along Skinner's Run, Independence-Parma Twp. boundary; CLEVELAND SOUTH.

Mineral occurrence: Cushing and others, 1931, p. 43; Prosser, 1912, p. 67.

6. Layer of pyrite in Bedford Shale. Outcrop along tributary of West Branch Rocky River 0.8 mile N of intersection of Columbia and John Rds., Olmsted Twp.; NORTH OLMSTED.

Mineral occurrence: Prosser, 1912, p. 476-477; Van Horn and Van Horn, 1933, p. 291.

7. Concretions of pyrite in Cleveland Shale Member, Ohio Shale. Outcrop near mouth of small tributary on W side of West Branch Rocky River about ¾ mile W of junction of West and East Branches, Olmsted Twp.; NORTH OLMSTED.

Mineral occurrence: Cushing and others, 1931, p. 35-40; Prosser, 1912, p. 477-478.

8. Concretions of pyrite in Cleveland Shale Member, Ohio Shale. Outcrop in valley of West Branch Rocky River between "Little Cedar Point" and Olmsted Falls, Olmsted Twp.; NORTH OLMSTED.

Mineral occurrence: Van Horn and Van Horn, 1933, p. 291-292.

General geology: Cushing and others, 1931, p. 35-40; Prosser, 1912, p. 474-476.

9. Concretions of pyrite in Cleveland Shale Member, Ohio Shale. Outcrop in valley of Big Creek near W. 130th St., Parma Heights; LAKEWOOD.

Mineral occurrence: Van Horn and Van Horn, 1933, p. 291-292.

General geology: Cushing and others, 1931, p. 36-37.

DELAWARE COUNTY

1. Nodules of pyrite in Olentangy Shale. Also marcasite. Cliff exposure along E bank of Olentangy River ¼ mile S of Penn Central Railroad bridge and opposite sewage disposal plant at Delaware, Delaware Twp.; DELAWARE. Identified by x-ray.

General geology: Janssens, 1969, p. 1.7-1.8; Stauffer, 1909, p. 88-89; Westgate, 1926, p. 33-34, 56.

2. Abundant pyrite in Columbus Limestone and *Delaware Limestone*. Also calcite. Old Miami Stone Co. quarry on W side of Olentangy River W of Ohio Rte. 315, 1.8 miles N of Ohio Rte. 750 intersection, Liberty Twp.; POWELL.

Mineral occurrence: Bernhagen and others, 1953, p. 4.

General geology: Wells, 1944b, p. 299.

3. Cubic and octahedral crystals of pyrite in Olentangy Shale. Outcrop at Camp Lazarus Boy Scout Camp in W-flowing unnamed tributary of Olentangy River in vicinity of "Eagle Rock" 4.9 miles S of Delaware and 0.6 mile W of U.S. Rte. 23, Liberty Twp.; POWELL.

4. Concretions of pyrite in *Olentangy Shale* and *Ohio Shale*. Also melanterite. Exposures of shale banks, no specific localities given.
  Mineral occurrence: Westgate, 1926, p. 51, 56, 63.

ERIE COUNTY
1. Nodules of pyrite in Cleveland Shale Member, Ohio Shale. Also barite and calcite. Outcrop about 0.5 mile N of Birmingham on W bank of Vermilion River, Florence Twp.; KIPTON. Identified by x-ray.
  General geology: Herdendorf, 1963, p. 168-170.
2. Small crystals of pyrite perched on and included in calcite crystals in dolostones of *Detroit River Group* and Columbus and Delaware Limestones. Also celestite, fluorite, and sphalerite. Sandusky Crushed Stone Co. quarry, Parkertown, just S of Portland Rd., Groton Twp.; BELLEVUE. Identified by x-ray.
  General geology: Janssens, 1970b, p. 10-12.
3. Large cubes of pyrite in Olentangy Shale. Outcrop near pond in railroad yard about ½ mile E of intersection of Ohio Rtes. 4 and 113 E of Bellevue, Groton Twp.; BELLEVUE.
  Mineral occurrence: Green, R., 1970a, p. 585.
  General geology: Stauffer, 1909, p. 115-116.
4. Concretions of pyrite in Huron Shale Member, Ohio Shale. Also barite, calcite, dolomite, ferroan dolomite, and quartz. Outcrop just W of Milan on N side of Huron River and W side of U.S. Rte. 250 bridge, Milan Twp.; MILAN.
  Mineral occurrence: Feldmann and others, 1977, p. 48-49; Prosser, 1913, p. 327-328.
5. Small aggregates of pyrite with barite, calcite, dolomite, ferroan dolomite, and whewellite in veins of large limestone concretions from lower Huron Shale Member, Ohio Shale. Outcrop along Huron River about 1 mile W of Milan, Milan Twp.; KIMBALL. Identified by x-ray.
  Mineral occurrence: Hyde, C., and Landy, 1966, p. 228; Leavens, 1968, p. 456-457.
  General geology: Prosser, 1913, p. 324-341.
6. Concretions of pyrite in Olentangy Shale. Outcrop along Plum Creek about 2 miles ENE of Prout, Perkins Twp.; KIMBALL.
  Mineral occurrence: Stauffer, 1916, p. 476-478.
  General geology: Stauffer, 1909, p. 120-121.
7. Pyrite in *Columbus Limestone* and *Delaware Limestone*. Wagner Quarries Co. Soldier's Home quarry, Sandusky, SE of State Soldier's Home, Perkins Twp.; SANDUSKY.
  Mineral occurrence: Nelson, 1967, p. 74, 76; Stout, 1941, p. 366.
  General geology: Stauffer, 1909, p. 125-126; Summerson and others, 1957, p. 59.

FAYETTE COUNTY
1. Pyrite in Greenfield Dolomite. Also calcite, quartz, and sphalerite. American Aggregates Corp. Blue Rock quarry about ¾ mile N of intersection of Ohio Rtes. 41 and 753, SE Perry Twp.; NEW MARTINSBURG.
  Mineral occurrence: Botoman and Stieglitz, 1978, p. 5, 9.
  General geology: Stout, 1941, p. 133-134.

FRANKLIN COUNTY
1. Concretions of pyrite in Ohio Shale. Also barite and calcite. Outcrops along Narrows of Olentangy River about 1¼ miles N of Worthington, Sharon Twp.; NORTHWEST COLUMBUS.
  Mineral occurrence: Foster, J. W., 1838, p. 105; Karhi, 1948, p. 26-27; Orton, 1878, p. 635; Stauffer and others, 1911, p. 26-27, pl. 4.
2. Shells of finely crystalline pyrite on smaller limestone concretions of lower Ohio Shale. Old highway construction site on Olentangy River Rd. between Worthington and Mount Air, Sharon Twp.; NORTHWEST COLUMBUS. Identified by x-ray.
  Mineral occurrence: Barth, 1975, p. 162-163.
3. Shells of fine-grained pyrite on limestone concretions from lower Huron Shale Member, Ohio Shale. Also calcite and whewellite. Road cut along Interstate 270 about 2 miles N of Worthington, Sharon Twp.; NORTHWEST COLUMBUS.
  Mineral occurrence: Criss and others, 1988, p. 4.

GALLIA COUNTY
1. Thick pyrite layers in Pittsburgh (No. 8) coal, Monongahela Group. Old Kerns bank, NE¼ sec. 15, Harrison Twp.; MERCERVILLE.
  Mineral occurrence: Bownocker and Dean, 1929, p. 239; Bownocker and others, 1908, p. 93-94.

GREENE COUNTY
1. Small crystals of pyrite with dolomite and marcasite in cavities of Cedarville Dolomite. Also calcite and quartz. American Aggregates Corp. quarry 1 mile SE of Cedarville on N side of Turnbull Rd., Cedarville Twp.; CEDARVILLE. Identified by x-ray.
  General geology: Stith, 1983, p. 11-12, 14.

GUERNSEY COUNTY
1. Lenses of pyrite in Lower Kittanning (No. 5) coal, Allegheny Group. Old Mary Jean mine near Cambridge, Cambridge Twp.; CAMBRIDGE.
  Mineral occurrence: Tucker, 1919, p. 207, 216.
2. Large masses of pyrite in channels of sandstone associated with Upper Freeport (No. 7) coal, Allegheny Group. Old Minnehaha and Harreyette mines near Byesville, Jackson Twp.; BYESVILLE.
  Mineral occurrence: Tucker, 1919, p. 205, 216-218.
3. Lenses of pyrite in Lower Kittanning (No. 5) coal, Allegheny Group. Old Walters mine, Kimbolton, Liberty Twp.; KIMBOLTON.
  Mineral occurrence: Tucker, 1919, p. 207, 216.

HANCOCK COUNTY
1. Crystals and granular aggregates of coarsely crystalline pyrite in cavities and fractures of *Tymochtee Dolomite* and dolostones of undifferentiated Salina Group; may fill molds of gypsum crystals. Also asphalt, calcite, celestite, fluorite, and sphalerite. National Lime & Stone Co. quarry, Findlay, sec. 24 and NE¼ sec. 25, Liberty Twp.; FINDLAY. Identified by x-ray.
  Mineral occurrence: Strogonoff, 1966, p. 56.
  General geology: Janssens, 1971, p. 35; Stout, 1941, p. 342-343.
2. Crystals of iridescent pyrite with barite, calcite, celestite, and fluorite in cavities of Tymochtee Dolomite. Tarbox-McCall Stone Co. quarry, Findlay, W½ sec. 24, Liberty Twp.; FINDLAY.
  General geology: Janssens, 1977, p. 3.
3. Crystals and granular aggregates of coarsely crystalline pyrite in cavities of Tymochtee Dolomite. Also calcite and fluorite. Pifer Stone Co. quarry, Williamstown, SE¼ sec. 24, Madison Twp.; DUNKIRK. Identified by x-ray.
  General geology: Janssens, 1977, p. 3; Stout, 1941, p. 338-340.

HARDIN COUNTY
1. Crystals and thin crusts of finely crystalline iridescent pyrite in cavities of Lockport Dolomite. Also calcite and dolomite. Standard Slag Co. quarry, Forest, SW¼ sec. 19, Jackson Twp.; FOREST. Identified by x-ray.
  General geology: Cumings, 1930, p. 203; Janssens, 1974, p. 81-86; 1977, p. 3, 22; Stout, 1941, p. 270-272; Summerson and others, 1963, p. 38-39.

2. Crystals and thin crusts of finely crystalline pyrite in cavities and fractures of Tymochtee Dolomite. Also asphalt, calcite, dolomite, fluorite, and sphalerite. Hardin Quarry Co. quarry, Blanchard, NW¼ sec. 6, Pleasant Twp.; FORAKER. Identified by x-ray.
General geology: Janssens, 1977, p. 3; Stout, 1941, p. 274-276.

HARRISON COUNTY
1. Nodules of pyrite in Meigs Creek (No. 9) coal, Monongahela Group. Old Culbertson bank S of New Athens, Athens Twp.; HARRISVILLE.
Mineral occurrence: Bownocker and others, 1908, p. 126-127.
2. Concretions of pyrite in Pittsburgh (No. 8) coal, Monongahela Group. Old Glover Coal Co. mine, SW¼ sec. 5, Cadiz Twp.; JEWETT.
Mineral occurrence: Bownocker and Dean, 1929, p. 202; Bownocker and others, 1908, p. 58.
3. Lenses of pyrite in Lower Freeport (No. 6A) coal, Allegheny Group. Consolidation Coal Co. Oak Park mine, sec. 3, Cadiz Twp.; CADIZ. Identified by x-ray.
General geology: Brant, 1956, p. 23, 29.
4. Lenses of pyrite in Pittsburgh (No. 8) coal, Monongahela Group. Old Rose and Howard mines, Hopedale, Green Twp.; CADIZ.
Mineral occurrence: Tucker, 1919, p. 204, 216.
5. Lenses of pyrite in Pittsburgh (No. 8) coal, Monongahela Group. Old Pittsburgh Block Coal Co. mine, Kenwood, Green Twp.; CADIZ.
Mineral occurrence: Bownocker and others, 1908, p. 57; Tucker, 1919, p. 204, 216.
6. Nodules of pyrite in Pittsburgh (No. 8) coal, Monongahela Group. Old Mansfield opening, sec. 17, Moorefield Twp.; PIEDMONT.
Mineral occurrence: Stevenson, 1878, p. 210.
7. Lenses and layers of pyrite in Pittsburgh (No. 8) coal, Monongahela Group. Old Adena Mining Co. workings near Adena, NE¼ sec. 2, Short Creek Twp.; HARRISVILLE.
Mineral occurrence: Bownocker and Dean, 1929, p. 203; Bownocker and others, 1908, p. 56; Tucker, 1919, p. 204, 216.
8. Lenses of pyrite in Pittsburgh (No. 8) coal, Monongahela Group. Old Majestic mine near Blairmont, Short Creek Twp.; HARRISVILLE.
Mineral occurrence: Tucker, 1919, p. 204, 216.
9. Nodules and lenses of pyrite in Middle Kittanning (No. 6) coal, Allegheny Group. Old Tippecanoe mine near Tippecanoe, Washington Twp.; TIPPECANOE.
Mineral occurrence: Tucker, 1919, p. 206, 216.

HENRY COUNTY
1. Pyrite with calcite in Dundee Formation or dolostones of Traverse Group. Old quarry along W bank of Maumee River a short distance SW of Florida, Flatrock Twp.; FLORIDA.
Mineral occurrence: Stout, 1941, p. 399; Winchell, 1874, p. 417.

HIGHLAND COUNTY
1. Nodules of pyrite in Bisher Dolomite. Also calcite. Outcrop along Sinking Spring Rd. on W bluff of Baker Fork of Ohio Brush Creek 0.5 mile W of Sinking Spring, Brush Creek Twp.; SINKING SPRING. OGS section no. 12683.
Mineral occurrence: Bowman, 1956, p. 111-113.
General geology: Summerson and others, 1963, p. 3-4.
2. Pyrite in Brassfield Formation. Also barite, calcite, and sphalerite. Davon, Inc., Highland Plant quarry about 1 mile SE of Fairview on E side of Danville Rd., NE Hamer Twp.; NEW MARKET. OGS section no. 13610.

Mineral occurrence: Botoman and Stieglitz, 1978, p. 5.
General geology: Hopkins, 1954, p. 85.
3. Crystals of pyrite in Lilley Dolomite. Also calcite. Exposure S of old woolen mill along Factory Branch of Rocky Fork, about 2(?) miles SE of Rainsboro, SE Paint Twp.; RAINSBORO (BAINBRIDGE 15-minute).
Mineral occurrence: Rogers, J. K., 1936, p. 84-85.
4. Pyrite in Ohio Shale. Also melanterite. Exposures along E margin of county, no specific localities given.
Mineral occurrence: Rogers, 1936, p. 84-85.

HOCKING COUNTY
1. Nodules of pyrite in Lower Kittanning (No. 5) coal, Allegheny Group. Strip mine, SW¼NE¼ sec. 26, Falls Gore Twp.; GORE.
Mineral occurrence: Merrill, 1950, p. 169-170, 408-409.
2. Nodules of pyrite in Upper Freeport (No. 7) coal, Allegheny Group. Strip mine, SW¼ sec. 17, Ward Twp.; NEW STRAITSVILLE.
Mineral occurrence: Merrill, 1948, p. 72; 1950, p. 198-199.
3. Nodules of pyrite in Lower Freeport (No. 6A) coal, Allegheny Group. Outcrop in second gully E of road intersection, NE¼NE¼ sec. 29, Ward Twp.; NEW STRAITSVILLE.
Mineral occurrence: Merrill, 1950, p. 434.

HURON COUNTY
1. Small aggregates of granular pyrite with barite, calcite, dolomite, ferroan dolomite, quartz, and sphalerite in veins of large limestone concretions from lower Huron Shale Member, Ohio Shale. Also aragonite. Outcrop about 2 miles N of Monroeville at Lamereaux Rd. bridge on E side of West Branch Huron River, Ridgefield Twp.; KIMBALL. Identified by x-ray.
Mineral occurrence: Carlson, 1977, p. 24-25.
General geology: Broadhead and others, 1980, p. 10-15; Prosser, 1913, p. 324-341.
2. Nodules of pyrite in Huron Shale Member, Ohio Shale. Also barite, gypsum, and halotrichite-pickeringite. Cliff exposure about 2 miles N of Monroeville and ¼ mile SW of Lamereaux Rd. bridge on W side of West Branch Huron River, Ridgefield Twp.; KIMBALL. Identified by x-ray.
General geology: Broadhead and others, 1980, p. 10-15; Prosser, 1913, p. 324-341.

JACKSON COUNTY
1. Lenses of pyrite in Clarion (No. 4A) coal, Allegheny Group. Old mines near Wellston, N Milton Twp.; MULGA.
Mineral occurrence: Bownocker and Dean, 1929, p. 43-44; Stout, 1916, p. 207; Tucker, 1919, p. 208.

JEFFERSON COUNTY
1. Pyrite ("sulphur") balls and thick pyrite band in Pittsburgh (No. 8) coal, Monongahela Group. Old Cross Creek Coal Co. mine near head of Wells Run, sec. 5, Cross Creek Twp.; STEUBENVILLE WEST.
Mineral occurrence: Lamborn, 1930, p. 194.
2. Stalactitic masses and aggregates of granular pyrite in veins of ironstone concretions from shales above Brush Creek coal, Conemaugh Group; may be associated with barite, calcite, sphalerite, and wurtzite. Road cut near Alikanna on E side of Ohio Rte. 7 just N of Ohio Rte. 213 intersection, N½ sec. 31, Island Creek Twp.; KNOXVILLE. Identified by x-ray.
Mineral occurrence: Hollenbaugh and Carlson, 1983, p. 697-701.
General geology: Condit, 1912, p. 204-205; Lamborn, 1930, p. 123; Seaman and Hamilton, 1950, p. 47.
3. Lenses of pyrite in Pittsburgh (No. 8) coal, Monongahela Group. Old mines near Dillonvale, N Mount Pleasant Twp.; DILLONVALE.

Mineral occurrence: Bownocker and Dean, 1929, p. 201; Bownocker and others, 1908, p. 44; Tucker, 1919, p. 204, 216.
4. Lenses of pyrite in Pittsburgh (No. 8) coal, Monongahela Group. Old Dunglen mine, Dunglen, Mount Pleasant Twp.; DILLONVALE.
Mineral occurrence: Tucker, 1919, p. 204, 216.
5. Lenses of pyrite in Pittsburgh (No. 8) coal, Monongahela Group. Old U.S. Coal Co. mine, NE¼ sec. 36, Smithfield Twp.; SMITHFIELD.
Mineral occurrence: Bownocker, 1917, p. 66; Bownocker and Dean, 1929, p. 190; Bownocker and others, 1908, p. 47.
6. Lenses of pyrite in Pittsburgh (No. 8) coal, Monongahela Group. Old Crow Hollow mine, secs. 3 and 4, Smithfield Twp.; DILLONVALE.
Mineral occurrence: Bownocker and Dean, 1929, p. 190-191; Bownocker and others, 1908, p. 46; Tucker, 1919, p. 204, 216.
7. Nodules and large masses of pyrite in Middle Kittanning (No. 6) coal, Allegheny Group. Old mines near Amsterdam and Bergholz, Springfield Twp.; AMSTERDAM.
Mineral occurrence: Tucker, 1919, p. 207, 216.
8. Balls of pyrite in Pittsburgh (No. 8) coal, Monongahela Group. Old Tweed's mine, NW¼ sec. 34, Steubenville Twp.; STEUBENVILLE WEST.
Mineral occurrence: Brown, 1888, p. 598.
9. Lenses of pyrite in Pittsburgh (No. 8) coal, Monongahela Group. Old Rush Run No. 4 mine near Rush Run, Warren Twp.; TILTONSVILLE.
Mineral occurrence: Tucker, 1919, p. 205, 216.
10. Balls and lenses of pyrite in Pittsburgh (No. 8) coal, Monongahela Group. Old McFadden mine 2 miles NE of Hopedale, N-central sec. 33, Wayne Twp.; SMITHFIELD.
Mineral occurrence: Bownocker and Dean, 1929, p. 187; Bownocker and others, 1908, p. 53; Brown, 1888, p. 597.

LAWRENCE COUNTY
1. Large masses of pyrite in Redstone (Pomeroy) (No. 8A) coal, Monongahela Group. Old mine on E side of Paddy Creek about 1½ miles NE of Rome, Rome Twp.; BARBOURSVILLE.
Mineral occurrence: Bownocker and others, 1908, p. 123.

LOGAN COUNTY
1. Trapezohedral crystals and granular aggregates of coarsely crystalline pyrite in cavities of dolostones of undifferentiated Salina Group. Also asphalt, calcite, dolomite, fluorite, and sphalerite. C. E. Duff & Son, Inc., quarry just E of Ohio Rte. 117 about 2 miles N of Huntsville, Richland Twp.; HUNTSVILLE.
Mineral occurrence: Anderson, 1979a, p. 42; Fisher, H. H., 1976, p. 293; Gait, 1980, p. 97-99; Richards and Chamberlain, 1987, p. 391-398.
General geology: Janssens, 1971, p. 35.
2. Crystals and granular aggregates of coarsely crystalline pyrite in cavities of dolostones of undifferentiated Salina Group. Also asphalt, calcite, dolomite, and fluorite. Northwood Stone & Asphalt Co. quarry ½ mile W of Northwood on S side of County Hwy. 105 just W of intersection with County Hwy. 106, Richland Twp.; RUSHSYLVANIA. Identified by x-ray.
General geology: Summerson and others, 1963, p. 37; Stout, 1941, p. 245-247.

LORAIN COUNTY
1. Nodules of pyrite and small masses of pyrite with barite and quartz in veins of barite nodules from Cleveland Shale Member, Ohio Shale. Also calcite and pickeringite. Along banks of Vermilion River at Mill Hollow-Bacon Woods Park, Brownhelm Twp.; VERMILION EAST. Identified by x-ray.
Mineral occurrence: Holden and Carlson, 1979, p. 227-232.
General geology: Broadhead and others, 1980, p. 23-30; Herdendorf, 1963, map; Prosser, 1913, p. 348.
2. Nodules of pyrite in Bedford Shale. Outcrops along bluffs of Vermilion River at Peasley Rd. bridge over Chance Creek, Brownhelm Twp.; KIPTON.
Mineral occurrence: Herdendorf, 1963, p. 51, 170-171.
3. Concretions of pyrite in Cleveland Shale Member, Ohio Shale. Outcrops near shore of Lake Erie on old L. B. Elles farm about 2 miles SW of Beach Park, Sheffield Twp.; AVON (OBERLIN 15-minute).
Mineral occurrence: Prosser, 1913, p. 355-356.

LUCAS COUNTY
1. Pyrite as nodules and replacements of fossils in *Silica Formation* and *Tenmile Creek Dolomite*. Also barite, calcite, celestite, dolomite, sphalerite, and strontianite. France Stone Co. North quarry (formerly Medusa Portland Cement Co.), S-central sec. 7 and NE¼ sec. 18, Sylvania Twp.; SYLVANIA, BERKEY. Identified by x-ray.
Mineral occurrence: Bingaman and others, 1978, p. 20; Carman and others, 1962, p. 5; Ehlers, G. M., and others, 1951, p. 19; Nussman, 1961, p. 101; Stewart, 1927, p. 7-8; Strogonoff, 1966, p. 26.
2. Nodules of pyrite in Tenmile Creek Dolomite. Also calcite. Outcrop along Tenmile Creek, SE¼ sec. 19, Sylvania Twp.; SYLVANIA.
Mineral occurrence: Ehlers, G. M., and others, 1951, p. 21; Stauffer, 1909, p. 145-146.
3. Thin coatings of finely crystalline iridescent pyrite in cavities and fractures of Tymochtee Dolomite and dolostones of undifferentiated Salina Group; may be associated with calcite and celestite. Also asphalt, fluorite, gypsum, halite, sphalerite, and sulfur. France Stone Co. quarry, Waterville, secs. 38 and 39, Waterville Twp.; BOWLING GREEN NORTH. Identified by x-ray.
Mineral occurrence: Strogonoff, 1966, p. 38.
General geology: Janssens, 1977, p. 25-30; Kahle and Floyd, 1968, p. 21-24; 1971, p. 2082-2086; 1972, p. 68; Stout, 1941, p. 402-404.
4. Thin coatings of finely crystalline pyrite in fractures and cavities of Lockport Dolomite and *Greenfield Dolomite*. Also asphalt, calcite, celestite, dolomite, fluorite, gypsum, sphalerite, and sulfur. Stoneco quarry (formerly Maumee Stone Co.), Maumee, sec. 35, Waynesfield Twp.; MAUMEE. Identified by x-ray.
Mineral occurrence: Botoman and Stieglitz, 1978, p. 5; Strogonoff, 1966, p. 33.
General geology: Kahle, 1974, p. 31-54; 1978, p. 63-115; Kahle and Floyd, 1972, p. 70-81; Summerson and others, 1963, p. 44-45; Textoris and Carozzi, 1966, p. 1375-1388.

MAHONING COUNTY
1. Small crystals and coatings of pyrite in veins of ironstone concretions from shales below Lower Mercer limestone, Pottsville Group; may be associated with barite, calcite, chalcopyrite, kaolinite, and sphalerite. Outcrop along West Branch Meander Creek just E of junction with Ohio Rte. 45 about ¾ mile S of Ellsworth, Ellsworth Twp.; CANFIELD. Identified by x-ray.
Mineral occurrence: Greene, 1935, p. 883.
General geology: Lamb, 1910, p. 114.
2. Small crystals and coatings of iridescent pyrite in veins

of ironstone concretions from shales below Vanport(?) limestone, Allegheny Group; may be associated with barite, chalcopyrite, and sphalerite. Keller mine S of Middletown Rd., NE¼ sec. 19, Smith Twp.; ALLIANCE. Identified by x-ray.

General geology: DeLong and White, 1963, p. 42, 45; Lamb, 1910, p. 109.

MARION COUNTY
1. Thin crusts of finely crystalline pyrite in fractures of *Columbus Limestone* and Delaware Limestone. Also calcite and fluorite. National Lime & Stone Co. quarry, Marion, secs. 2 and 3, Marion Twp., and sec. 34, Grand Prairie Twp.; MONNETT. Identified by x-ray.

General geology: Hall and Alkire, 1956, p. 5, 32-35; Janssens, 1970b, p. 3.

MEIGS COUNTY
1. Lenses of pyrite in Redstone (Pomeroy) (No. 8A) coal, Monongahela Group. Old mines at Pomeroy, Salisbury Twp.; POMEROY.

Mineral occurrence: Bownocker and Dean, 1929, p. 243; Bownocker and others, 1908, p. 107-109; Tucker, 1919, p. 203, 212.

MERCER COUNTY
1. Thin crusts of finely crystalline pyrite in cavities of Lockport Dolomite and Greenfield Dolomite. Also asphalt, calcite, dolomite, quartz, and sphalerite. Stoneco quarry (formerly John W. Karch Stone Co.) 4 miles W of Celina, E½ sec. 8, Jefferson Twp.; ERASTUS. Identified by x-ray.

General geology: Shaver, 1974, p. 95-97; Stout, 1941, p. 265-266.

MIAMI COUNTY
1. Small pyritohedrons of pyrite on partings of *Brassfield Formation* and Dayton Formation. Also calcite, dolomite, and glauconite. Armco, Inc., quarry (formerly Piqua Stone Products Co.), Piqua, W½ sec. 29, Spring Creek Twp.; PIQUA EAST, TROY.

General geology: Stith, 1983, p. 11-12, 16; Stout, 1941, p. 187-190.

MORGAN COUNTY
1. Large masses of pyrite ("sulphur") in Pittsburgh (No. 8) coal, Monongahela Group. Old E. M. Blower mine, center sec. 28, Homer Twp.; CORNING.

Mineral occurrence: Bownocker and Dean, 1929, p. 228.

MUSKINGUM COUNTY
1. Small crystals, stringers, and lenses of finely crystalline pyrite in Meigs Creek (No. 9) coal, Monongahela Group. Central Ohio Coal Co. strip mine, Meigs Twp.; CUMBERLAND.

Mineral occurrence: Scheihing and others, 1978, p. 723-732.

NOBLE COUNTY
1. Nodules of pyrite in channels cutting Meigs Creek (No. 9) coal, Monongahela Group. Old mines, NE Elk Twp.; STAFFORD.

Mineral occurrence: Bownocker and others, 1908, p. 145.

2. Nodules of pyrite in Meigs Creek (No. 9) coal, Monongahela Group. Old Barnes and Mellon mine, NW¼ sec. 13, Elk Twp.; DALZELL.

Mineral occurrence: Dean, 1949, p. 15.

3. Concretions of pyrite in Meigs Creek (No. 9) coal, Monongahela Group. Old mine, SE¼ sec. 12, Marion Twp.; SUMMERFIELD.

Mineral occurrence: Bownocker and Dean, 1929, p. 262; Bownocker and others, 1908, p. 143.

4. Balls and lenses of pyrite in Meigs Creek (No. 9) coal, Monongahela Group. Bank on old L. C. Harper farm near Olive Green, Sharon Twp.; CALDWELL SOUTH.

Mineral occurrence: Bownocker and others, 1908, p. 152.

5. Concretions of pyrite in Meigs Creek (No. 9) coal, Monongahela Group. Exposure on farm, NW¼ sec. 25, Stock Twp.; SUMMERFIELD.

Mineral occurrence: Bownocker and Dean, 1929, p. 266; Bownocker and others, 1908, p. 144.

OTTAWA COUNTY
1. Thin coatings of finely crystalline iridescent pyrite in cavities and fractures of *Lockport Dolomite* and Greenfield Dolomite; may be associated with calcite and celestite. Also dolomite, fluorite, galena, gypsum, and sphalerite. Edward Kraemer & Sons, Inc., White Rock quarry, Clay Center, SE¼ sec. 9 and NE¼ sec. 16, Allen Twp.; GENOA. Identified by x-ray.

Mineral occurrence: Botoman and Faure, 1976, p. 69; Botoman and Stieglitz, 1978, p. 5; Carman and others, 1962, p. 13-14; Morrison, 1934, p. 20; 1935, p. 784; Sparling, 1965, p. 171, 239-240; Strogonoff, 1966, p. 12.

General geology: Janssens, 1974, p. 82, 84; 1977, p. 22; Sparling, 1971, p. 19; Stout, 1941, p. 415-418.

2. Thin coatings of finely crystalline pyrite in cavities and fractures of *Lockport Dolomite* and Greenfield Dolomite; may be associated with calcite and celestite. Also asphalt, dolomite, fluorite, sphalerite, and sulfur. Stoneco quarry (formerly Maumee Stone Co.) N of Rocky Ridge, sec. 23, Benton Twp.; OAK HARBOR. Identified by x-ray.

General geology: Botoman and Stieglitz, 1978, p. 6; Forsyth, 1971, p. 14; Sparling, 1965, p. 172.

3. Thin crusts of finely crystalline pyrite associated with celestite in cavities of Lockport Dolomite. Also calcite, dolomite, fluorite, galena, marcasite, and sphalerite. GenLime Group, L. P., quarry (formerly U.S. Gypsum Co.), Genoa, W½ sec. 3, Clay Twp.; GENOA. Identified by x-ray.

Mineral occurrence: Carlson, 1986, p. 4-9.

General geology: Forsyth, 1971, p. 15-16; Janssens, 1977, p. 3, 22; Sparling, 1965, p. 236-237; Stout, 1941, p. 413-414.

4. Crystalline coatings of pyrite in dolostones of undifferentiated Salina Group. Also anhydrite and gypsum. Celotex Corp. quarry, W½ sec. 10, Portage Twp.; VICKERY.

Mineral occurrence: Strogonoff, 1966, p. 21.

General geology: Forsyth, 1971, p. 13-14; Janssens, 1977, p. 36-38; Sparling, 1965, p. 174-175, 253-254.

5. Thin layers of finely crystalline pyrite in cavities and fractures of Bass Islands Dolomite. Also barite, calcite, celestite, and fluorite. Fox Stone Products, Inc., quarry, N side of Langram Rd., S part of South Bass Island, Put-in-Bay Twp.; PUT-IN-BAY. Identified by x-ray.

General geology: Janssens, 1977, p. 27-30; Sparling, 1971, p. 19-22.

PAULDING COUNTY
1. Thin coatings of finely crystalline pyrite in cavities and fractures of dolostones of *Detroit River Group* and Dundee Formation; may be associated with calcite. Also asphalt, fluorite, quartz, and sphalerite. Stoneco Auglaize quarry (formerly Maumee Stone Co.), Junction, NW¼ sec. 32, Auglaize Twp.; JUNCTION. Identified by x-ray.

Mineral occurrence: Feldmann and others, 1977, p. 32-33; Nelson, 1967, p. 46; Stauffer, 1909, p. 153; Strogonoff, 1966, p. 61.

General geology: Janssens, 1970a, p. 21; Stout, 1941, p. 324-325.

PERRY COUNTY
1. Lenses and nodules of pyrite in Middle Kittanning (No.

6) coal, Allegheny Group. Also copiapite and melanterite. Old Congo coal mine, Congo, SW¼ sec. 7, Monroe Twp.; NEW STRAITSVILLE.

Mineral occurrence: Tucker, 1919, p. 206, 214.

General geology: Flint, 1951, p. 82-83.

2. Nodules of pyrite in Upper Freeport (No. 7) coal, Allegheny Group. Old Hatfield wagon mine, sec. 35, Monroe Twp.; CORNING.

Mineral occurrence: Dean, 1949, p. 8.

3. Lenses and nodules of pyrite in Middle Kittanning (No. 6) coal, Allegheny Group. Old mines near Moxahala, Pleasant Twp.; NEW LEXINGTON.

Mineral occurrence: Tucker, 1919, p. 206, 214.

General geology: Orton, 1884a, p. 903-904.

PICKAWAY COUNTY

1. Nodules of pyrite in Ohio Shale. Also asphalt and calcite. Exposures in cliffs and in bed of Deer Creek at Williamsport, Deer Creek Twp.; CLARKSBURG, WILLIAMSPORT.

Mineral occurrence: Andrews, 1874b, p. 590; Hildreth, 1834, p. 249-250.

2. Pyrite with dolomite and marcasite in Columbus Limestone. Also calcite. Melvin Stone Co. quarry (formerly F. H. Brewer Co.) about 1 mile E of Crownover Mill on N side of Williamsport-Crownover Mill Rd., N Perry Twp.; CLARKSBURG.

Mineral occurrence: Botoman and Stieglitz, 1978, p. 6, 9.

General geology: Stout, 1941, p. 140-141.

PREBLE COUNTY

1. Pyrite in Brassfield Formation. Also hematite and sphalerite. Old Marble Cliff quarry, Lewisburg, SW¼ sec. 21, Harrison Twp.; LEWISBURG.

Mineral occurrence: Botoman and Stieglitz, 1978, p. 6.

General geology: Horvath and Sparling, 1967, p. 2-3; Shaver and others, 1961, p. 31-32; Stout, 1941, p. 170.

PUTNAM COUNTY

1. Pyrite in Tymochtee Dolomite and dolostones of undifferentiated Salina Group. Also calcite, fluorite, and sphalerite. Ottawa Stone Co., Inc., quarry, W½ sec. 27, Blanchard Twp.; LEIPSIC.

Mineral occurrence: Botoman and Stieglitz, 1978, p. 6.

General geology: Janssens, 1971, p. 35; 1977, p. 29.

2. Thin crusts of finely crystalline pyrite in cavities and fractures of Tymochtee Dolomite and dolostones of undifferentiated Salina Group. Also asphalt, calcite, fluorite, and sphalerite. Putnam Stone Co., Inc., quarry, NW¼ sec. 6, Riley Twp.; BLUFFTON. Identified by x-ray.

Mineral occurrence: Botoman and Stieglitz, 1978, p. 6.

General geology: Janssens, 1971, p. 35; 1977, p. 29.

ROSS COUNTY

1. Concretions of pyrite in Huron Shale Member, Ohio Shale. Also barite, calcite, dolomite, halotrichite-pickeringite, melanterite, and quartz. Cliff exposure at Copperas Mountain about 1 mile ESE of Seip Mound State Memorial on SE side of Paint Creek, Paxton Twp.; MORGANTOWN. Identified by x-ray.

Mineral occurrence: Briggs, 1838, p. 77-78; Carlson, 1987b, p. 428; Dana, E. S., 1892, p. 942, 1085; Dana, J. D., 1858, p. 385, 495; 1868, p. 646, 784; Knille and Gibbs, 1942, p. 318-320; Orton, 1874, p. 647; Seyfried, 1953, p. 18-25; Shetrone, 1926, p. 190-191.

General geology: Kepferle and others, 1981, p. 294-295.

2. Nodules of pyrite in Ohio Shale. Outcrops in gullies W of Chillicothe and near Frankfort, no specific localities given. Identified by x-ray.

Mineral occurrence: Hyde, J. E., 1921, p. 147; McAllister, 1941, p. 203.

SANDUSKY COUNTY

1. Thin crusts of finely crystalline pyrite in fractures and cavities of Lockport Dolomite. Also barite, calcite, celestite, dolomite, fluorite, galena, sphalerite, and strontianite. Martin Marietta Chemicals quarry (S part formerly Woodville Lime & Chemical Co. quarry), Woodville, E½ sec. 21 and W½ sec. 22, Woodville Twp.; ELMORE. Identified by x-ray.

Mineral occurrence: Carlson, 1986, p. 9-13.

General geology: Stout, 1941, p. 375; Summerson and others, 1963, p. 42.

2. Thin crusts of finely crystalline pyrite in cavities of Lockport Dolomite. Also barite, calcite, celestite, dolomite, fluorite, galena, and sphalerite. Steetley Resources, Inc., Ohio Lime Co. quarry, Woodville, W½ sec. 34, Woodville Twp.; WOODVILLE. Identified by x-ray.

General geology: Floyd, 1971, p. 167-169; Kahle and Floyd, 1968, p. 31-35.

SENECA COUNTY

1. Thin crusts of finely crystalline pyrite in cavities and fractures of *Lockport Dolomite* and Greenfield Dolomite. Also calcite, celestite, dolomite, fluorite, galena, marcasite, sphalerite, and strontianite. Maple Grove Stone Co. quarry (formerly Basic Refractories), Maple Grove, sec. 11 and N½ sec. 14, Liberty Twp.; TIFFIN NORTH. Identified by x-ray.

General geology: Floyd, 1971, p. 167, 173-174; Janssens, 1971, p. 35; 1974, p. 82, 84; 1977, p. 3, 22.

STARK COUNTY

1. Finely crystalline iridescent pyrite with calcite and sphalerite in veins of ironstone concretions in shale beds of Putnam Hill limestone, Allegheny Group. East Ohio Limestone Co. quarry N of Cairo, sec. 21, Lake Twp.; HARTVILLE. Identified by x-ray.

General geology: DeLong and White, 1963, p. 45-49, 180-181.

2. Lenses of pyrite in Lower Kittanning (No. 5) coal, Allegheny Group. Old Robertsville strip mine, NW¼NW¼SE¼ sec. 23, Osnaburg Twp.; ROBERTSVILLE.

Mineral occurrence: DeLong and White, 1963, p. 80; Denton and others, 1961, p. 184-185.

3. Finely crystalline pyrite with barite and sphalerite in veins of ironstone concretions in shales of Allegheny Group. Penn Central Railroad cut at Warren Rd. intersection about ½ mile NE of Paris, SW¼ sec. 4, Paris Twp.; ROBERTSVILLE. Identified by x-ray.

General geology: DeLong and White, 1963, p. 75, 81.

4. Lenses of pyrite in Lower Kittanning (No. 5) coal, Allegheny Group. Abandoned strip mine, SW¼NW¼NW¼ sec. 21, Sandy Twp.; WAYNESBURG.

Mineral occurrence: DeLong and White, 1963, p. 69.

SUMMIT COUNTY

1. Pyrite with calcite, chalcopyrite, kaolinite, and sphalerite in veins of ironstone concretions from Meadville Shale Member, Cuyahoga Formation. Outcrop along small tributary that enters Cuyahoga River from N side about ¼ mile W of foot of dam, Cuyahoga Gorge Park, Cuyahoga Falls; AKRON WEST. Identified by x-ray.

General geology: Kent State University, *in* Frank, 1969, p. 1.4-1.7; Szmuc, 1957, p. 159-161.

2. Spherical concretions of pyrite in Orangeville Shale Member, Cuyahoga Formation. Outcrop in ravine on N face of Cuyahoga River 0.7 mile E of Ohio Rte. 8 bridge and S of Highbridge Ave., Cuyahoga Gorge Park, Cuyahoga Falls; AKRON WEST.

Mineral occurrence: Szmuc, 1957, p. 161.

General geology: Kent State University, *in* Frank, 1969, p. 1.4-1.7.

3. Pyrite as concretions and fossil replacements in Sharpsville Shale Member, Cuyahoga Formation. Also sphalerite. Outcrop along Brandywine Creek near Cleveland-Akron Rd., Northfield Twp.; NORTHFIELD (CLEVELAND 15-minute).
   Mineral occurrence: Cushing and others, 1931, p. 51; Szmuc, 1957, p. 152.

TRUMBULL COUNTY
1. Pyrite with sphalerite as fossil replacements in Meadville Shale Member, Cuyahoga Formation. Outcrop along a tributary that enters Pymatuning Creek from E side 0.2 mile N of Kinsman-Vernon Twp. boundary, SE Kinsman Twp.; KINSMAN.
   Mineral occurrence: Szmuc, 1957, p. 132-133.
2. Concretions of pyrite in Sharpsville Shale Member, Cuyahoga Formation. Outcrop along Mill Creek near Ohio Rte. 88 bridge 0.85 mile W of Vernon, Vernon Twp.; KINSMAN.
   Mineral occurrence: Szmuc, 1957, p. 131.

TUSCARAWAS COUNTY
1. Nodules of pyrite in Middle Kittanning (No. 6) coal, Allegheny Group. Old Jacob Groh mine, sec. 17, Auburn Twp.; STONE CREEK.
   Mineral occurrence: Bownocker and Dean, 1929, p. 86; Bownocker and others, 1908, p. 240.
2. Pyrite with barite and sphalerite in veins of ironstone concretions from shales of the Allegheny Group. Old strip mine on W side of Winfield Rd. about ½ mile NE of intersection with U.S. Rte. 250, Dover Twp.; DOVER.
   General geology: Lamborn, 1956, p. 168, pl. 1.
3. Pyrite with barite and sphalerite in veins of ironstone concretions in shales above Lower Kittanning (No. 5) coal, Allegheny Group. Eberhart Coal Co., Inc., strip mine, Dover(?) Twp., specific location not given.
   Mineral occurrence: Orr and others, 1982, p. 52-54.
   General geology: Lamborn, 1956, p. 125-140.
4. Lenses, nodules, and thick layers of pyrite in Middle Kittanning (No. 6) coal, Allegheny Group. Old mines near New Philadelphia; Dover, Fairfield, Goshen, and York Twps.; DOVER, NEW PHILADELPHIA.
   Mineral occurrence: Orton, 1884a, p. 266-271; Tucker, 1919, p. 206-207, 215-217.
5. Thick band of pyrite in Middle Kittanning (No. 6) coal, Allegheny Group. Old mines S of Uhrichsville, Mill Twp.; UHRICHSVILLE.
   Mineral occurrence: Lamborn, 1956, p. 178; Tucker, 1919, p. 206, 216.
6. Lenses, nodules, and layers of pyrite in Middle Kittanning (No. 6) coal, Allegheny Group. Old mines near Uhrichsville, Mill Twp.; UHRICHSVILLE.
   Mineral occurrence: Tucker, 1919, p. 206, 215-217.
7. Nodules and thick bands of pyrite in Middle Kittanning (No. 6) coal, Allegheny Group. Old mines near Midvale, N Mill Twp. and SW Union Twp.; UHRICHSVILLE.
   Mineral occurrence: Lamborn, 1956, p. 177; Tucker, 1919, p. 207, 216.
8. Lenses, nodules, and thick bands of pyrite in Lower Kittanning (No. 5) coal, Allegheny Group. Old Buckhorn mine NE of Newcomerstown, Oxford Twp.; NEWCOMERSTOWN.
   Mineral occurrence: Tucker, 1919, p. 207, 216.
9. Lenses and thick bands of pyrite in *Lower Kittanning (No. 5) coal* and *Middle Kittanning (No. 6) coal*, Allegheny Group. Old mines at Mineral City, Sandy Twp.; MINERAL CITY.
   Mineral occurrence: Bownocker and Dean, 1929, p. 62-63, 81; Bownocker and others, 1908, p. 191-192, 238-239; Tucker, 1919, p. 207, 208, 216.
10. Pyrite with calcite, sphalerite, and wurtzite in veins of ironstone concretions from shales of Allegheny Group. Puskarich Mining, Inc., strip mine about 1 mile S of New Cumberland, SW¼ sec. 28, Warren Twp.; MINERAL CITY. Identified by x-ray.
    General geology: Lamborn, 1956, p. 140, 175.
11. Lenses of pyrite in Lower Kittanning (No. 5) coal, Allegheny Group. C. A. Wallick strip mine, SW¼SW¼ sec. 17, Wayne Twp.; STRASBURG.
    Mineral occurrence: White, G. W., 1949, p. 216.
12. Lenses of pyrite in Lower Kittanning (No. 5) coal, Allegheny Group. Mullet Coal Co. strip mine about ½ mile NE of old Chestnut Ridge School, Wayne Twp.; WILMOT (NAVARRE 15-minute).
    Mineral occurrence: Lamborn, 1956, p. 133.

UNION COUNTY
1. Thin crusts of finely crystalline pyrite in fractures of dolostones of Salina Group. Also calcite. L. G. Rockhold & Sons, Inc., quarry ½ mile N of York Center on S side of Twp. Hwy. 212, York Twp.; YORK CENTER. Identified by x-ray.
   General geology: Stout, 1941, p. 238-239.

VAN WERT COUNTY
1. Pyrite in Tymochtee Dolomite and dolostones of undifferentiated Salina Group. Also calcite, dolomite, fluorite, and sphalerite. Ridge Township Quarry 2 miles W of Middle Point, NE¼ sec. 22, Ridge Twp.; MIDDLE POINT.
   Mineral occurrence: Botoman and Stieglitz, 1978, p. 6.
   General geology: Janssens, 1971, p. 35.
2. Thin crusts of finely crystalline pyrite in cavities of dolostones of undifferentiated Salina Group. Also asphalt, calcite, dolomite, fluorite, and sphalerite. Stoneco quarry (formerly Maumee Stone Co.) about 4 miles SW of Scott, sec. 8, Union Twp.; CONVOY. Identified by x-ray.
   General geology: Janssens, 1971, p. 35; 1977, p. 3, 29; Stout, 1941, p. 319-320.
3. Small crystals of pyrite in Tymochtee Dolomite and dolostones of undifferentiated Salina Group. Also asphalt, calcite, dolomite, fluorite, and sphalerite. Suever Stone Co., Inc., quarry (formerly Delphos Quarries Co.), Delphos, sec. 25, Washington Twp.; DELPHOS.
   Mineral occurrence: Medici and Robinson, 1988, p. 128.
   General geology: Janssens, 1971, p. 35; Stout, 1941, p. 313.

VINTON COUNTY
1. Concretions of pyrite in Middle Kittanning (No. 6) coal, Allegheny Group. Exposure near head of west fork of Wildcat Hollow about 1½ miles NW of Hope Furnace, Brown Twp.; MINERAL.
   Mineral occurrence: Stout, 1927, p. 317, 330.
2. Pyrite in Middle Kittanning (No. 6) coal, Allegheny Group. Also halotrichite, melanterite, and rozenite. Abandoned mine along upper reaches of Sandy Run, NE Brown Twp.; MINERAL.
   Mineral occurrence: Ehlers, E. G., and Stiles, 1965, p. 1457-1458.
   General geology: Brant and Foster, 1959, p. 187-188.
3. Lenses of pyrite in Clarion (No. 4A) coal, Allegheny Group. Old Vinton Coal Co. mine, N-central sec. 33, Vinton Twp.; MCARTHUR.
   Mineral occurrence: Bownocker and Dean, 1929, p. 49.
4. Small crystals of pyrite in Vanport limestone, Allegheny Group. Also calcite, galena, quartz, and sphalerite. No specific localities given.
   Mineral occurrence: Stout, 1927, p. 265-266.
   General geology: Lamborn, 1951, p. 344-349.

WASHINGTON COUNTY

1. Lenses of pyrite in Meigs Creek (No. 9) coal, Monongahela Group. Exposure 1 mile SW of Elba, NW¼ sec. 28, Aurelius Twp.; LOWER SALEM.
   Mineral occurrence: Bownocker and Dean, 1929, p. 273; Bownocker and others, 1908, p. 162.
2. Masses of pyrite ("sulphur rock") in Meigs Creek (No. 9) coal, Monongahela Group. Old Hamilton mine, Smoky Fork, NW of Moss Run P.O., Lawrence Twp.; BELMONT.
   Mineral occurrence: Bownocker and others, 1908, p. 169.

WAYNE COUNTY

1. Small crystalline masses of pyrite with barite, calcite, chalcopyrite, galena, and sphalerite in veins of ironstone concretions from shales of lower Pottsville Group. Penn Central Railroad cut N of Marshallville, W-central sec. 33, Chippewa Twp.; DOYLESTOWN. Identified by x-ray.
   Mineral occurrence: Ver Steeg, 1940, p. 259; 1942, p. 223.
   General geology: Conrey, 1921, p. 92; Ver Steeg, 1948, p. 185.
2. Pyrite with calcite, galena, and sphalerite in veins of ironstone nodules from shales of Wooster Shale Member, Cuyahoga Formation. Also aragonite. Old quarry E of County Rd. 22 behind City of Wooster Service and Maintenance Facility, NE¼ sec. 5, Wooster Twp.; WOOSTER.
   Mineral occurrence: Ver Steeg, 1940, p. 259.
   General geology: Conrey, 1921, p. 62-63; Szmuc, 1957, p. 193-195.

WOOD COUNTY

1. Pyrite in Tymochtee Dolomite. Also calcite, fluorite, gypsum, marcasite, and sphalerite. France Stone Co. North Baltimore quarry, W½ sec. 26, Henry Twp.; NORTH BALTIMORE.
   Mineral occurrence: Botoman and Stieglitz, 1978, p. 6.
   General geology: Janssens, 1971, p. 35; 1977, p. 26; Kahle and Floyd, 1972, p. 46-48; Stout, 1941, p. 394-395.
2. Small crystals of pyrite in cavities and fractures in dolostones of *Detroit River Group* and Dundee Formation. Also asphalt, barite, calcite, celestite, dolomite, fluorite, glauconite, hexahydrite, marcasite, and sphalerite. France Stone Co. Custar quarry (formerly Pugh Quarry Co.) about 4 miles W of Weston, SW¼ sec. 6, Milton Twp.; MCCLURE.
   Mineral occurrence: Botoman and Faure, 1976, p. 69; Botoman and Stieglitz, 1978, p. 6; Green, R., 1970a, p. 584; Parr and Chang, 1977, p. 213-222.
   General geology: Forsyth, 1966a, p. 204-205; Janssens, 1970a, p. 7, 22; Orton and Peppel, 1906, p. 133; Stout, 1941, p. 395-396.
3. Fine-grained coatings of pyrite in cavities and fractures of *Lockport Dolomite* and Greenfield Dolomite; may be associated with calcite and sphalerite. Also barite, celestite, dolomite, fluorite, hexahydrite, and strontianite. MacRitchie Materials, Inc., quarry (formerly Brough Stone Co.), West Millgrove, SE¼ sec. 4, Perry Twp.; FOSTORIA. Identified by x-ray.
   General geology: Janssens, 1971, p. 35; 1974, p. 82, 84; 1977, p. 22; Shaver, 1977, p. 1414; Stout, 1941, p. 392.
4. Tiny balls of pyrite on calcite crystals in *Lockport Dolomite* and Greenfield Dolomite. Also aragonite, barite, celestite, dolomite, fluorite, galena, gypsum, sphalerite, strontianite, and sulfur. Stoneco quarry (formerly Maumee Stone Co.), Lime City, SW¼ sec. 11, Perrysburg Twp.; ROSSFORD. Identified by x-ray.
   General geology: Janssens, 1971, p. 35; 1974, p. 82, 84; 1977, p. 22; Kahle and Floyd, 1968, p. 28-30; 1972, p. 50-52.

WYANDOT COUNTY

1. Crystals and granular aggregates of coarsely crystalline iridescent pyrite in *Lockport Dolomite* and Greenfield Dolomite. Also calcite, celestite, dolomite, fluorite, gypsum, sphalerite, and strontianite. National Lime & Stone Co. quarry, Carey, N½ sec 15 and N½ sec. 16, Crawford Twp.; CAREY, MCCUTCHENVILLE. Identified by x-ray.
   Mineral occurrence: Summerson and others, 1963, p. 39-40.
   General geology: Carlson, 1987c, p. 101-102; Cumings, 1930, p. 201-202; Hall and Alkire, 1956, p. 7, 31-33; Janssens, 1974, p. 82, 84; 1977, p. 22; Stout, 1941, p. 294-295.

QUARTZ
(including CHALCEDONY, CHERT, and FLINT)
SiO$_2$

Chemical class: Silicate
Crystallization: Hexagonal (Trigonal); trigonal trapezohedral; 32
Habit: Crystals commonly prismatic and terminated by two sets of rhombohedrons; commonly granular or massive
Physical properties: Fracture: conchoidal to uneven. H: 7. G: 2.65. Luster: vitreous; may be greasy or waxy in massive varieties (flint, chaledony). Color: commonly white or colorless; also gray, brown, or purple; flint may be red, brown, green, gray, or black if impurities are present. Streak: white
Varieties: Of the two massive varieties of quartz in this report, flint and chalcedony, flint refers to relatively pure opaque-appearing material of various color in sedimentary nodules and beds; chalcedony refers to silicified wood and to the banded, bluish-white, translucent material lining cavity walls in concretions, geodes, and flint beds (see Chapter 3 for discussion of flint vs. chert)
Occurrence: Flint beds important as a source of lapidary materials in Coshocton, Licking, and Muskingum Counties with fractures and cavities lined with chalcedony and crystals of quartz; siliceous dolostones in the western half of the state locally with quartz-lined cavities, and in Adams and Highland Counties with chalcedony- and quartz-bearing geodes; crystals and granular aggregates of quartz in veins of large septarian limestone concretions from the Ohio Shale in central Ohio; fragments of silicified wood loose along creek and stream beds and imbedded in sandstones and shales in the southeastern part of the state. Sites in addition to those below are given by Stout and Schoenlaub (1945, p. 13-106) for flint, and by Mitchell (1951, p. 253-255) for silicified wood. Quartz pebbles suitable for tumbling occur at sites too numerous to be listed below; the interested reader is referred to reports by Bingaman and others (1978, p. 19) and Read (1878b, p. 526)

ADAMS COUNTY

1. Small quartz crystals with calcite in cavities of Bisher Dolomite. Serpent Mound area, no specific localities given, Bratton and Franklin Twps.; SINKING SPRING.
   Mineral occurrence: Reidel, 1972, p. 26, 92; Rogers, J. K.,

1936, p. 72; Stout, 1941, p. 79.
General geology: Reidel, 1975, map.
2. Quartz with barite, calcite, and pyrite in veins of large limestone concretions from lower Ohio Shale. Abandoned Norfolk and Western Railroad cut at Beaver Pond, Franklin Twp.; JAYBIRD.
Mineral occurrence: Hoskins and Blickle, 1940, p. 474.
General geology: Seyfried, 1953, p. 30.
3. Quartz crystals with asphalt, barite, calcite, and dolomite in veins of large limestone concretions from lower Ohio Shale. Also pyrite. Old quarry and cliff exposure on W side of Hackleshin Rd. 4 miles NE of Locust Grove, Franklin Twp.; JAYBIRD.
Mineral occurrence: Wuestner, 1938, p. 259-261.
General geology: Kepferle and others, 1981, p. 290-293; Lamborn, 1927, p. 712-714; Seyfried, 1953, p. 28.
4. Flint nodules in Bisher Dolomite and Lilley Dolomite. Old Southern Ohio Quarries Co. quarry, ½ mile W of Peebles on N side of Norfolk and Western Railroad tracks, Meigs Twp.; PEEBLES.
Mineral occurrence: Schmidt and others, 1961, p. 283-284; Stout, 1941, p. 55-56.
General geology: Rexroad and others, 1965, p. 27-28.

ATHENS COUNTY
1. Silicified wood weathers out of shales and sandstones of upper Conemaugh or lower Monongahela Group. Fragments scattered along tributaries of Federal Creek, Ames and Bern Twps.; AMESVILLE, JACKSONVILLE.
Mineral occurrence: Hildreth, 1838, p. 43; Stout, 1945, p. 150; 1946, p. 31.
General geology: Andrews, 1873, p. 270-277.
2. Silicified wood weathers out of shales above Pittsburgh (No. 8) coal, Monongahela Group. Fragments scattered along head of Middle Branch of Shade River, SE corner Athens Twp.; ATHENS.
Mineral occurrence: Andrews, 1873, p. 287-288; Condit, 1912, p. 119-120; Hildreth, 1838, p. 43; Mitchell, 1951, p. 253; Murphy, 1973, p. 29-30; Stout, 1945, p. 146, 150-151.
3. Silicified wood weathers out of shales and sandstones of upper Conemaugh Group. Loose fragments along Coates Run and Rock Riffle Run, N-flowing tributaries of Hocking River that join main stream SE of Athens, E Athens Twp.; ATHENS.
Mineral occurrence: Hildreth, 1838, p. 43; Murphy, 1973, p. 29-30.
4. Silicified wood weathers out of shales and sandstones of lower Monongahela Group. Loose fragments scattered along Long Run, a tributary of Middle Branch Shade River, N-central Lodi Twp.; ATHENS.
Mineral occurrence: Andrews, 1873, p. 287-289; Arnold, 1947, p. 195-196; Hildreth, 1838, p. 43; Lesquereux, 1880, p. 336.
5. Silicified wood in shales above Pittsburgh (No. 8) or Redstone (Pomeroy) (No. 8A) coal, Monongahela Group. Loose fragments in bed and bank of Fossil Run, a tributary of Middle Branch Shade River, NE¼ sec. 21, central Lodi Twp.; SHADE.
Mineral occurrence: Good and Taylor, 1974, p. 287, 290; Hildreth, 1838, p. 43; Morgan, E. J., 1959, p. 66, 106; Stout, 1945, p. 150.
General geology: Sturgeon and associates, 1958, p. 480.
6. Silicified wood in sandstone above Redstone (Pomeroy) (No. 8A) coal, Monongahela Group. Exposure on former Philip Haning property, sec. 32, Lodi Twp.; SHADE.
Mineral occurrence: Andrews, 1873, p. 287-288; Stout, 1945, p. 151-152.

AUGLAIZE COUNTY
1. Small crystals of quartz in *Lockport Dolomite* and *Greenfield Dolomite*. Also calcite, pyrite, and sphalerite. National Lime & Stone Co. Buckland quarry, E½ sec. 10, Moulton Twp.; MOULTON.
General geology: Janssens, 1971, p. 35; 1974, p. 82, 84; Shaver, 1974, p. 89-95.

BELMONT COUNTY
1. Petrified wood in Pittsburgh sandstone, Monongahela Group. Strip mine N of U.S. Rte. 40, NW¼ sec. 20, Kirkwood Twp.; FAIRVIEW.
Mineral occurrence: Berryhill, 1963, p. 18, 24-25.
2. Petrified wood in Pittsburgh sandstone, Monongahela Group. Strip mine 2 miles N of Barnesville, SW¼ sec. 17, Warren Twp.; FAIRVIEW.
Mineral occurrence: Berryhill, 1963, p. 18, 24-25.
3. Silicified wood weathers out of sandstones and shales of Monongahela or Dunkard Group. Fragments scattered along Captina Creek and its tributaries, including Bend Fork, Washington and York Twps.; ARMSTRONGS MILLS, BUSINESSBURG, POWHATAN POINT.
Mineral occurrence: Andrews, 1874a, p. 569; Mitchell, 1951, p. 253-254.
General geology: Berryhill, 1963, pl. 1.

COSHOCTON COUNTY
1. Massive bed of black flint in Upper Mercer limestone, Pottsville Group. Road cut on N side of Twp. Hwy. 53, 0.9 mile N of junction with Ohio Rte. 79, W-central Jefferson Twp.; WARSAW.
Mineral occurrence: Lamborn, 1954, p. 93.
General geology: Stout and Schoenlaub, 1945, p. 55-56.
2. Massive bed of black flint in Upper Mercer limestone, Pottsville Group. Also manganese oxides. Road cut along County Hwy. 82, 0.6 mile W of junction with Twp. Hwy. 59, SW Jefferson Twp.; WARSAW.
Mineral occurrence: Lamborn, 1954, p. 93; Morningstar, 1922, p. 107-108; Stout and Schoenlaub, 1945, p. 56.
3. Massive bed of black flint in Upper Mercer limestone, Pottsville Group. Road cut along N side of Twp. Hwy. 81 just E of Flint Run crossing, S-central Jefferson Twp.; WARSAW.
Mineral occurrence: Lamborn, 1954, p. 92-94; Meyers, 1929, p. 51-52; Morningstar, 1922, p. 108; Stout and Schoenlaub, 1945, p. 54-56.
4. Massive bed of black flint in Upper Mercer limestone, Pottsville Group. Road cut on County Hwy. 41 about 0.6 mile E of junction with Ohio Rte. 60, SE Jefferson Twp.; WARSAW.
Mineral occurrence: Lamborn, 1954, p. 94; Meyers, 1929, p. 52.
General geology: Stout and Schoenlaub, 1945, p. 55-56.
5. Massive bed of black flint in Upper Mercer limestone, Pottsville Group. Road cut on W side of Twp. Hwy. 31, 1.1 miles N of Warsaw, E-central sec. 10, Jefferson Twp.; RANDLE.
Mineral occurrence: Lamborn, 1954, p. 92-93.
General geology: Stout and Schoenlaub, 1945, p. 55-56.
6. Fragments of silicified wood in rocks of Pottsville and Allegheny Groups. No specific localities given.
Mineral occurrence: Stout, 1946, p. 31.
General geology: Lamborn, 1954, p. 34-190.

ERIE COUNTY
1. Granular masses of quartz with barite in veins of barite nodules from Cleveland Shale Member, Ohio Shale. Banks and bed of Vermilion River N and S of Garfield Rd. bridge about 0.6 mile S of Birmingham, Florence Twp.; KIPTON.

Mineral occurrence: Holden and Carlson, 1979, p. 227-232.

General geology: Herdendorf, 1963, map.

2. Granular masses of colorless quartz with barite, calcite, dolomite, and ferroan dolomite in veins of large limestone concretions from lower Huron Shale Member, Ohio Shale. Also aragonite and sphalerite. Borrow pit at Huron just S of U.S. Rte. 6, 0.4 mile W of Rye Beach Rd. intersection, Huron Twp.; HURON.

General geology: Explorer, 1961, p. 5; Prosser, 1913, p. 324-341.

3. Crystals and granular masses of colorless quartz with barite, calcite, dolomite, and ferroan dolomite in veins of large limestone concretions from lower Huron Shale Member, Ohio Shale. Also pyrite. Outcrop just W of Milan on N side of Huron River and W side of U.S. Rte. 250 bridge, Milan Twp.; MILAN.

Mineral occurrence: Feldmann and others, 1977, p. 48-49.

General geology: Prosser, 1913, p. 327-328.

4. Quartz crystals in chert nodules of Lucas Dolomite and *Columbus Limestone*. Also calcite and sphalerite. Kellstone (South Side) quarry, SW Kelleys Island, Kelleys Island Twp.; KELLEYS ISLAND.

General geology: Feldmann and Bjerstedt, 1987, p. 395-398; Feldmann and others, 1977, p. 43-47; Fisher, M., 1922, p. 8, 41; Forsyth, 1971, p. 7; Stauffer, 1909, p. 136-137.

5. Quartz crystals in chert nodules of Lucas Dolomite and *Columbus Limestone*. Also calcite and sphalerite. North Side quarry N of Titus Rd., NW Kelleys Island, Kelleys Island Twp.; KELLEYS ISLAND.

General geology: Feldmann and Bjerstedt, 1987, p. 395-398; Feldmann and others, 1977, p. 43-47; Fisher, M., 1922, p. 8, 40; Forsyth, 1971, p. 6; Stauffer, 1909, p. 139.

FAYETTE COUNTY

1. Quartz with sphalerite in Greenfield Dolomite. Also calcite and pyrite. American Aggregates Corp. Blue Rock quarry about ¾ mile N of intersection of Ohio Rtes. 41 and 753, SE Perry Twp.; NEW MARTINSBURG.

Mineral occurrence: Botoman and Stieglitz, 1978, p. 5, 9.

General geology: Stout, 1941, p. 133-134.

GALLIA COUNTY

1. Silicified wood in sandstone of Conemaugh or Monongahela Group. Cliff exposure about 2 miles above Gallipolis and ½ mile from Ohio River, Gallipolis Twp.; GALLIPOLIS.

Mineral occurrence: Hildreth, 1827, p. 205-206.

General geology: Condit, 1912, p. 80-81.

2. Silicified wood weathers from shales of Conemaugh Group. Fragments scattered along Raccoon Creek and its eastern tributaries, Green, Perry, Raccoon and Springfield Twps.; RODNEY, VINTON.

Mineral occurrence: Stout, 1916, p. 657; 1946, p. 31.

3. Silicified wood weathers from red shales above Ames limestone, Conemaugh Group. Fragments scattered along Campaign Creek and its tributaries, Morgan Twp.; VINTON.

Mineral occurrence: Hildreth, 1838, p. 43; Mitchell, 1951, p. 253-254; Stout, 1945, p. 146, 150.

4. Thin bed of dark-gray Brush Creek flint, Conemaugh Group. Exposure in sec. 32, Walnut Twp.; WATERLOO.

Mineral occurrence: Carskadden and Donaldson, 1973, p. 20-21; Morgan, R., 1929, p. 52-53.

GEAUGA AND TRUMBULL COUNTIES

1. Doubly terminated quartz crystals known locally as "Swine Creek diamonds." Along Swine Creek, Middlefield Twp., Geauga Co.; Farmington and Mesopotamia Twps., Trumbull Co.; MIDDLEFIELD, WEST FARMINGTON.

Mineral occurrence: Gettings, 1955, p. 485; Van Winkle, 1953, p. 35.

General geology: Baker, 1957, pls. 2, 6; White, G.W., 1971, map (author's note: the source reference incorrectly locates Swine Creek in Ashtabula County).

GREENE COUNTY

1. Small crystals of colorless quartz in cavities of Cedarville Dolomite. Also calcite, dolomite, marcasite, and pyrite. American Aggregates Corp. quarry 1 mile SE of Cedarville on N side of Turnbull Rd., Cedarville Twp.; CEDARVILLE.

General geology: Stith, 1983, p. 11-12, 14.

GUERNSEY COUNTY

1. Loose fragments of silicified wood from rocks below Cambridge limestone, Conemaugh Group. In bed of tributary of North Crooked Creek, just E of New Concord, Adams and Westland Twps.; BLOOMFIELD, NEW CONCORD.

Mineral occurrence: Mitchell, 1951, p. 253.

HIGHLAND COUNTY

1. Colorless quartz crystals in cavities of Lilley Dolomite. Also calcite and sphalerite. Abandoned quarry on N side of County Hwy. 54 and exposures along and near road 1 mile W of Elmville and a short distance SW of Dunkard Ridge Church, Brush Creek-Jackson Twp. boundary; SINKING SPRING. OGS section no. 12961.

General geology: Bowman, 1956, p. 114-115; Rogers, J. K., 1936, p. 101.

2. Quartz in Greenfield Dolomite. Also asphalt, calcite, and sphalerite. Havens Limestone Co. quarry about 2 miles SW of Leesburg, S Fairfield Twp.; LEESBURG.

Mineral occurrence: Botoman and Stieglitz, 1978, p. 5, 9.

3. Quartz crystals in geodes of Bisher Dolomite. Geodes accumulate on surface in upper part of valley of Setty Branch of Middle Fork Ohio Brush Creek, E Jackson Twp.; SINKING SPRING.

Mineral occurrence: Orton, 1871b, p. 276, 303-304; Rogers, J. K., 1936, p. 101.

4. Quartz-lined geodes in Bisher Dolomite. Outcrop along a small tributary of Clear Creek, E of old Bates School about 3¼ miles NE of Hillsboro off Ohio Rte. 138, Liberty Twp.; HILLSBORO (HILLSBORO 15-minute).

Mineral occurrence: Rogers, J. K., 1936, p. 103-104; Stout, 1941, p. 82; Stout and Schoenlaub, 1945, p. 17, 19.

5. Quartz-lined geodes in Lilley Dolomite. Old quarries of Col. Collins, N side of Hillsboro, Liberty Twp.; HILLSBORO.

Mineral occurrence: Orton, 1871b, p. 276, 303-304.

General geology: Rogers, J. K., 1936, p. 74.

6. Quartz-filled cavities in Bisher Dolomite and *Lilley Dolomite*. Old Carey Brothers quarry on W side of Hillsboro just S of U.S. Rte. 50, Liberty Twp.; NEW MARKET. OGS section no. 12747.

Mineral occurrence: Bowman, 1956, p. 95.

General geology: Stout, 1941, p. 79-81; Stout and Schoenlaub, 1945, p. 17-18.

7. Quartz-filled cavities in Lilley Dolomite. Abandoned quarry near E edge of Hillsboro 0.5 mile S of Ohio Rte. 124, Liberty Twp.; HILLSBORO. OGS section no. 12979.

Mineral occurrence: Bowman, 1956, p. 97-98.

8. Crystals of quartz in silicified stromatoporoids in *Lilley Dolomite* and Peebles Dolomite. Also calcite. Fossils accumulate along road gutter of Ohio Rte. 124, ½ mile NE of Harriett, Marshall Twp.; RAINSBORO, SINKING SPRING. OGS section no. 12748.

Mineral occurrence: Orton, 1871b, p. 276, 303-304; Rogers, J. K., 1936, p. 106-107; Summerson and others, 1963, p. 5-6.
General geology: Bowman, 1956, p. 126-127.

9. Crystals of quartz with calcite in silicified stromatoporoids in Lilley Dolomite. Exposure along Franklin Branch of Rocky Fork at intersection of Marshall Twp. Rd. 250A about 0.6 mile S of McCoppin Mill, NE Marshall Twp.; RAINSBORO.
Mineral occurrence: Bingaman and others, 1978, p. 17.
General geology: Bowman, 1956, p. 106-107; Summerson and others, 1963, p. 25-26.

10. Quartz geodes in Bisher Dolomite. Old Cashman quarry W of Ohio Rte. 73 a little over 1 mile NW of Berrysville, Washington Twp.; HILLSBORO.
Mineral occurrence: Rogers, J. K., 1936, p. 107.
General geology: Stout, 1941, p. 86-87.

HOCKING COUNTY
1. Bed of black Upper Mercer flint, Pottsville Group. Exposure in hollow in E-central sec. 23, Green Twp.; GORE.
Mineral occurrence: Stout and Schoenlaub, 1945, p. 43.

HOLMES COUNTY
1. Massive bed of black flint with small quartz-filled cavities in Upper Mercer limestone, Pottsville Group. Exposure along Twp. Hwy. 177 just N of junction with Twp. Hwy. 159, 2¼ miles W of Trail, Walnut Creek Twp.; SUGAR CREEK.
Mineral occurrence: Stout and Schoenlaub, 1945, p. 58; White, G. W., 1949, p. 148, 151, 320.

HURON COUNTY
1. Crystals and granular aggregates of quartz with barite, calcite, dolomite, ferroan dolomite, and sphalerite in veins of large limestone concretions from lower Huron Shale Member, Ohio Shale. Also aragonite and pyrite. Outcrop about 2 miles N of Monroeville at Lamereaux Rd. bridge on E side of West Branch Huron River, Ridgefield Twp.; KIMBALL.
Mineral occurrence: Bingaman and others, 1978, p. 16; Carlson, 1977, p. 24-25.
General geology: Broadhead and others, 1980, p. 10-15; Prosser, 1913, p. 324-341.

JACKSON COUNTY
1. Bed of light-colored Vanport flint, Allegheny Group. Exposure along Kisor Rd., SW corner sec. 9, Milton Twp.; WELLSTON.
Mineral occurrence: Stout and Schoenlaub, 1945, p. 74-76.

2. Silicified wood in Bolivar clay, Allegheny Group. Unspecified locality in E Milton Twp.; MULGA.
Mineral occurrence: Mitchell, 1951, p. 254.
General geology: Stout, 1916, p. 269-273; Stout and others, 1943, generalized section of rocks in Ohio.

3. Bed of black Zaleski flint, Allegheny Group. Several exposures in secs. 21 and 22, Washington Twp.; HAMDEN.
Mineral occurrence: Morningstar, 1922, p. 131-133; Stout and Schoenlaub, 1945, p. 62.

JEFFERSON COUNTY
1. Nodular brown flint in Fishpot limestone, Monongahela Group. Exposures in N Mount Pleasant and S Smithfield Twps.; DILLONVALE.
Mineral occurrence: Murphy, 1976, p. 23.

LAWRENCE COUNTY
1. Thin bed of dark-gray Brush Creek flint, Conemaugh Group. Exposure in sec. 5, Mason Twp.; WATERLOO.
Mineral occurrence: Carskadden and Donaldson, 1973, p. 20-21; Morgan, R., 1929, p. 52-53.

2. Silicified wood in red shales of upper Conemaugh Group. Unspecified locality in E part of county.
Mineral occurrence: Mitchell, 1951, p. 253.
General geology: Stout, 1916, p. 412-424.

LICKING COUNTY
1. Massive bed of gray flint with chalcedony and quartz crystals lining small pockets in Vanport limestone, Allegheny Group. Also manganese oxides. Road cut along County Hwy. 668 just N of Flint Ridge State Memorial, Hopewell Twp.; GLENFORD.
Mineral occurrence: Carlson, 1987a, p. 415-418; Denison University, in Frank, 1969, p. 19.12-19.14; Stout and Schoenlaub, 1945, p. 81.
General geology: DeLong, 1972, map; Mills, 1921, p. 90-161.

2. Massive bed of gray flint with chalcedony and quartz crystals lining pockets in Vanport limestone, Allegheny Group. Also barite. Prehistoric quarries near Flint Ridge State Memorial, intersection of County Hwys. 668 and 312, Hopewell Twp.; GLENFORD.
Mineral occurrence: Mills, 1921, p. 96, 115-123.
General geology: DeLong, 1972, map; Stout and Schoenlaub, 1945, p. 80-83.

3. Massive bed of gray flint with chalcedony and quartz crystals lining small pockets in Vanport limestone, Allegheny Group. Clayton Mason property about ½ mile E of Flint Ridge State Memorial on S side of County Hwy. 312, Hopewell Twp.; GLENFORD.
Mineral occurrence: Bingaman and others, 1978, p. 13; Carlson, 1987a, p. 415-418.
General geology: DeLong, 1972, map; Mills, 1921, p. 90-161; Stout and Schoenlaub, 1945, p. 81.

LICKING AND MUSKINGUM COUNTIES
1. Quartz crystals and chalcedony in cavities of massive flint bed in Vanport limestone, Allegheny Group. Also barite and calcite. Prehistoric quarries and exposures along Flint Ridge, no specific localities given, Hopewell Twp., Licking Co., and Hopewell Twp., Muskingum Co.; GLENFORD, GRATIOT, TOBOSO.
Mineral occurrence: Atwater, 1820, p. 130-131; Foster, J. W., 1838, p. 90-91; Frondel, 1962, p. 200, 207; Hildreth, 1829, p. 157; 1834, p. 233-234; Moorehead, 1892, p. 35; Read, 1878a, p. 353-354; Smith, C. M., 1885, p. 859.
General geology: DeLong, 1972, map; Stout and Schoenlaub, 1945, p. 79-85.

LOGAN COUNTY
1. Small colloform masses of white chalcedony with dolomite in cavities of Columbus Limestone. Also calcite. Connolly Construction Co., Inc., quarry 1¼ miles W of East Liberty on N side of Ohio Rte. 347 near intersection with U.S. Rte. 33, Perry Twp.; EAST LIBERTY.
General geology: Stout, 1941, p. 255-257.

LORAIN COUNTY
1. White chalcedony and granular masses of colorless quartz with barite, calcite, and pyrite in veins of barite nodules from Cleveland Shale Member, Ohio Shale. Also pickeringite. Along banks of Vermilion River at Mill Hollow-Bacon Woods Park, Brownhelm Twp.; VERMILION EAST.
Mineral occurrence: Holden and Carlson, 1979, p. 227-232.
General geology: Broadhead and others, 1980, p. 23-30; Herdendorf, 1963, map; Prosser, 1913, p. 348.

MAHONING COUNTY
1. Bed of mottled blue and gray Plum Run flint, Allegheny Group. Old quarry in SW¼ sec. 31, Smith Twp.; ALLIANCE.
Mineral occurrence: Murphy and Blank, 1970, p. 198-199; Stout and Schoenlaub, 1945, p. 61.

MEIGS COUNTY
1. Silicified wood weathers from red shales of upper Conemaugh Group. Fragments scattered along bed of Leading Creek, Columbia, Rutland, and Salem Twps.; ALBANY, RUTLAND.
   Mineral occurrence: Hildreth, 1838, p. 43; Mitchell, 1951, p. 253; Stout, 1945, p. 150; 1946, p. 31.

MERCER COUNTY
1. Small crystals of quartz in cavities of Lockport Dolomite and Greenfield Dolomite. Also asphalt, calcite, dolomite, pyrite, and sphalerite. Stoneco quarry (formerly John W. Karch Stone Co.) 4 miles W of Celina, E½ sec. 8, Jefferson Twp.; ERASTUS.
   General geology: Shaver, 1974, p. 95-97; Stout, 1941, p. 265-266.

MONROE COUNTY
1. Silicified wood weathers from Monongahela or Dunkard Group. Scattered fragments near Beallsville, Sunbury Twp.; WOODSFIELD.
   Mineral occurrence: Mitchell, 1951, p. 254; Stout, 1946, p. 31.
   General geology: Condit, 1923, p. 137-142.
2. Fragments of silicified wood from rocks of upper Conemaugh Group or lower Monongahela Group. In bed of Sunfish Creek and its tributaries, N part of county.
   Mineral occurrence: Mitchell, 1951, p. 253.
   General geology: Condit, 1923, p. 15-18, 89-151.

MORGAN COUNTY
1. Silicified wood weathers from shales above Ames limestone, Conemaugh Group. Fragments scattered on hills and along upper branches of Federal Creek, Homer Twp.; CORNING, RINGGOLD.
   Mineral occurrence: Condit, 1912, p. 140; Hildreth, 1838, p. 43; Mitchell, 1951, p. 253; Stout, 1945, p. 146, 150; 1946, p. 31.
2. Bed of light-gray Brush Creek flint, Conemaugh Group. Exposure in SE¼ sec. 25, York Twp.; DEAVERTOWN.
   Mineral occurrence: Carskadden and Donaldson, 1973, p. 20-21.

MUSKINGUM COUNTY
1. Bed of black Boggs flint, Pottsville Group. Exposures in Licking River valley in vicinity of Dillon Falls, NW Falls Twp.; ZANESVILLE WEST.
   Mineral occurrence: Morton and Carskadden, 1972, p. 15-17; Stout and Schoenlaub, 1945, p. 36-38.
2. Massive bed of color-banded flint with chalcedony and quartz crystals lining small pockets in Vanport limestone, Allegheny Group. Also barite. John Nethers property along County Hwy. 8, NW¼ sec. 6, Hopewell Twp.; TOBOSO.
   Mineral occurrence: Bingaman and others, 1978, p. 13; Carlson, 1987a, p. 415-418; Stout and Schoenlaub, 1945, p. 87.
   General geology: DeLong, 1972, map; Mills, 1921, p. 90-161.
3. Massive bed of gray flint in Vanport limestone, Allegheny Group. Basil Norris property along Twp. Hwy. 413, NE¼ sec. 4, Hopewell Twp.; TOBOSO.
   Mineral occurrence: Stout and Schoenlaub, 1945, p. 87-88.
   General geology: DeLong, 1972, map; Mills, 1921, p. 90-161.
4. Massive bed of gray flint in Vanport limestone, Allegheny Group. Gene Wyrick property along N side of Twp. Hwy. 292, SW¼ sec. 4, Hopewell Twp.; TOBOSO.
   Mineral occurrence: Stout and Schoenlaub, 1945, p. 87.
   General geology: DeLong, 1972, map; Mills, 1921, p. 90-161.
5. Fragments of silicified wood from rocks below Lower Mercer limestone, Pottsville Group. In stream bed W of Muskingum River W of Rock Cut, Muskingum Twp.; ADAMSVILLE.
   Mineral occurrence: Mitchell, 1951, p. 254.
6. Fragments of silicified wood in red shales above Ames limestone, Conemaugh Group. Unspecified hillside locality SW of New Concord, Union Twp.; NORWICH.
   Mineral occurrence: Mitchell, 1951, p. 253.
   General geology: Stout, 1918, p. 254-263.
7. Bed of black flint in Upper Mercer limestone, Pottsville Group. Several exposures mainly in N part of county.
   Mineral occurrence: Morgan, R., 1929, p. 46-50; Morton and Carskadden, 1972, p. 15-20; Stout, 1916, p. 104-108; Stout and Schoenlaub, 1945, p. 51-54.

PAULDING COUNTY
1. Tiny quartz crystals lining cavities in dolostones of *Detroit River Group* and Dundee Formation. Also asphalt, calcite, fluorite, pyrite, and sphalerite. Stoneco Auglaize quarry (formerly Maumee Stone Co.), Junction, NW¼ sec. 32, Auglaize Twp.; JUNCTION.
   General geology: Janssens, 1970a, p. 21; Stauffer, 1909, p. 152-153; Stout, 1941, p. 324-325.

PERRY COUNTY
1. Bed of light-gray Brush Creek flint, Conemaugh Group. Exposure in NW¼ sec. 1, Bearfield Twp.; DEAVERTOWN.
   Mineral occurrence: Carskadden and Donaldson, 1973, p. 20-21.
2. Massive bed of black flint with quartz veins and chalcedony in Upper Mercer limestone, Pottsville Group. Outcrops at New Lexington, sec. 9, Pike Twp.; NEW LEXINGTON.
   Mineral occurrence: Fowke, 1928, p. 512.
   General geology: Flint, 1951, p. 129-130.
3. Massive bed of black and gray flint with quartz crystals lining cavities in Upper Mercer limestone, Pottsville Group. Exposure along County Hwy. 95, E-central sec. 3, about 2 miles SW of Cannon, Clayton Twp.; FULTONHAM.
   Mineral occurrence: Stout and Schoenlaub, 1945, p. 44-46.
   General geology: Flint, 1951, p. 37-38.

ROSS COUNTY
1. Quartz crystals in cavities of Greenfield Dolomite; may be associated with sphalerite. Also asphalt and calcite. Old Rucker quarry E of Greenfield and just E of Paint Creek about ¼ mile N of Ohio Rte. 4, Buckskin Twp.; SOUTH SALEM.
   Mineral occurrence: Knille and Gibbs, 1942, p. 320; Napper, 1916, p. 155-159; 1917, p. 7-13; Orton, 1871b, p. 291; Rogers, J. K., 1936, p. 113-114, 135; Wuestner, 1938, p. 262.
   General geology: Stout, 1941, p. 71; Summerson and others, 1963, p. 27.
2. Granular masses of quartz with barite, calcite, and dolomite in veins of large limestone concretions from lower Huron Shale Member, Ohio Shale. Also halotrichite-pickeringite, melanterite, and pyrite. Cliff exposure at Copperas Mountain about 1 mile ESE of Seip Mound State Memorial on SE side of Paint Creek, Paxton Twp.; MORGANTOWN.
   Mineral occurrence: Bingaman and others, 1978, p. 10; Carlson, 1987b, p. 428; Seyfried, 1953, p. 13-25.
   General geology: Briggs, 1838, p. 77-78; Kepferle and others, 1981, p. 294-295; Orton, 1874, p. 647.

TRUMBULL COUNTY—see Geauga County

VINTON COUNTY
1. Bed of black Zaleski flint, Allegheny Group. Exposure on Elk Twp. road, SE¼ sec. 11 and SW¼ sec. 12, Elk Twp.; ZALESKI.
   Mineral occurrence: Morningstar, 1922, p. 134-135; Stout, 1927, p. 182-183.
   General geology: Stout and Schoenlaub, 1945, p. 62-70.

2. Bed of dark-gray to black Brush Creek flint, Conemaugh Group. Exposures on ridges in secs. 18, 23, 24, and 30, Madison Twp.; MINERAL, ZALESKI.
Mineral occurrence: Carskadden and Donaldson, 1973, p. 20-21; Morgan, R., 1929, p. 52-53.
3. Quartz in cavities of Vanport limestone, Allegheny Group. Also calcite, galena, pyrite, and sphalerite. No specific localities given.
Mineral occurrence: Stout, 1927, p. 265-266.
General geology: Lamborn, 1951, p. 344-349.

ROZENITE
$FeSO_4 \cdot 4H_2O$

Chemical class: Sulfate
Crystallization: Monoclinic; prismatic; 2/m
Habit: Commonly a powdery crust; crystals small and platy
Physical properties: Cleavage: {010} good pinacoidal. H: soft. G: 2.2. Luster: dull. Color: white, greenish white. Streak: white. Rozenite is unstable and may hydrate to melanterite or dehydrate to szomolnokite
Occurrence: As an efflorescence, especially on pyrite, in coal beds of eastern Ohio

CARROLL COUNTY
1. Efflorescence of rozenite with melanterite and szomolnokite on Lower Kittanning (No. 5) coal, Allegheny Group. Also barite, pyrite, sphalerite, and wurtzite. James Bros. Coal Co. strip mine about 3 miles SE of Mineral City, N½ sec. 25, Rose Twp.; MINERAL CITY.
General geology: Lamborn, 1942, p. 10, 13.

LORAIN COUNTY
1. Efflorescence of rozenite with melanterite on gray Bedford Shale. Cliff exposure on W bank of Black River near junction of West and East Branches, S end of Cascade Park, Elyria, Elyria Twp.; GRAFTON.
General geology: Newberry, 1874b, p. 211-212.

VINTON COUNTY
1. Fine powder of rozenite with melanterite and halotrichite on pyrite from Middle Kittanning (No. 6) coal, Allegheny Group. Abandoned coal mines along upper reaches of Sandy Run, NE Brown Twp.; MINERAL.
Mineral occurrence: Ehlers, E. G., and Stiles, 1965, p. 1458.
General geology: Brant and Foster, 1959, p. 187-188.

SMITHSONITE
$ZnCO_3$

Chemical class: Carbonate
Crystallization: Hexagonal (Trigonal); ditrigonal scalenohedral; $\bar{3}m$
Habit: Rarely well crystallized; commonly compact, massive, earthy, and friable; porous or cellular boxworks; colloform coatings
Physical properties: Cleavage: {10$\bar{1}$1} good rhombohedral. H: 4-4½. G: 4.4. Luster: vitreous to dull. Color: brown, gray, white. Streak: white. Soluble in cold dilute HCl with effervescence
Occurrence: Associated with hydrozincite and hemimorphite as a weathering product of sphalerite in Serpent Mound area

ADAMS COUNTY
1. Finely crystalline boxworks of brown smithsonite with hydrozincite and sulfur as an alteration of sphalerite in undifferentiated Peebles-Greenfield-Tymochtee Dolomites. Also calcite and dolomite. Outcrop and small quarry 0.7 mile E of entrance to Serpent Mound State Memorial on Ohio Rte. 73 and 1.4 miles N on E side of Twp. Hwy. 116, Bratton Twp.; SINKING SPRING.
Mineral occurrence: Heyl and Brock, 1962, p. D95; Koucky, 1975, p. 22; Reidel and Koucky, 1981, p. 391-403; Wedow and Heyl, 1968, p. 454, 464.
General geology: Koucky and Reidel, 1987, p. 431-436; Reidel, 1975, map; Reidel and others, 1982, p. 1343-1377.
2. Smithsonite with hydrozincite as an alteration of sphalerite in Peebles Dolomite. Outcrop in gully behind museum at Serpent Mound State Memorial, Bratton Twp.; SINKING SPRING.
Mineral occurrence: Koucky, 1975, p. 16.
General geology: Koucky and Reidel, 1987, p. 431-436; Reidel, 1975, map; Reidel and Koucky, 1981, p. 391-403; Reidel and others, 1982, p. 1343-1377.
3. Finely crystalline boxworks of brown smithsonite with hydrozincite and sphalerite in cavities of brecciated Tymochtee Dolomite. Hillside exposure 1.0 mile E of entrance to Serpent Mound State Memorial on Ohio Rte. 73 and 0.4 mile S on E side of Wallace Rd., Bratton Twp.; SINKING SPRING.
Mineral occurrence: Koucky and Reidel, 1987, p. 432-435; Reidel and Koucky, 1981, p. 397-398.
General geology: Reidel and others, 1982, p. 1343-1377.
4. Smithsonite with asphalt, calcite, hydrozincite, and sphalerite in breccias of Silurian dolostone and limestone. Numerous exposures within the Serpent Mound disturbance (in addition to Adams County sites 1, 2, 3, and 5 given here), Bratton and Franklin Twps.; SINKING SPRING.
Mineral occurrence: Reidel, 1972, p. 98.
General geology: Koucky and Reidel, 1987, p. 431-436; Reidel, 1975, map; Reidel and Koucky, 1981, p. 391-403; Reidel and others, 1982, p. 1343-1377.
5. Small crystals of brown smithsonite with hemimorphite and hydrozincite as an alteration of sphalerite in undifferentiated Peebles-Greenfield-Tymochtee Dolomites. Exposure on small hill 0.1 mile W of Ohio Rte. 41 and 1.8 miles N of intersection with Ohio Rte. 73, Franklin Twp.; SINKING SPRING.
General geology: Koucky, 1975, p. 27-28; Koucky and Reidel, 1987, p. 431-436; Reidel and Koucky, 1981, p. 391-403; Reidel and others, 1982, p. 1343-1377.

SPHALERITE
$(Zn,Fe)S$

Chemical class: Sulfide
Crystallization: Isometric; hextetrahedral; $\bar{4}3m$
Habit: Commonly well crystallized; tetrahedral or complex crystals; crystal faces commonly curved; tabular or granular aggregates
Physical properties: Cleavage: {011} perfect dodecahedral. H: 3½-4. G: 4.1. Luster: resinous, adamantine, submetallic. Color: yellowish brown, orange, red, black, greenish yellow. Streak: brown to yellow
Occurrence: Commonly as crystals and granular masses in cavities and fractures of dolostones especially along the crest and flanks of the Findlay Arch in northwestern Ohio and in the Serpent Mound disturbance in southwestern Ohio. Lustrous masses of black sphalerite are very common in veins of septarian ironstone nodules of eastern Ohio

ADAMS COUNTY
1. Granular masses of brownish-orange sphalerite with dolomite, hydrozincite, smithsonite, and sulfur in fractures and pockets of undifferentiated Peebles-

Greenfield-Tymochtee Dolomites. Also calcite. Outcrop and small quarry 0.7 mile E of entrance to Serpent Mound State Memorial on Ohio Rte. 73 and 1.4 miles N on E side of Twp. Hwy. 116, Bratton Twp.; SINKING SPRING.

Mineral occurrence: Heyl and Brock, 1962, p. 95-97; Jolly and Heyl, 1968, p. 10-11; Koucky, 1975, p. 22; Koucky and Reidel, 1987, p. 431-436; Reidel, 1975, map; Reidel and Koucky, 1981, p. 391-403; Wedow and Heyl, 1968, p. 454, 464.

General geology: Reidel and others, 1982, p. 1343-1377.

2. Sphalerite with hydrozincite and smithsonite in Peebles Dolomite. Outcrop in gully behind museum at Serpent Mound State Memorial, Bratton Twp.; SINKING SPRING.

Mineral occurrence: Koucky, 1975, p. 16; Koucky and Reidel, 1987, p. 431-436; Reidel, 1975, map; Reidel and Koucky, 1981, p. 391-403.

General geology: Reidel and others, 1982, p. 1343-1377.

3. Brown sphalerite with hydrozincite and smithsonite in cavities of brecciated Tymochtee Dolomite. Hillside exposure 1.0 mile E of entrance to Serpent Mound State Memorial on Ohio Rte. 73 and 0.4 mile S on E side of Wallace Rd.; Bratton Twp.; SINKING SPRING.

Mineral occurrence: Koucky and Reidel, 1987, p. 432-435; Reidel and Koucky, 1981, p. 397-398.

General geology: Reidel and others, 1982, p. 1343-1377.

4. Sphalerite in Brassfield Formation. Also calcite and hematite. Exposure on S side of Ohio Rte. 73, 1.5 miles W of Louden, Bratton Twp.; SINKING SPRING. OGS section no. 14350.

Mineral occurrence: Botoman and Stieglitz, 1978, p. 5.

General geology: Hopkins, 1954, p. 88; Koucky, 1975, p. 14-15.

5. Yellow to purple sphalerite with asphalt, calcite, hydrozincite, and smithsonite in fractures and cavities of Silurian dolostones and limestones. Numerous exposures within Serpent Mound disturbance (in addition to Adams County sites 1, 2, 3, and 7 given here), Bratton and Franklin Twps.; SINKING SPRING.

Mineral occurrence: Reidel, 1972, p. 72-98; 1975, map.

General geology: Koucky and Reidel, 1987, p. 431-436; Reidel and Koucky, 1981, p. 391-403; Reidel and others, 1982, p. 1343-1377.

6. Sphalerite in Peebles Dolomite. Old Lynx quarry 1¼ miles E of Lynx on Burr Run Creek on S side of Ohio Rte. 125, Brush Creek Twp.; LYNX.

Mineral occurrence: Reidel, 1972, p. 94.

General geology: Stout, 1941, p. 61.

7. Brown sphalerite in fractures and pockets of undifferentiated Peebles-Greenfield-Tymochtee Dolomites. Also hemimorphite, hydrozincite, and smithsonite. Exposure on a small hill 0.1 mile W of Ohio Rte. 41 and 1.8 miles N of intersection with Ohio Rte. 73, Franklin Twp.; SINKING SPRING.

Mineral occurrence: Koucky, 1975, p. 27-28; Reidel, 1975, map; Reidel and Koucky, 1981, p. 391-403.

General geology: Koucky and Reidel, 1987, p. 431-436; Reidel and others, 1982, p. 1343-1377.

8. Sphalerite in Lilley Dolomite, Peebles Dolomite, *Greenfield Dolomite*, Tymochtee Dolomite, and Ohio Shale. Also calcite and pyrite. Davon, Inc., Plum Run quarry about 1 mile S on Twp. Hwy. 126 from intersection with Ohio Rte. 74 at Bacon Flat, Franklin-Meigs Twp. boundary; JAYBIRD.

Mineral occurrence: Schmidt and others, 1961, p. 285-288; Summerson and others, 1963, p. 18-23.

General geology: Rexroad and others, 1965, p. 29; Stith, 1983, p. 11-12, 15.

9. Sphalerite with calcite near base of Brassfield Formation. Also barite. Exposure along Beasley Fork of Ohio Brush Creek about 1 mile S of West Union near Ohio Rte. 247, Tiffin Twp.; WEST UNION. OGS section no. 12667.

Mineral occurrence: Botoman and Stieglitz, 1978, p. 5.

ALLEN COUNTY

1. Sphalerite in cavities of Tymochtee Dolomite and dolostones of undifferentiated Salina Group. Also asphalt, calcite, dolomite, fluorite, and pyrite. National Lime & Stone Co. quarry, Lima, sec. 29, Bath Twp.; LIMA.

Mineral occurrence: Botoman and Stieglitz, 1978, p. 5; Carlson, 1983, p. 427, 430.

General geology: Janssens, 1977, p. 3.

2. Sphalerite in Tymochtee Dolomite. Also calcite and pyrite. National Lime & Stone Co. quarry (formerly Western Ohio Stone Co.), Lima, W½ sec. 29, Bath Twp.; LIMA.

Mineral occurrence: Botoman and Stieglitz, 1978, p. 5; Carlson, 1983, p. 427, 430.

General geology: Janssens, 1977, p. 3; Stout, 1941, p. 305.

3. Small crystals of reddish-brown sphalerite in cavities and fractures of Tymochtee Dolomite and dolostones of undifferentiated Salina Group. Also calcite, dolomite, fluorite, and pyrite. Bluffton Stone Co. quarry, Bluffton, NW¼ sec. 12, Richland Twp.; BLUFFTON.

General geology: Janssens, 1977, p. 3; Stout, 1941, p. 310.

ATHENS COUNTY

1. Sphalerite in ironstone concretions from shale below Upper Freeport (No. 7) coal, Allegheny Group. Exposure on former property of L. Weethee, sec. 18, Dover Twp.; JACKSONVILLE.

Mineral occurrence: Andrews, 1873, p. 264.

General geology: Condit, 1912, p. 92.

AUGLAIZE COUNTY

1. Sphalerite in Lockport Dolomite and Greenfield Dolomite. Also calcite, pyrite, and quartz. National Lime & Stone Co. Buckland quarry, E½ sec. 10, Moulton Twp.; MOULTON.

Mineral occurrence: Botoman and Stieglitz, 1978, p. 5; Carlson, 1983, p. 427, 430.

General geology: Janssens, 1971, p. 35; 1974, p. 82, 84; Shaver, 1974, p. 89-95.

CARROLL COUNTY

1. Sphalerite in veins of ironstone nodules 15 ft below Upper Freeport (No. 7) coal, Allegheny Group. Exposure near old steam sawmill about halfway between former village of Cannonsburg (S½ sec. 36, Monroe Twp.) and Carrollton (N½ sec. 31, Center Twp.); CARROLLTON, DELLROY.

Mineral occurrence: Stevenson, 1878, p. 185.

2. Black sphalerite with barite, pyrite, and wurtzite in veins of ironstone concretions from shales above both Lower Kittanning (No. 5) coal and Middle Kittanning (No. 6) coal, Allegheny Group. Also melanterite, rozenite, and szomolnokite. James Bros. Coal Co. strip mine about 3 miles SE of Mineral City, N½ sec. 25, Rose Twp.; MINERAL CITY.

General geology: Lamborn, 1942, p. 10, 13.

COLUMBIANA COUNTY

1. Black sphalerite with barite, calcite, chalcopyrite, kaolinite, pyrite, and wurtzite in veins of ironstone concretions from shales above Lower Kittanning (No. 5) coal, Allegheny Group. Also copiapite and gypsum. Metrel, Inc., quarry S of Negley, sec. 13, Middleton Twp.; EAST PALESTINE.

Mineral occurrence: Hollenbaugh, 1979, p. 9, 16-22; Hollenbaugh and Carlson, 1983, p. 697-703.

General geology: Stout and Lamborn, 1924, p. 111.

CUYAHOGA COUNTY
1. Granular masses of dark-brown sphalerite with barite in veins of pyrite nodules from Chagrin Shale Member, Ohio Shale. Cliff exposure along N side of Chippewa Creek about ½ mile downstream from Ohio Rte. 82 bridge, Brecksville Reservation, E Brecksville Twp.; NORTHFIELD.
   General geology: Kent State University, *in* Frank, 1969, p. 1.4-1.9; Prosser, 1912, p. 119.

ERIE COUNTY
1. Granular masses of brownish-orange sphalerite in cavities of dolostones of *Detroit River Group* and Columbus and Delaware Limestones; may be associated with calcite. Also celestite, fluorite, and pyrite. Sandusky Crushed Stone Co. quarry, Parkertown, just S of Portland Rd., Groton Twp.; BELLEVUE.
   Mineral occurrence: Carlson, 1983, p. 427, 430.
   General geology: Janssens, 1970b, p. 10-12.
2. Small masses of brown sphalerite in veins of large limestone concretions from lower Huron Shale Member, Ohio Shale. Also aragonite, barite, calcite, dolomite, ferroan dolomite, and quartz. Borrow pit at Huron just S of U.S. Rte. 6, 0.4 mile W of Rye Beach Rd. intersection, Huron Twp.; HURON.
   Mineral occurrence: Reported by C. Hyde and Landy (1966, p. 228) from near Milan, but according to Clarence Raver (personal commun., 1976) the sphalerite comes from the Rye Beach locality.
   General geology: Explorer, 1961, p. 5; Prosser, 1913, p. 324-341.
3. Small brown sphalerite crystals in cherty zones of Lucas Dolomite and *Columbus Limestone*. Also calcite and quartz. Kellstone (South Side) quarry, SW Kelleys Island, Kelleys Island Twp.; KELLEYS ISLAND.
   General geology: Feldmann and Bjerstedt, 1987, p. 395-398; Feldmann and others, 1977, p. 43-47; Fisher, M., 1922, p. 8, 41; Forsyth, 1971, p. 7; Stauffer, 1909, p. 136-137.
4. Small brown sphalerite crystals in cherty zones of Lucas Dolomite and *Columbus Limestone*. Also calcite and quartz. North Side quarry N of Titus Rd., NW Kelleys Island, Kelleys Island Twp.; KELLEYS ISLAND.
   General geology: Feldmann and Bjerstedt, 1987, p. 395-398; Feldmann and others, 1977, p. 43-47; Fisher, M., 1922, p. 8, 40; Forsyth, 1971, p. 6; Stauffer, 1909, p. 139.

FAYETTE COUNTY
1. Yellowish-brown sphalerite with quartz in Greenfield Dolomite. Also calcite and pyrite. American Aggregates Corp. Blue Rock quarry about ¾ mile N of intersection of Ohio Rtes. 41 and 753, SE Perry Twp.; NEW MARTINSBURG.
   Mineral occurrence: Botoman and Stieglitz, 1978, p. 5, 9.
   General geology: Stout, 1941, p. 133-134.

GUERNSEY COUNTY
1. Sphalerite in veins of ironstone nodules from shales above Middle Kittanning (No. 6) coal, Allegheny Group. Exposures along Wills and Indian Camp Creeks in Liberty, Wheeling, and Knox Twps.; BLOOMFIELD, CAMBRIDGE, KIMBOLTON, PLAINFIELD.
   Mineral occurrence: Stevenson, 1878, p. 224, 231-234, 236.
2. Black sphalerite with kaolinite in veins of ironstone nodules from black shales of Brush Creek horizon, Conemaugh Group. Exposure in hollow, S½SE¼ sec. 7, Washington Twp.; BIRMINGHAM.
   General geology: Condit, 1912, p. 172.

HANCOCK COUNTY
1. Small crystals of brownish-red sphalerite in pockets of *Tymochtee Dolomite* and dolostones of undifferentiated Salina Group. Also asphalt, calcite, celestite, fluorite, gypsum, and pyrite. National Lime & Stone Co. quarry, Findlay, sec. 24 and NE¼ sec. 25, Liberty Twp.; FINDLAY.
   Mineral occurrence: Carlson, 1983, p. 427, 430.
   General geology: Janssens, 1971, p. 35; Stout, 1941, p. 342-343.

HARDIN COUNTY
1. Crystals of reddish-brown sphalerite in cavities of Tymochtee Dolomite. Also asphalt, calcite, dolomite, fluorite, and pyrite. Hardin Quarry Co., Inc., quarry, Blanchard, NW¼ sec. 6, Pleasant Twp.; FORAKER.
   Mineral occurrence: Botoman and Stieglitz, 1978, p. 5; Carlson, 1983, p. 427, 430.
   General geology: Janssens, 1977, p. 3; Stout, 1941, p. 274-276.

HIGHLAND COUNTY
1. Yellow-brown sphalerite with calcite in a fault breccia of Bisher-Lilley Dolomites. Outcrop about ½ mile S of Sinking Spring on E side of Ohio Rte. 41, Brush Creek Twp.; SINKING SPRING.
   Mineral occurrence: Galbraith, 1968, p. 25-26, 32.
   General geology: Reidel, 1975, map.
2. Granular masses of sphalerite in fractures and cavities of undifferentiated Peebles-Greenfield-Tymochtee Dolomites. Three exposures W of Ohio Rte. 41 and S of Sinking Spring Rd., SE corner Brush Creek Twp.; SINKING SPRING.
   Mineral occurrence: Reidel, 1975, map.
3. Brown sphalerite with calcite in fossil cavities of Lilley Dolomite. Also quartz. Abandoned quarry on N side of County Hwy. 54 and exposures along and near road 1 mile W of Elmville and a short distance W of Dunkard Ridge Church, Brush Creek-Jackson Twp. boundary; SINKING SPRING. OGS section no. 12961.
   General geology: Bowman, 1956, p. 114-115; Rogers, J. K., 1936, p. 101.
4. Sphalerite with calcite in Brassfield Formation. Also hematite. Outcrop along tributary of Little West Fork of Ohio Brush Creek near intersection of Pondlick and Richardson Rds. about 2¼ miles SE of Sugar Tree Ridge, central Concord Twp.; SUGAR TREE RIDGE. OGS section no. 9732.
   Mineral occurrence: Botoman and Stieglitz, 1978, p. 5.
   General geology: Hopkins, 1954, p. 87; Rogers, J. K., 1936, p. 95.
5. Honey-yellow sphalerite in Greenfield Dolomite. Also asphalt, calcite, and quartz. Havens Limestone Co. quarry about 2 miles SW of Leesburg, S Fairfield Twp.; LEESBURG.
   Mineral occurrence: Botoman and Stieglitz, 1978, p. 5, 9.
6. Sphalerite in Brassfield Formation. Also barite, calcite, and pyrite. Davon, Inc., Highland Plant quarry about 1 mile SE of Fairview on E side of Danville Rd., NE Hamer Twp.; NEW MARKET. OGS section no. 13610.
   Mineral occurrence: Botoman and Stieglitz, 1978, p. 5.
   General geology: Hopkins, 1954, p. 85.
7. Crystals of sphalerite with calcite in Brassfield Formation. Road cut on Peach Orchard Rd. just E of bridge across Ohio Brush Creek 1 mile NW of Belfast, Jackson Twp.; BELFAST. OGS section no. 13609.
   Mineral occurrence: Botoman and Stieglitz, 1978, p. 5; Rogers, J. K., 1936, p. 93.
8. Brown to black sphalerite with asphalt in Lilley Dolomite and Peebles Dolomite. Also calcite. Marshall Quarry, Inc., quarry about 1¼ miles W of Marshall on S side of Ohio Rte. 124, W Marshall Twp.; HILLSBORO.
   Mineral occurrence: Botoman and Stieglitz, 1978, p. 5, 9.

9. Crystalline aggregates of sphalerite in Greenfield Dolomite. Old Smith quarry on a hill about 2 miles N of Samantha and 1½ miles S of Highland near old School No. 4, N-central Penn Twp.; LEESBURG (SABINA 15-minute).
   Mineral occurrence: Jolly and Heyl, 1968, p. 10; Rogers, J. K., 1936, p. 114, 136; Wedow and Heyl, 1968, p. 464.
   General geology: Stout, 1941, p. 98-99.
10. Sphalerite in Greenfield Dolomite. Abandoned quarry 1 mile E of locality 9 above, N-central Penn Twp.; LEESBURG (SABINA 15-minute).
    Mineral occurrence: Rogers, J. K., 1936, p. 114.

HURON COUNTY
1. Small granular masses of brown sphalerite with dolomite in veins of large limestone concretions from lower Huron Shale Member, Ohio Shale. Also aragonite, barite, calcite, ferroan dolomite, pyrite, and quartz. Outcrop about 2 miles N of Monroeville at Lamereaux Rd. bridge on E side of West Branch Huron River, Ridgefield Twp.; KIMBALL.
   General geology: Broadhead and others, 1980, p. 10-15; Prosser, 1913, p. 324-341.

JEFFERSON COUNTY
1. Granular masses of brown to black sphalerite with barite, calcite, pyrite, and wurtzite in veins of ironstone nodules from shales above Brush Creek coal, Conemaugh Group. Road cut near Alikanna on E side of Ohio Rte. 7 just N of Ohio Rte. 213 intersection, N½ sec. 31, Island Creek Twp.; KNOXVILLE.
   Mineral occurrence: Hollenbaugh and Carlson, 1983, p. 697-701.
   General geology: Condit, 1912, p. 204-205; Lamborn, 1930, p. 123; Seaman and Hamilton, 1950, p. 47.

LOGAN COUNTY
1. Small crystals of dark sphalerite with calcite and dolomite in fractures and cavities of dolostones of undifferentiated Salina Group. Also asphalt, fluorite, and pyrite. C. E. Duff & Son quarry, just E of Ohio Rte. 117 about 2 miles N of Huntsville, Richland Twp.; HUNTSVILLE.
   Mineral occurrence: Richards and Chamberlain, 1987, p. 391-392.
   General geology: Janssens, 1971, p. 35.

LUCAS COUNTY
1. Small crystals of yellowish-brown sphalerite with calcite in cavities of Silica Formation and *Tenmile Creek Dolomite*. Also barite, celestite, dolomite, pyrite, and strontianite. W wall of France Stone Co. North quarry (formerly Medusa Portland Cement Co.), Sylvania, S-central sec. 7, Sylvania Twp.; SYLVANIA, BERKEY.
   Mineral occurrence: Carlson, 1983, p. 427, 430.
   General geology: Carman and others, 1962, p. 5-6; Ehlers, G. M., and others, 1951, p. 4.
2. Crystals and granular masses of brown sphalerite with calcite in cavities of Tymochtee Dolomite and dolostones of *undifferentiated Salina Group*. Also asphalt, celestite, fluorite, gypsum, halite, pyrite, and sulfur. France Stone Co. quarry, Waterville, secs. 38 and 39, Waterville Twp.; BOWLING GREEN NORTH.
   General geology: Janssens, 1977, p. 25-30; Kahle and Floyd, 1971, p. 2082-2086; 1972, p. 65-68; Stout, 1941, p. 402-404.
3. Crystals and granular aggregates of reddish-brown to yellowish-brown sphalerite in cavities of *Lockport Dolomite* and Greenfield Dolomite. Also asphalt, calcite, celestite, dolomite, fluorite, gypsum, pyrite, and sulfur. Stoneco quarry (formerly Maumee Stone Co.), Maumee, sec. 35, Waynesfield Twp.; MAUMEE.

   Mineral occurrence: Botoman and Stieglitz, 1978, p. 5, 8; Carlson, 1983, p. 427, 430; Kahle, 1974, p. 34; Mychkovsky, 1978b, p. 42.
   General geology: Kahle, 1978, p. 63-115; Kahle and Floyd, 1972, p. 70-81; Summerson and others, 1963, p. 44-45; Textoris and Carozzi, 1966, p. 1375-1388.

MAHONING COUNTY
1. Brown to black sphalerite with barite, calcite, chalcopyrite, kaolinite, and pyrite in veins of ironstone concretions from shales below Lower Mercer limestone, Pottsville Group. Outcrop along West Branch Meander Creek just E of junction with Ohio Rte. 45 about ¾ mile S of Ellsworth, Ellsworth Twp.; CANFIELD.
   Mineral occurrence: Anonymous, 1936, p. 462; Greene, 1935, p. 883; Whittlesey, 1838, p. 66.
   General geology: Lamb, 1910, p. 114.
2. Sphalerite in ironstone nodules from shale of Pottsville or Allegheny Group. Cliff exposure along Yellow Creek near Poland, Poland Twp.; CAMPBELL.
   Mineral occurrence: Hildreth, 1837, p. 25.
   General geology: Newberry, 1878, p. 803-806.
3. Brown to black sphalerite with barite, chalcopyrite, and pyrite in veins of ironstone concretions from shales below Vanport(?) limestone, Allegheny Group. Keller mine S of Middletown Rd., NE¼ sec. 19, Smith Twp.; ALLIANCE.
   General geology: DeLong and White, 1963, p. 42; Lamb, 1910, p. 109.

MARION COUNTY
1. Granular masses of reddish-brown sphalerite in cavities of Lockport Dolomite and *Greenfield Dolomite*. Also calcite, celestite, dolomite, fluorite, marcasite, and strontianite. Tri-County Limestone Co. quarry (formerly Laubis Stone Co.), 2 miles SW of Marseilles, center sec. 19, Grand Twp.; MARSEILLES.
   General geology: Cumings, 1930, p. 202-203; Hall and Alkire, 1956, p. 5, 32-35; Stith, 1983, p. 15; Stout, 1941, p. 281-282.

MERCER COUNTY
1. Crystals of brownish-red sphalerite in pockets of Lockport Dolomite and Greenfield Dolomite. Also asphalt, calcite, dolomite, pyrite, and quartz. Stoneco quarry (formerly John W. Karch Stone Co.) 4 miles W of Celina, E½ sec. 8, Jefferson Twp.; ERASTUS.
   Mineral occurrence: Carlson, 1983, p. 427, 430.
   General geology: Shaver, 1974, p. 95-97; Stout, 1941, p. 265-266.

MIAMI COUNTY
1. Sphalerite with calcite in Brassfield Formation. Road cut on N side of Ohio Rte. 571 about 0.3 mile E of West Milton, sec. 21, Union Twp.; WEST MILTON. OGS section no. 12771.
   Mineral occurrence: Botoman and Stieglitz, 1978, p. 5.
   General geology: Stout, 1941, p. 190.

MUSKINGUM COUNTY
1. Sphalerite with calcite in ironstone nodules from shales above Lower Mercer limestone, Pottsville Group. Outcrop at Zanesville along E side of Muskingum River; ZANESVILLE EAST, ZANESVILLE WEST.
   Mineral occurrence: Foster, J. W., 1838, p. 86-88.
   General geology: Stout, 1918, p. 84.

OTTAWA COUNTY
1. Crystals and aggregates of reddish-brown to yellowish-brown sphalerite in cavities and fractures of *Lockport Dolomite* and Greenfield Dolomite; may be associated with celestite or fluorite. Also calcite, dolomite, galena, gypsum, and pyrite. Edward Kraemer & Sons, Inc., White Rock quarry, Clay Center, SE¼ sec. 9 and NE¼ sec. 16, Allen Twp.; GENOA.

Mineral occurrence: Botoman and Faure, 1976, p. 69; Botoman and Stieglitz, 1978, p. 5, 8; Carlson, 1983, p. 427, 430; Carman and others, 1962, p. 13-14; Howard, 1959, p. 129; Morrison, 1934, p. 20-21; 1935, p. 784; Mychkovsky, 1978b, p. 26, 42; Nelson, 1967, p. 78; Roedder, 1967, p. 355; 1979, p. 92; Sparling, 1965, p. 171, 239-240; Strogonoff, 1966, p. 13, 15.

General geology: Janssens, 1974, p. 82, 84; 1977, p. 22; Sparling, 1971, p. 19; Stout, 1941, p. 415-418.

2. Sphalerite in cavities of *Lockport Dolomite* and Greenfield Dolomite. Also asphalt, calcite, celestite, dolomite, fluorite, pyrite, and sulfur. Stoneco quarry (formerly Maumee Stone Co.) N of Rocky Ridge, sec. 23, Benton Twp.; OAK HARBOR.

Mineral occurrence: Botoman and Stieglitz, 1978, p. 6; Carlson, 1983, p. 427, 430.

General geology: Forsyth, 1971, p. 14; Sparling, 1965, p. 172.

3. Reddish-brown sphalerite in vugs and fractures of Lockport Dolomite; may be associated with calcite. Also celestite, dolomite, fluorite, galena, marcasite, and pyrite. GenLime Group, L. P., quarry (formerly U.S. Gypsum Co.), Genoa, W½ sec. 3, Clay Twp.; GENOA.

Mineral occurrence: Botoman, 1975, p. 45; Carlson, 1983, p. 427, 430; 1986, p. 4-9; Mychkovsky, 1978b, p. 42; Sparling, 1965, p. 171, 236-237; Strogonoff, 1966, p. 19.

General geology: Forsyth, 1971, p. 15-16; Janssens, 1977, p. 3, 22; Sparling, 1965, p. 236-237; Stout, 1941, p. 413-414.

4. Sphalerite in Lockport Dolomite. Also fluorite. Old Purtee quarry, Genoa, S½NE¼ sec. 4, Clay Twp.; GENOA.

Mineral occurrence: Botoman and Stieglitz, 1978, p. 6, 8; Carlson, 1983, p. 427, 430; Green, R., 1970a, p. 585.

PAULDING COUNTY

1. Granular masses of yellowish- to reddish-brown sphalerite in dolostones of *Detroit River Group* and Dundee Formation. Also asphalt, calcite, fluorite, pyrite, and quartz. Stoneco Auglaize quarry (formerly Maumee Stone Co.), Junction, NW¼ sec. 32, Auglaize Twp.; JUNCTION.

Mineral occurrence: Botoman, 1975, p. 45; Botoman and Stieglitz, 1978, p. 6, 9; Carlson, 1983, p. 427, 430; Feldmann and others, 1977, p. 32-33; Nelson, 1967, p. 46.

General geology: Janssens, 1970a, p. 21; Stauffer, 1909, p. 152-153; Stout, 1941, p. 324-325.

PIKE COUNTY

1. Sphalerite in fractures and cavities of undifferentiated Peebles-Greenfield-Tymochtee Dolomites. SW corner Mifflin Twp.; SINKING SPRING.

Mineral occurrence: Reidel, 1975, map.

PORTAGE COUNTY

1. Brown to black sphalerite with barite, calcite, chalcopyrite, and kaolinite in veins of ironstone concretions from shales of lower Pottsville Group. Outcrop along SE shore of Michael J. Kirwan Reservoir at mouth of Silver Creek just W of Alliance Rd., NE Edinburg Twp.; WINDHAM.

General geology: Winslow and White, 1966, p. 79.

PREBLE COUNTY

1. Sphalerite in Brassfield Formation. Also hematite and pyrite. Old Marble Cliff quarry, Lewisburg, SW¼ sec. 21, Harrison Twp.; LEWISBURG.

Mineral occurrence: Botoman and Stieglitz, 1978, p. 6.

General geology: Horvath and Sparling, 1967, p. 2-3; Shaver and others, 1961, p. 31-32; Stout, 1941, p. 170.

2. Sphalerite in Brassfield Formation. Also calcite. Exposure along N side of a branch of Twin Creek on E side of Ohio Rte. 503 about 1/3 mile N of intersection with Brennersville-Pyrmont Rd., NW¼SW¼ sec. 10, Twin Twp.; LEWISBURG. OGS section no. 15772.

Mineral occurrence: Botoman and Stieglitz, 1978, p. 6.

PUTNAM COUNTY

1. Sphalerite in Tymochtee Dolomite and dolostones of undifferentiated Salina Group. Also calcite, fluorite, and pyrite. Ottawa Stone Co., Inc., quarry, W½ sec. 27, Blanchard Twp.; LEIPSIC.

Mineral occurrence: Botoman and Stieglitz, 1978, p. 6; Carlson, 1983, p. 427, 430.

General geology: Janssens, 1971, p. 35; 1977, p. 29.

2. Reddish-brown sphalerite in Tymochtee Dolomite and dolostones of undifferentiated Salina Group. Also asphalt, calcite, fluorite, and pyrite. Putnam Stone Co. quarry, NW¼ sec. 6, Riley Twp.; BLUFFTON.

Mineral occurrence: Botoman, 1975, p. 45; Botoman and Stieglitz, 1978, p. 6; Carlson, 1983, p. 427, 430.

General geology: Janssens, 1971, p. 35; 1977, p. 29.

3. Sphalerite in Tymochtee Dolomite and dolostones of undifferentiated Salina Group. Also calcite and fluorite. National Lime & Stone Co. quarry, Rimer, secs. 6, 7, and 8, Sugar Creek Twp.; KALIDA.

Mineral occurrence: Botoman and Stieglitz, 1978, p. 6; Carlson, 1983, p. 427, 430.

General geology: Janssens, 1971, p. 35; 1977, p. 29; Stith, 1983, p. 11-13; Stout, 1941, p. 327-328.

ROSS COUNTY

1. Yellowish-brown to black sphalerite in cavities of Greenfield Dolomite; may be associated with quartz. Also asphalt and calcite. Old Rucker quarry E of Greenfield and just E of Paint Creek about ¼ mile N of Ohio Rte. 4, Buckskin Twp.; SOUTH SALEM.

Mineral occurrence: Bownocker, 1915, p. 42-43; Hawes, 1884, p. 622-623; Knille and Gibbs, 1942, p. 320; Napper, 1916, p. 155-159; 1917, p. 7-13; Orton, 1871b, p. 290-291; 1888c, p. 730; Rogers, J. K., 1936, p. 113-114, 135; Wedow and Heyl, 1968, p. 464; Wuestner, 1938, p. 262.

General geology: Stout, 1941, p. 71; Summerson and others, 1963, p. 27.

SANDUSKY COUNTY

1. Small crystals and granular aggregates of reddish-brown sphalerite with fluorite in Lockport Dolomite. Also calcite, celestite, and galena. Charles Pfizer & Co., Inc., quarry, NW of Gibsonburg, sec. 14, Madison Twp.; ELMORE.

Mineral occurrence: Botoman, 1975, p. 45-46; Botoman and Faure, 1976, p. 69; Botoman and Stieglitz, 1978, p. 8; Carlson, 1983, p. 427, 430; Mychkovsky, 1978b, p. 25, 42; Strogonoff, 1966, p. 53.

General geology: Floyd, 1971, p. 167; Janssens, 1977, p. 3, 22; Stith, 1983, p. 11-13.

2. Dark-brown sphalerite in vugs and fractures of Lockport Dolomite. Also barite, calcite, celestite, dolomite, fluorite, galena, and pyrite. Steetley Resources, Inc., Ohio Lime Co. quarry, Woodville, W½ sec. 34, Woodville Twp.; ELMORE.

Mineral occurrence: Botoman, 1975, p. 45-46; Carlson, 1983, p. 427, 430; Green, R., 1971, p. 281; Strogonoff, 1966, p. 54.

General geology: Floyd, 1971, p. 167-169; Kahle and Floyd, 1968, p. 31-35.

3. Crystals and granular aggregates of orange to brown sphalerite in cavities of Lockport Dolomite. Also barite, calcite, celestite, dolomite, fluorite, galena, pyrite, and strontianite. Martin Marietta Chemicals quarry, (S part formerly Woodville Lime & Chemical Co. quarry), Woodville, E½ sec. 21 and W½ sec. 22, Woodville Twp.; ELMORE.

Mineral occurrence: Botoman, 1975, p. 45; Botoman and Stieglitz, 1978, p. 6; Carlson, 1983, p. 427, 430; 1986, p. 9-13; Mychkovsky, 1978b, p. 43.

General geology: Stout, 1941, p. 375; Summerson and others, 1963, p. 42.

SENECA COUNTY
1. Crystals of reddish-brown sphalerite in Lockport Dolomite or Greenfield Dolomite. Also calcite, celestite, dolomite, fluorite, galena, strontianite, and sulfur. Old quarries at Tiffin, Clinton Twp.; TIFFIN SOUTH.

Mineral occurrence: Carlson, 1983, p. 427, 430; Chesterman, 1978, p. 813; also unpublished information from mineral collection at Heidelberg College.

General geology: Carman, 1927, p. 487; Janssens, 1977, p. 3; Winchell, 1873, p. 616-618.

2. Crystals of reddish-brown sphalerite in *Lockport Dolomite* and Greenfield Dolomite. Also calcite, celestite, dolomite, fluorite, galena, marcasite, pyrite, and strontianite. Maple Grove Stone Co. quarry (formerly Basic Refractories), Maple Grove, sec. 11 and N½ sec. 14, Liberty Twp.; TIFFIN NORTH.

General geology: Floyd, 1971, p. 167, 173-174; Janssens, 1971, p. 35; 1974, p. 82, 84; 1977, p. 3, 22; Stout, 1941, p. 348-349.

STARK COUNTY
1. Granular masses of brownish-black sphalerite with calcite and pyrite in veins of ironstone concretions in shale beds of Putnam Hill limestone, Allegheny Group. East Ohio Limestone Co. quarry N of Cairo, sec. 21, Lake Twp.; HARTVILLE.

General geology: DeLong and White, 1963, p. 45-49, 180-181.

2. Black sphalerite with barite and pyrite in veins of ironstone concretions from shales of Allegheny Group. Penn Central Railroad cut at Warren Rd. intersection about ½ mile NE of Paris, SW¼ sec. 4, Paris Twp.; ROBERTSVILLE.

General geology: DeLong and White, 1963, p. 75, 81.

SUMMIT COUNTY
1. Granular masses of brown to black sphalerite with calcite, chalcopyrite, kaolinite, and pyrite in veins of ironstone concretions from Meadville Shale Member, Cuyahoga Formation. Outcrop along small tributary that enters Cuyahoga River from N side about ¼ mile W of foot of dam, Cuyahoga Gorge Park, Cuyahoga Falls; AKRON WEST.

General geology: Kent State University, *in* Frank, 1969, p. 1.5-1.7; Szmuc, 1957, p. 159-161.

2. Sphalerite in fossil cavities of Sharpsville Shale Member, Cuyahoga Formation. Also pyrite. Outcrop along Brandywine Creek near Cleveland-Akron Rd., Northfield Twp.; NORTHFIELD (CLEVELAND 15-minute).

Mineral occurrence: Cushing and others, 1931, p. 51.
General geology: Szmuc, 1957, p. 152.

TRUMBULL COUNTY
1. Sphalerite with pyrite as fossil replacements in Meadville Shale Member, Cuyahoga Formation. Outcrop along tributary that enters Pymatuning Creek from E side 0.2 mile N of Kinsman-Vernon Twp. boundary, SE Kinsman Twp.; KINSMAN.

Mineral occurrence: Szmuc, 1957, p. 132-133.

TUSCARAWAS COUNTY
1. Sphalerite with barite and pyrite in veins of ironstone concretions from shales of Allegheny Group. Old strip mine on W side of Winfield Rd. about ½ mile NE of intersection with U.S. Rte. 250, Dover Twp.; DOVER.

General geology: Lamborn, 1956, p. 168, pl. 1.

2. Tabular crystals of dark-brown sphalerite with barite and pyrite in veins of ironstone concretions in shales above Lower Kittanning (No. 5) coal, Allegheny Group. Eberhart Coal Co., Inc., strip mine, Dover(?) Twp., specific location not given.

Mineral occurrence: Orr and others, 1982, p. 52-54.
General geology: Lamborn, 1956, p. 125-140.

3. Brown to black sphalerite with calcite, pyrite, and wurtzite in veins of ironstone concretions from shales of Allegheny Group. Puskarich Mining, Inc., strip mine about 1 mile S of New Cumberland, SW¼ sec. 28, Warren Twp.; MINERAL CITY.

General geology: Lamborn, 1956, p. 140, 175.

4. Sphalerite with barite in veins of ironstone concretions from shales of Pottsville Group. Belden Brick Co. quarry, just N of Dundee, Wayne Twp.; STRASBURG.

General geology: Lamborn, 1956, pl. 1.

VAN WERT COUNTY
1. Sphalerite in Tymochtee Dolomite and dolostones of undifferentiated Salina Group. Also calcite, dolomite, fluorite, and pyrite. Ridge Township Quarry 2 miles W of Middle Point, NE¼ sec. 22, Ridge Twp.; MIDDLE POINT.

Mineral occurrence: Botoman and Stieglitz, 1978, p. 6; Carlson, 1983, p. 427, 430.

General geology: Janssens, 1971, p. 35.

2. Tiny crystals of reddish-brown and yellowish-brown sphalerite in cavities of dolostones of undifferentiated Salina Group. Also asphalt, calcite, dolomite, fluorite, and pyrite. Stoneco quarry (formerly Maumee Stone Co.) about 4 miles SW of Scott, sec. 8, Union Twp.; CONVOY.

General geology: Janssens, 1971, p. 35; 1977, p. 3, 29; Stout, 1941, p. 319-320.

3. Sphalerite in Tymochtee Dolomite and dolostones of undifferentiated Salina Group. Also asphalt, calcite, dolomite, fluorite, and pyrite. Suever Stone Co., Inc., quarry (formerly Delphos Quarries Co.), Delphos, sec. 25, Washington Twp.; DELPHOS.

Mineral occurrence: Botoman and Stieglitz, 1978, p. 6; Carlson, 1983, p. 427, 430.

General geology: Janssens, 1971, p. 35; Stout, 1941, p. 313.

VINTON COUNTY
1. Small crystals of sphalerite in Vanport limestone, Allegheny Group. Also calcite, galena, pyrite, and quartz. No specific localities given.

Mineral occurrence: Stout, 1927, p. 265-266.
General geology: Lamborn, 1951, p. 344-349.

WAYNE COUNTY
1. Brown to black sphalerite with barite, calcite, chalcopyrite, galena, and pyrite in veins of ironstone concretions from shales of lower Pottsville Group. Penn Central Railroad cut N of Marshallville, W-central sec. 33, Chippewa Twp.; DOYLESTOWN.

Mineral occurrence: Ver Steeg, 1940, p. 259; 1942, p. 223.
General geology: Conrey, 1921, p. 92; Ver Steeg, 1948, p. 185.

2. Sphalerite as crystals in shale, as fossil fillings, and with calcite, galena, and pyrite in veins of ironstone nodules from shales of Wooster Shale Member, Cuyahoga Formation. Also aragonite. Old quarry E of County Rd. 22 behind City of Wooster Service and Maintenance Facility, NE¼ sec. 5, Wooster Twp.; WOOSTER.

Mineral occurrence: Ver Steeg, 1940, p. 259.
General geology: Conrey, 1921, p. 62-63; Szmuc, 1957, p. 193-195.

WOOD COUNTY
1. Sphalerite in Tymochtee Dolomite. Also calcite, fluorite, gypsum, marcasite, and pyrite. France Stone Co. North Baltimore quarry, W½ sec. 26, Henry Twp.; NORTH BALTIMORE.

Mineral occurrence: Botoman and Stieglitz, 1978, p. 6; Carlson, 1983, p. 427, 430.

General geology: Janssens, 1971, p. 35; 1977, p. 26; Kahle

and Floyd, 1972, p. 46-48; Stout, 1941, p. 394-395.
2. Small crystals and spherical aggregates of yellowish-orange sphalerite with celestite and marcasite as cavity and fracture fillings in dolostones of *Detroit River Group* and Dundee Formation. Also asphalt, barite, calcite, dolomite, fluorite, glauconite, hexahydrite, and pyrite. France Stone Co. Custar quarry (formerly Pugh Quarry Co.) about 4 miles W of Weston, SW¼ sec. 6, Milton Twp.; MCCLURE.

Mineral occurrence: Bingaman and others, 1978, p. 18; Botoman, 1975, p. 45; Botoman and Stieglitz, 1978, p. 6, 9; Carlson, 1983, p. 427, 430; Feldmann and others, 1977, p. 35-37; Gettings, 1950, p. 601; Nelson, 1967, p. 74; Parr and Chang, 1978, p. 272-279.

General geology: Forsyth, 1966a, p. 204-205; Janssens, 1970a, p. 7, 22; Orton and Peppel, 1906, p. 133; Stout, 1941, p. 395-396.

3. Crystals and aggregates of yellowish-brown to reddish-brown sphalerite in vugs and fractures of *Lockport Dolomite* and Greenfield Dolomite; may be associated with barite and pyrite. Also calcite, celestite, dolomite, fluorite, hexahydrite, and strontianite. MacRitchie Materials, Inc., quarry (formerly Brough Stone Co.), West Millgrove, SE¼ sec. 4, Perry Twp.; FOSTORIA.

Mineral occurrence: Carlson, 1983, p. 427, 430; Mychkovsky, 1978b, p. 23-24, 43.

General geology: Janssens, 1971, p. 35; 1974, p. 82, 84; 1977, p. 22; Shaver, 1977, p. 1414; Stout, 1941, p. 392.

4. Crystals and aggregates of reddish-brown sphalerite in vugs and fractures of *Lockport Dolomite* and *Greenfield Dolomite;* may be associated with calcite. Also aragonite, barite, celestite, dolomite, fluorite, galena, gypsum, marcasite, pyrite, strontianite, and sulfur. Stoneco quarry (formerly Maumee Stone Co.), Lime City, SW¼ sec. 11, Perrysburg Twp.; ROSSFORD.

Mineral occurrence: Botoman, 1975, p. 45; Botoman and Stieglitz, 1978, p. 6, 8; Carlson, 1983, p. 427, 430; Haden, 1977, p. 25, 28; Mychkovsky, 1978b, p. 24, 26, 38, 42; Strogonoff, 1966, p. 43-44.

General geology: Janssens, 1971, p. 35; 1974, p. 82, 84; 1977, p. 22; Kahle and Floyd, 1968, p. 28-30; 1972, p. 50-52.

5. Granular masses of brownish-orange sphalerite in cavities of *Lockport Dolomite* and Greenfield Dolomite. Also calcite, celestite, dolomite, gypsum, and sulfur. Stoneco quarry (formerly Maumee Stone Co.) SE of Portage, sec. 7, Portage Twp.; BOWLING GREEN SOUTH.

General geology: Carlson,1987c, p. 96-104; Floyd,1971, p. 188; Janssens, 1971, p. 35; 1974, p. 82, 84; 1977, p. 22.

WYANDOT COUNTY
1. Yellowish-brown sphalerite in *Lockport Dolomite* and Greenfield Dolomite. Also calcite, celestite, dolomite, fluorite, gypsum, pyrite, and strontianite. National Lime & Stone Co. quarry, Carey, N½ sec. 15 and N½ sec. 16, Crawford Twp.; CAREY, MCCUTCHENVILLE.

Mineral occurrence: Botoman and Stieglitz, 1978, p. 6; Carlson, 1983, p. 427, 430.

General geology: Carlson, 1987c, p. 101-102; Cumings, 1930, p. 201-202; Hall and Alkire, 1956, p. 7, 31-33; Janssens, 1974, p. 82, 84; 1977, p. 22; Stout, 1941, p. 294-295; Summerson and others, 1963, p. 39-40.

2. Yellow sphalerite in fractures of Tymochtee Dolomite and dolostones of undifferentiated Salina Group. Also calcite, celestite, gypsum, and sulfur. McCarthy Stone Quarry 3½ miles SE of Upper Sandusky, N½ sec. 15, Pitt Twp.; NEVADA.

Mineral occurrence: Botoman and Stieglitz, 1978, p. 6; Carlson, 1983, p. 427, 430.

General geology: Carlson, 1987c, p. 97-101; Janssens, 1977, p. 3, 29; Stout, 1941, p. 299.

STRONTIANITE
SrCO₃

Chemical class: Carbonate
Crystallization: Orthorhombic; dipyramidal; mmm
Habit: Commonly in acicular or fibrous radial aggregates; individual crystals commonly with steep pyramidal terminations; may be in granular or powdery masses
Physical properties: Cleavage: {110} good prismatic. H: 3½. G: 3.8. Luster: vitreous. Color: white, pale yellow, colorless. Streak: white. Commonly fluorescent and phosphorescent. Will effervesce in cold dilute hydrochloric acid
Occurrence: Radiating aggregates of fibrous crystals commonly associated with celestite; appears to form as an alteration of celestite; in cavities of dolostones in northwestern Ohio, where it is commonly confused with aragonite

LUCAS COUNTY
1. Fibrous aggregates of fluorescent white strontianite with calcite and celestite in fossil cavities of Silica Formation and *Tenmile Creek Dolomite*. Also barite, dolomite, pyrite, and sphalerite. W wall of France Stone Co. North quarry (formerly Medusa Portland Cement Co.), Sylvania, S-central sec. 7, Sylvania Twp.; SYLVANIA, BERKEY.

General geology: Carman and others, 1962, p. 5-6; Ehlers, G. M., and others, 1951, p. 4.

MARION COUNTY
1. Fibrous masses of white strontianite in cavities of *Lockport Dolomite* and Greenfield Dolomite. Also calcite, celestite, dolomite, fluorite, marcasite, and sphalerite. Tri-County Limestone Co. quarry (formerly Laubis Stone Co.) 2 miles SW of Marseilles, center sec. 19, Grand Twp.; MARSEILLES.

General geology: Cumings, 1930, p. 202-203; Hall and Alkire, 1956, p. 5, 32-35; Stith, 1983, p. 15; Stout, 1941, p. 281-282.

SANDUSKY COUNTY
1. Fibrous aggregates of fluorescent white strontianite with calcite and celestite in small vugs of Lockport Dolomite. Also barite, dolomite, fluorite, galena, pyrite, and sphalerite. Martin Marietta Chemicals quarry (S part formerly Woodville Lime & Chemical Co. quarry), Woodville, E½ sec. 21 and W½ sec. 22, Woodville Twp.; ELMORE.

Mineral occurrence: Carlson, 1986, p. 9-13.

General geology: Stout, 1941, p. 375; Summerson and others, 1963, p. 42.

SENECA COUNTY
1. Radiating aggregates of fibrous white strontianite in cavities of Lockport Dolomite or Greenfield Dolomite. Also calcite, celestite, dolomite, fluorite, galena, sphalerite, and sulfur. Old quarries at Tiffin, Clinton Twp.; TIFFIN SOUTH.

Mineral occurrence: unpublished information from mineral collection at Heidelberg College.

General geology: Carman, 1927, p. 487; Janssens, 1977, p. 3; Winchell, 1873, p. 616-618.

2. Finely granular masses of white strontianite altering from celestite in *Lockport Dolomite* and Greenfield Dolomite. Also calcite, dolomite, fluorite, galena,

marcasite, pyrite, and sphalerite. Maple Grove Stone Co. quarry (formerly Basic Refractories), Maple Grove, sec. 11 and N½ sec. 14, Liberty Twp.; TIFFIN NORTH.

General geology: Floyd, 1971, p. 167, 173-174; Janssens, 1971, p. 35; 1974, p. 82, 84; 1977, p. 3, 22; Stout, 1941, p. 348-349.

WOOD COUNTY
1. Aggregates of fibrous, radiating crystals of white strontianite in cavities of *Lockport Dolomite* and *Greenfield Dolomite*. Also barite, calcite, celestite, dolomite, fluorite, hexahydrite, pyrite, and sphalerite. MacRitchie Materials, Inc., quarry (formerly Brough Stone Co.), West Millgrove, SE¼ sec. 4, Perry Twp.; FOSTORIA.

General geology: Janssens, 1971, p. 35; 1974, p. 82, 84; 1977, p. 22; Shaver, 1977, p. 1414; Stout, 1941, p. 392.

2. Acicular crystals of fluorescent pale-yellow strontianite coating celestite from Lockport Dolomite and *Greenfield Dolomite*. Also aragonite, barite, calcite, dolomite, fluorite, galena, gypsum, marcasite, pyrite, sphalerite, and sulfur. Stoneco quarry (formerly Maumee Stone Co.), Lime City, SW¼ sec. 11, Perrysburg Twp.; ROSSFORD.

Mineral occurrence: Haden, 1977, p. 28; Strogonoff, 1966, p. 41.

General geology: Janssens, 1971, p. 35; 1974, p. 82, 84; 1977, p. 22; Kahle and Floyd, 1968, p. 28-30; 1972, p. 50-52.

WYANDOT COUNTY
1. Balls of fibrous radiating crystals of fluorescent white strontianite in cavities of Lockport Dolomite and *Greenfield Dolomite*. Also calcite, celestite, dolomite, fluorite, gypsum, pyrite, and sphalerite. National Lime & Stone Co. quarry, Carey, N½ sec. 15 and N½ sec. 16, Crawford Twp.; CAREY, MCCUTCHENVILLE.

Mineral occurrence: Carlson, 1987c, p. 101-102.

General geology: Cumings, 1930, p. 201-202; Hall and Alkire, 1956, p. 7, 31-33; Janssens, 1974, p. 82, 84; 1977, p. 22; Stout, 1941, p. 294-295; Summerson and others, 1963, p. 39-40.

SULFUR
S

Chemical class: Native element
Crystallization: Orthorhombic; dipyramidal; mmm
Habit: Dipyramidal crystals common; generally in finely crystalline granular masses
Physical properties: Cleavage: imperfect. Fracture: conchoidal to uneven. H: 1½-2½. G: 2.1. Luster: resinous to greasy. Color: lemon yellow. Streak: white. Burns with a blue flame
Occurrence: Fine-grained aggregates of small crystals rare as coatings on bedded gypsum or associated with calcite or celestite in cavities of dolostones in western Ohio. The numerous notations in the Ohio geological literature to efflorescences of sulfur on shale most likely refer instead to the mineral copiapite

ADAMS COUNTY
1. Sulfur with hydrozincite and smithsonite as an alteration of sphalerite in undifferentiated Peebles-Greenfield-Tymochtee Dolomites. Also calcite and dolomite. Outcrop and small quarry 0.7 mile E of entrance to Serpent Mound State Memorial on Ohio Rte. 73 and 1.4 miles N on E side of Twp. Hwy. 116, Bratton Twp.; SINKING SPRING.

General geology: Heyl and Brock, 1962, p. 95; Koucky, 1975, p. 22; Koucky and Reidel, 1987, p. 431-436; Reidel, 1975, map; Reidel and Koucky, 1981, p. 391-403; Reidel and others, 1982, p. 1343-1377.

LUCAS COUNTY
1. Sulfur with calcite and celestite in cavities of and on nodular gypsum in *Tymochtee Dolomite* and dolostones of undifferentiated Salina Group. Also asphalt, fluorite, halite, pyrite, and sphalerite. France Stone Co. quarry, Waterville, secs. 38 and 39, Waterville Twp.; BOWLING GREEN NORTH.

Mineral occurrence: Kahle and Floyd, 1968, p. 21-24; Nelson, 1967, p. 81; Strogonoff, 1966, p. 38, 41.

General geology: Janssens, 1977, p. 25-30; Kahle and Floyd, 1971, p. 2082-2086; 1972, p. 65-68; Stout, 1941, p. 402-404.

2. Sulfur with calcite in vugs of Lockport Dolomite and *Greenfield Dolomite*. Also asphalt, celestite, dolomite, fluorite, gypsum, pyrite, and sphalerite. Stoneco quarry (formerly Maumee Stone Co.), Maumee, sec. 35, Waynesfield Twp.; MAUMEE.

Mineral occurrence: Strogonoff, 1966, p. 35.

General geology: Kahle, 1974, p. 31-54; 1978, p. 63-115; Kahle and Floyd, 1972, p. 70-81; Summerson and others, 1963, p. 44-45; Textoris and Carozzi, 1966, p. 1375-1388.

OTTAWA COUNTY
1. Sulfur with calcite in cavities of *Lockport Dolomite* and Greenfield Dolomite. Also asphalt, celestite, dolomite, fluorite, pyrite, and sphalerite. Stoneco quarry (formerly Maumee Stone Co.) N of Rocky Ridge, sec. 23, Benton Twp.; OAK HARBOR.

General geology: Botoman and Stieglitz, 1978, p. 6; Forsyth, 1971, p. 14; Sparling, 1965, p. 172.

2. Sulfur with calcite and celestite in Bass Islands Dolomite. South Bass Island, no specific locality given, Put-in-Bay Twp.; PUT-IN-BAY.

Mineral occurrence: Dana, E. S., 1892, p. 1085; Dana, J. D., 1868, p. 784; Hamilton, 1953, p. 134; Newberry, 1873a, p. 106; 1874b, p. 202; 1875, p. 106.

General geology: Janssens, 1977, p. 27-30; Mohr, 1931, p. 28; Sparling, 1971, p. 19-22.

SENECA COUNTY
1. Small granular masses of sulfur with calcite or celestite in cavities of Lockport Dolomite or Greenfield Dolomite. Also dolomite, fluorite, galena, sphalerite, and strontianite. Old quarries at Tiffin, Clinton Twp.; TIFFIN SOUTH.

Mineral occurrence: unpublished information from mineral collection at Heidelberg College.

General geology: Carman, 1927, p. 487; Janssens, 1977, p. 3; Winchell, 1873, p. 616-618.

WOOD COUNTY
1. Sulfur with calcite in cavities of Lockport Dolomite and *Greenfield Dolomite*. Also aragonite, barite, celestite, dolomite, fluorite, galena, gypsum, marcasite, pyrite, sphalerite, and strontianite. Stoneco quarry (formerly Maumee Stone Co.), Lime City, SW¼ sec. 11, Perrysburg Twp.; ROSSFORD.

Mineral occurrence: Haden, 1977, p. 25, 29.

General geology: Janssens, 1971, p. 35; 1974, p. 82, 84; 1977, p. 22; Kahle and Floyd, 1968, p. 28-30; 1972, p. 50-52.

2. Fine-grained sulfur as a coating of Lockport Dolomite and *Greenfield Dolomite*. Also calcite, celestite, dolomite, gypsum, and sphalerite. Stoneco quarry (formerly Maumee Stone Co.) SE of Portage, sec. 7, Portage Twp.; BOWLING GREEN SOUTH.

Mineral occurrence: Carlson, 1987c, p. 102-104.

General geology: Floyd, 1971, p. 188; Janssens, 1971, p. 35; 1974, p. 82, 84; 1977, p. 22.

WYANDOT COUNTY
1. Sulfur with calcite in cavities of *Tymochtee Dolomite* and

dolostones of undifferentiated Salina Group. Also celestite, gypsum, and sphalerite. McCarthy Stone Quarry, 3½ miles SE of Upper Sandusky, N½ sec. 15, Pitt Twp.; NEVADA.
General geology: Carlson, 1987c, p. 97-101; Janssens, 1977, p. 3, 29; Stout, 1941, p. 299.

SZOMOLNOKITE
$FeSO_4 \cdot H_2O$

Chemical class: Sulfate
Crystallization: Monoclinic; prismatic; 2/m
Habit: Commonly in powdery or fibrous aggregates and crusts; dipyramidal crystals common
Physical properties: Fracture: conchoidal to uneven. H: 2½. G: 3.1. Luster: silky to dull. Color: white, pale yellow. Streak: white. Taste: bitter, astringent. Szomolnokite is unstable and hydrates readily to rozenite and melanterite
Occurrence: Finely crystalline aggregates rare as an efflorescence associated with pyrite in coal in eastern Ohio

BELMONT COUNTY
1. Efflorescence of white szomolnokite in Pittsburgh (No. 8) coal, Monongahela Group. Also pyrite. North American Coal Co., G-North sec., Powhatan No. 1 mine, sec. 14, Washington Twp.; CAMERON.
General geology: Berryhill, 1963, p. 19-21.

CARROLL COUNTY
1. Efflorescence of szomolnokite with melanterite and rozenite on *Lower Kittanning (No. 5) coal* and *Middle Kittanning (No. 6) coal*, Allegheny Group. Also barite, pyrite, sphalerite, and wurtzite. James Bros. Coal Co. strip mine about 3 miles SE of Mineral City, N½ sec. 25, Rose Twp.; MINERAL CITY.
General geology: Lamborn, 1942, p. 10, 13.

THENARDITE
Na_2SO_4

Chemical class: Sulfate
Crystallization: Orthorhombic; dipyramidal; mmm
Habit: Commonly a powdery crust; equant or tabular crystals
Physical properties: Cleavage: {010} perfect pinacoidal. H: 2½-3. G: 2.7. Luster: dull when powdery. Color: white, grayish white, colorless. Streak: white. Taste: slightly salty
Occurrence: Finely granular crusts rare as an efflorescence

SUMMIT COUNTY
1. Efflorescence of white thenardite with gypsum and potash alum on Sharon conglomerate, Pottsville Group. Kings's Creek Cave on N side of Cuyahoga River about 1/5 mile W of Mary Campbell Cave, Cuyahoga Gorge Park, Cuyahoga Falls; AKRON WEST.
Mineral occurrence: Connors, 1974, p. 37, 39-40.
General geology: Kent State University, *in* Frank, 1969, p. 1.4-1.7.

VIVIANITE
$Fe_3(PO_4)_2 \cdot 8H_2O$

Chemical class: Phosphate
Crystallization: Monoclinic; prismatic; 2/m
Habit: Crystals commonly prismatic, may be tabular; commonly massive
Physical properties: Cleavage: {010} perfect pinacoidal. H: 1½-2. G: 2.7. Luster: vitreous if well crystallized or dull if massive. Color: colorless or white when fresh; turns pale blue, greenish blue, or dark blue when exposed to air. Streak: white to bluish white
Occurrence: Crystals or earthy masses rare in glacial deposits; commonly associated with partially decomposed plant or bone debris

BROWN COUNTY
1. Crystals and earthy masses of deep-blue vivianite in Illinoian glacial beds of dark-brown clay. Outcrop on Miranda Run about 1 mile above junction with White Oak Creek about 3 miles NE of Hamersville, Clark Twp.; HAMERSVILLE.
Mineral occurrence: Sarles, 1951, p. 41; Wuestner, 1938, p. 267.
General geology: Goldthwait and others, 1961, map.

HAMILTON COUNTY
1. Small globular masses of vivianite in sand and loam. Along a small stream a short distance below a 110-ft-high bluff 3 miles W of Glendale, Springfield Twp.; GREENHILLS.
Mineral occurrence: Orton and Peppel, 1906, p. 71-72.

MEDINA COUNTY
1. Small earthy masses of vivianite in Wisconsinan glacial beds of dark-gray clay. Quillin Bros. Construction Co., Inc., gravel pit off Seville Rd. about 1 mile E of Ohio Rte. 83 intersection 3 miles SE of Lodi, Westfield Twp.; WESTFIELD CENTER (formerly LEROY).
General geology: Totten, 1976, p. 514.

MONTGOMERY COUNTY
1. Small masses of vivianite in pockets of Wisconsinan glacial gravel and clay. Outcrops along N and E banks of Twin Creek about 1 mile E of Germantown, German Twp.; FRANKLIN.
Mineral occurrence: Orton, 1870, p. 54-56; Orton, 1871a, p. 160-161.

WARREN COUNTY
1. Small crystals and earthy masses of dark-blue vivianite as coatings on glacial clay and boulders. Outcrop along a creek that parallels Ohio Rte. 48 and near bridge just E of junction with Loveland-Foster Rd., SW Hamilton Twp.; SOUTH LEBANON.
Mineral occurrence: Wuestner, 1938, p. 265-266.
2. Small crystals and earthy masses of dark-blue vivianite as coatings on glacial clay and boulders. Outcrops along Ertel Run E of junction with Loveland-Foster Rd. at Adams Rd. bridge, Hamilton Twp.; SOUTH LEBANON.
Mineral occurrence: Wuestner, 1938, p. 265-266.

WHEWELLITE
$Ca(C_2O_4) \cdot H_2O$

Chemical class: Oxalate
Crystallization: Monoclinic; prismatic; 2/m
Habit: Commonly well crystallized; equant or short prismatic crystals; coarsely crystalline aggregates common
Physical properties: Cleavage: {$\bar{1}$01} good pinacoidal. H: 2½-3. G: 2.2. Luster: greasy. Color: white. Streak: white
Occurrence: Granular aggregates associated with fossil fish debris in veins of large limestone concretions from Huron Shale Member of Ohio Shale

ERIE COUNTY
1. Coarsely crystalline aggregates of whewellite with barite,

calcite, dolomite, ferroan dolomite, and pyrite in veins of large limestone concretions from lower Huron Shale Member, Ohio Shale. Outcrops along Huron River about 1 mile W of Milan, Milan Twp.; KIMBALL.

Mineral occurrence: Hoefs, 1969, p. 396; Hyde, C., and Landy, 1966, p. 228-229; Leavens, 1968, p. 455-463.

General geology: Prosser, 1913, p. 324-341.

FRANKLIN COUNTY
1. Whewellite with calcite in veins of large limestone concretions from lower Huron Shale Member, Ohio Shale. Also pyrite. Road cut along Interstate 270 about 2 miles N of Worthington, Sharon Twp.; NORTHWEST COLUMBUS.

Mineral occurrence: Criss and others, 1988, p. 6.

WURTZITE
ZnS

Chemical class: Sulfide
Crystallization: Wurtzite crystallizes in two crystal classes:
  Hexagonal; dihexagonal pyramidal; 6mm
  Hexagonal (Trigonal); ditrigonal pyramidal; 3m
Habit: Pyramidal crystals (hexagonal or trigonal); may be acicular; commonly in radiating groups
Physical properties: Cleavage: $\{11\bar{2}0\}$ distinct prismatic. H: 3½-4. G: 4.1. Luster: adamantine to resinous. Color: brownish red to brown. Streak: brown to yellow
Occurrence: Crystals and crystalline aggregates rare in veins of ironstone concretions from black shales in eastern Ohio

ATHENS COUNTY
1. Small reddish-brown wurtzite crystals in veins of ironstone concretions from shales above Brush Creek limestone, Conemaugh Group. Old Glouster Brick quarry on E side of Sunday Creek 1/3 mile S of Glouster, sec. 9, Trimble Twp.; JACKSONVILLE.

Mineral occurrence: Frondel and Palache, 1950, p. 31; Hollenbaugh and Carlson, 1983, p. 698; Seaman and Hamilton, 1950, p. 48, 50.

General geology: Condit, 1912, p. 235-236; Lamborn and others, 1938, p. 193.

CARROLL COUNTY
1. Rare crystals of reddish-brown wurtzite with barite, pyrite, and sphalerite in veins of ironstone concretions from shales above *Lower Kittanning (No. 5) coal* and Middle Kittanning (No. 6) coal, Allegheny Group. Also melanterite, rozenite, and szomolnokite. James Bros. Coal Co. strip mine about 3 miles SE of Mineral City, N½ sec. 25, Rose Twp.; MINERAL CITY.

Mineral occurrence: Hollenbaugh and Carlson, 1983, p. 698.

General geology: Lamborn, 1942, p. 10, 13.

COLUMBIANA COUNTY
1. Small hexagonal and trigonal reddish-brown wurtzite crystals in veins of ironstone concretions from shales above Lower Kittanning (No. 5) coal, Allegheny Group; may be associated with barite and sphalerite. Also calcite, chalcopyrite, copiapite, gypsum, kaolinite, and pyrite. Metrel, Inc., quarry S of Negley, sec. 13, Middleton Twp.; EAST PALESTINE.

Mineral occurrence: Anderson, V., 1979b, p. 297; Hollenbaugh, 1979, p. 9, 16-22; Hollenbaugh and Carlson, 1983, p. 697-703.

General geology: Stout and Lamborn, 1924, p. 111.

2. Small reddish-brown wurtzite crystals in veins of ironstone concretions from shales above Vanport limestone, Allegheny Group. Exposure on North Fork of Little Beaver Creek just SE of Negley, SW¼ sec. 12, Middleton Twp.; EAST PALESTINE.

Mineral occurrence: Hollenbaugh, 1979, p. 9, 16-17; Hollenbaugh and Carlson, 1983, p. 697-698.

General geology: Stout and Lamborn, 1924, p. 67-77.

3. Small reddish-brown crystals of wurtzite in veins of ironstone concretions from shales above Lower Freeport (No. 6A) coal, Allegheny Group. Exposure on E side of Ohio Rte. 39 W of Wellsville, N-central sec. 16, Yellow Creek Twp.; WELLSVILLE.

Mineral occurrence: Hollenbaugh, 1979, p. 13, 16-17; Hollenbaugh and Carlson, 1983, p. 698.

General geology: Stout and Lamborn, 1924, p. 208-213.

JEFFERSON COUNTY
1. Small reddish-brown wurtzite crystals in veins of ironstone concretions from shales above Brush Creek coal, Conemaugh Group; may be associated with barite, calcite, pyrite, and sphalerite. Road cut near Alikanna on E side of Ohio Rte. 7 just N of Ohio Rte. 213 intersection, N½ sec. 31, Island Creek Twp.; KNOXVILLE.

Mineral occurrence: Hollenbaugh and Carlson, 1983, p. 697-701; Seaman and Hamilton, 1950, p. 47.

General geology: Condit, 1912, p. 204-205; Lamborn, 1930, p. 123.

STARK COUNTY
1. Small reddish-brown wurtzite crystals with a white clay in veins of ironstone concretions from shales below Middle Kittanning (No. 6) coal, Allegheny Group. Abandoned mine, SW¼NE¼ sec. 16, Paris Twp.; ROBERTSVILLE.

Mineral occurrence: Hollenbaugh and Carlson, 1983, p. 698; William Rice, personal commun., 1977; Seaman and Hamilton, 1950, p. 50.

General geology: DeLong and White, 1963, p. 71-73.

TUSCARAWAS COUNTY
1. Rare reddish-brown wurtzite crystals in veins of ironstone concretions from shales of Allegheny Group. Also calcite, pyrite, and sphalerite. Puskarich Mining, Inc., strip mine about 1 mile S of New Cumberland, SW¼ sec. 28, Warren Twp.; MINERAL CITY.

Mineral occurrence: Hollenbaugh and Carlson, 1983, p. 698.

General geology: Lamborn, 1956, p. 140, 175.

REFERENCES CITED

Allen, R. D., 1952, Variations in chemical and physical properties of fluorite: American Mineralogist, v. 37, p. 910-930.

Alling, H. L., and Briggs, L. I., 1961, Stratigraphy of the upper Silurian Cayugan evaporites: American Association of Petroleum Geologists Bulletin, v. 45, p. 515-547.

Andelfinger, G. F., and Fiedelman, H. W., 1966, Properties of the impurities in northern rock salt, in Bersticker, A. C., ed., Second Symposium on Salt, v. 1: Cleveland, Northern Ohio Geological Society, p. 365-368.

Anderson, G. M., and MacQueen, R. W., 1982, Ore deposits models-6, Mississippi Valley-type lead-zinc deposits: Geoscience Canada, v. 9, p. 108-117.

Anderson, Violet, 1979a, Microminerals: Mineralogical Record, v. 10, p. 41-43.

_____ 1979b, Microminerals: Mineralogical Record, v. 10, p. 297.

Andrews, E. B., 1860, An account of the fall of meteoric stones at New Concord, Ohio, May 1, 1860: American Journal of Science, 2nd series, v. 30, p. 103-111.

_____ 1871, Report of progress in the Second District: Ohio Division of Geological Survey Report of Progress in 1869, p. 55-142.

_____ 1873, Geology of Athens County: Ohio Division of Geological Survey, v. 1, p. 261-293.

_____ 1874a, Report on the geology of Belmont County (south half): Ohio Division of Geological Survey, v. 2, pt. 1, p. 543-569.

_____ 1874b, Report on the geology of Pickaway County: Ohio Division of Geological Survey, v. 2, pt. 1, p. 588-592.

Anonymous, 1936, Cleveland Mineralogical Society (Proceedings): American Mineralogist, v. 21, p. 461-462.

Arnold, C. A., 1947, An introduction to paleobotany: New York, McGraw-Hill Co., Inc., 433 p.

Atwater, Caleb, 1820, Description of antiquities discovered in the state of Ohio and other western states: Transactions of the American Antiquarian Society, v. 1, p. 105-267.

_____ 1838, A history of the state of Ohio, natural and civil (2nd ed.): Cincinnati, Glazen and Shepard, 407 p.

Baker, Jack, 1957, Glacial geology of Geauga County, Ohio: University of Illinois, Ph.D. dissertation (unpublished), 74 p.

Barth, V. D., 1975, Formation of concretions occurring in the Ohio Shale along the Olentangy River: Ohio Journal of Science, v. 75, p. 162-163.

Bassett, W. A., and Bassett, A. M., 1962, Hexagonal stalactite from Rushmore Cave, South Dakota: National Speleological Society Bulletin, v. 24, pt. 2, p. 88-94.

Bates, R. L., and Jackson J. A., eds., 1987, Glossary of geology (3rd ed.): Alexandria, Virginia, American Geological Institute, 788 p.

Baughman, A. G., 1904, The Bellville gold region: Ohio Archaeological and Historical Publication, v. 13, p. 83-87.

Bernhagen, R. J., Carman, J. E., Goldthwait, R. P., Marple, M. F., and Pincus, H. J., 1953, Geology of Columbus area—guide to twenty-eighth annual field conference of the Section of Geology: Ohio Academy of Science, 10 p.

Bernstein, L. R., 1979, Coloring mechanisms in celestite: American Mineralogist, v. 64, p. 160-168.

Berryhill, H. L., 1963, Geology and coal resources of Belmont County, Ohio: U.S. Geological Survey Professional Paper 380, 113 p.

Bigsby, J. J., 1822, Notices of the sulphate of strontian of Lake Erie and Detroit River: American Journal of Science, v. 4, p. 280-282.

Bingaman, Ann, Core, Doug, and Boyer, Richard, 1978, Rock and mineral collecting sites in Ohio: Ohio Historical Society Natural History Information Series, v. 5, no. 3, 22 p.

Birkheimer, L. B., 1938, Selenite near Charlestown, Ohio: Rocks and Minerals, v. 13, p. 331.

Blatchley, W. S., 1902, Gold and diamonds in Indiana: 27th Annual Report of the Indiana Department of Geology and Natural Resources, p. 11-47.

Boon, J. D., and Albritton, C. C., Jr., 1936, Meteorite craters and their possible relationship to "cryptovolcanic structures": Field and Laboratory, v. 5, p. 1-9.

Botoman, George, 1975, Precambrian and Paleozoic stratigraphy and potential mineral deposits along the Cincinnati Arch of Ohio: Ohio State University, M.S. thesis (unpublished), 137 p.

Botoman, George, and Faure, Gunter, 1976, Sulfur isotope composition of some sulfide and sulfate minerals in Ohio: Ohio Journal of Science, v. 76, p. 66-71.

Botoman, George, and Stieglitz, R. D., 1978, The occurrence of sulfide and associated minerals in Ohio: Ohio Division of Geological Survey Report of Investigations 104, 11 p.

Bowman, R. S., 1956, Stratigraphy and paleontology of the Niagaran Series in Highland County, Ohio: Ohio State University, Ph.D. dissertation (unpublished), 339 p.

Bownocker, J. A., 1915, Building stones of Ohio: Ohio Division of Geological Survey Bulletin 18, 160 p.

_____ 1917, Coal fields of Ohio: U.S. Geological Survey Professional Paper 100, p. 35-96.

_____ 1920, Gypsum deposits of Ohio, in Stone, R. W., and others, Gypsum deposits of the United States: U.S. Geological Survey Bulletin 697, p. 218-223.

_____ 1947, Geologic map of Ohio (revised ed.): Ohio Division of Geological Survey, map.

Bownocker, J. A., and Dean, E. S., 1929, Analyses of the coals of Ohio: Ohio Division of Geological Survey Bulletin 34, 360 p.

Bownocker, J. A., Lord, W. W., and Somermeier, E. E., 1908, Coal: Ohio Division of Geological Survey Bulletin 9, 342 p.

Boyle, R. W., 1979, The geochemistry of gold and its deposits: Geological Survey of Canada Bulletin 280, 584 p.

Brant, R. A., 1956, Coal resources of the upper part of the Allegheny Formation in Ohio: Ohio Division of Geological Survey Report of Investigations 29, 68 p.

Brant, R. A., and Foster, W. R., 1959, Magnesian halotrichite from Vinton County, Ohio: Ohio Journal of Science, v. 59, p. 187-192.

Briggs, Caleb, Jr., 1838, Report: Ohio Division of Geological Survey First Annual Report, p. 71-98.

Broadhead, R. F., Kepferle, R. C., and Potter, P. E., 1980, Lithologic descriptions of cores and exposures of Devonian shale and associated strata in Ohio along Lake Erie: U.S. Geological Survey Open-File Report 80-719, 94 p.

Brown, C. N., 1888, The Pittsburgh coal seam in Jefferson, Belmont and Guernsey Counties: Ohio Division of Geological Survey, v. 6, p. 595-626.

Brummer, J. J., 1978, Diamonds in Canada: Canadian Institute of Mining Bulletin, v. 71, no. 798, p. 64-79.

Bucher, W. H., 1936, Serpent Mound structure, Ohio, in Cryptovolcanic structures in the United States: Washington, D.C., Sixteenth International Geological Congress, 1933, Report, v. 2, p. 1060-1064.

Buchwald, V. F., 1975, Handbook of iron meteorites—their history, distribution, composition and structure: Berkeley, University of California Press (3 volumes), 1,418 p.

Calvert, W. L., Bernhagen, R. J., and Bowman, R. S., 1968, Detailed discussion of outcrops observed at Ohio field stops, in Geological aspects of the Maysville-Portsmouth region, southern Ohio and northeastern Kentucky: Joint field conference, Ohio Geological Society-Geological Society of Kentucky, Kentucky Geological Survey, p. 21-37.

Carlson, E. H., 1977, Mineralogy of the septarian concretions from Ohio (abs.): Tucson, Arizona, Third Mineralogical Society of America - Friends of Mineralogy Symposium, p. 24-25.

_____ 1978, Sedimentary chalcopyrite in eastern Ohio (abs.): Geological Society of America Abstracts with Programs, v. 10, no. 6, p. 248-249.

_____ 1983, The occurrence of Mississippi Valley-type mineralization in northwestern Ohio, in Kisvarsanyi, G., Grant, S. K., Pratt, W. P., and Koenig, J. W., eds., Proceedings, International Conference on Mississippi Valley Type Lead-Zinc Deposits: University of Missouri-Rolla, p. 424-435.

Carlson, E. H., 1986, Localization of Sr-F-Zn-Pb mineralization in Lockport mound structures, northwestern Ohio: Field trip guidebook, Geological Society of America North-Central Section annual meeting, Kent State University, 25 p.

———— 1987a, Flint Ridge, Ohio: Flint facies of the Pennsylvanian Vanport Limestone, *in* Biggs, D. L., ed., North-Central Section of the Geological Society of America: Geological Society of America, Centennial Field Guide, v. 3, p. 415-418.

———— 1987b, Copperas Mountain: Black shale facies of the Upper Devonian Ohio Shale in south-central Ohio, *in* Biggs, D. L., ed., North-Central Section of the Geological Society of America: Geological Society of America, Centennial Field Guide, v. 3, p. 427-430.

———— 1987c, Celestite replacements of evaporites in the Salina Group: Sedimentary Geology, v. 54, p. 93-112.

Carman, J. E., 1922, Some sub-surface rock channels and cavities filled with glacial material: Ohio Journal of Science, v. 22, p. 125-128.

———— 1927, The Monroe division of rocks in Ohio: Journal of Geology, v. 35, p. 481-506.

———— 1936, Sylvania sandstone of northwestern Ohio: Geological Society of America Bulletin, v. 47, p. 253-266.

———— 1946, The geologic interpretation of scenic features in Ohio: Ohio Journal of Science, v. 46, p. 241-283.

———— 1948, A study of the geology of Lucas County and the lime-dolomite belt—guide to twenty-third annual field conference of the Section of Geology: Ohio Academy of Science, 12 p.

———— 1960, The stratigraphy of the Devonian Holland quarry shale of Ohio: Chicago Natural History Museum, Fieldiana, Geology, v. 14, no. 1, 5 p.

Carman, J. E., Kneller, W. A., Farnsworth, D. W., and Forsyth, J. L., 1962, Geology of the Toledo area—guide to thirty-seventh annual field conference of the Section of Geology: Ohio Academy of Science, 14 p.

Carskadden, Jeff, and Donaldson, Gerald, 1973, Brush Creek Flint quarrying in Perry and Morgan Counties, Ohio: Ohio Archaeologist, v. 23, no. 1, p. 20-21.

Caster, K. E., Durrell, R. H., and Jenks, W. F., 1970, Cincinnatian strata from Oregonia to the Ohio River with notes on Pleistocene geology along the route (Warren and Clermont Counties)—guide to forty-fifth annual field conference of the Section of Geology: Ohio Academy of Science, 19 p.

Cavaroc, V. V., Jr., and Ferm, J. C., 1968, Siliceous spiculites as shoreline indicators in deltaic sequences: Geological Society of America Bulletin, v. 79, p. 263-272.

Chesterman, C. W., 1978, The Audubon Society field guide to North American rocks and minerals: New York, Random House, Inc., 856 p.

Clark, S. H. B., 1987, Metallogenic map of zinc, lead, and barium deposits and occurrences in Paleozoic sedimentary rocks, east-central United States: U.S. Geological Survey Miscellaneous Investigations Series Map I-1773 and text, 77 p.

Clark, T. H., and Stearn, C. W., 1968, Geological evolution of North America (2nd ed.): New York, Ronald Press, 570 p.

Cleaveland, Parker, 1816, Treatise on mineralogy and geology (1st ed.): Boston, Cummings and Hilliard, 668 p.

———— 1822, Treatise on mineralogy and geology (2nd ed.): Boston, Cummings and Hilliard, v. 1, 818 p.

Clifford, M. J., 1973, Silurian rock salt of Ohio: Ohio Division of Geological Survey Report of Investigations 90, 42 p.

Clifton, H. E., 1957, The carbonate concretions of the Ohio shale: Ohio Journal of Science, v. 57, p. 114-124.

Cohen, A. J., Bunch, T. E., and Reid, A. M., 1961, Coesite discoveries establish cryptovolcanics as fossil meteorite craters: Science, v. 134, p. 1624-1625.

Cohen, A. J., Reid, A. M., and Bunch, T. E., 1962, Central uplifts of terrestrial and lunar craters, part 1, Kentland and Serpent Mound structures (abs.): Journal of Geophysical Research, v. 67, p. 1632-1633.

Cohen, E. W., 1898, Uber das Meteoreisen von Cincinnati, Vereinigte Staaten: Königlich-preussische Akademie der Wissenschaften zu Berlin, Sitzungsberichte, p. 428-430.

Cole, Frank, 1968, Ohio's iron kettles: Earth Science, v. 21, p. 68.

Cole, G. A., Drozd, R. J., Sedivy, R. A., and Halpern, H. I., 1987, Organic geochemistry and oil-source correlations, Paleozoic of Ohio: American Association of Petroleum Geologists Bulletin, v. 71, p. 788-809.

Collins, H. R., 1979, The Mississippian and Pennsylvanian (Carboniferous) Systems in the United States—Ohio: U.S. Geological Survey Professional Paper 1110-E, p. E1-E26.

———— 1986, The Hanging Rock iron region of Ohio: Ohio Geology Newsletter, Winter, p. 1-5.

Collins, H. R., and Webb, D. K., Jr., 1966, The Hanging Rock iron region of Ohio: Ohio Historical Society, folded pamphlet.

Collins, R. F., 1924, Pickeringite from the Cleveland shale: Columbia University, M.S. thesis (unpublished), 14 p.

Comstock, J. L., 1837, An introduction to mineralogy (3rd ed.): New York, Robinson, Pratt and Co., 369 p.

Condit, D. D., 1912, Conemaugh formation in Ohio: Ohio Division of Geological Survey Bulletin 17, 363 p.

———— 1923, Economic geology of the Summerfield and Woodsfield quadrangles, Ohio, with descriptions of coal and other mineral resources except oil and gas: U.S. Geological Survey Bulletin 720, 156 p.

Connors, H. E., 1974, Thenardite and other efflorescence in northeastern Ohio: Compass, v. 51, no. 2, p. 35-40.

Conrey, G. W., 1921, Geology of Wayne County: Ohio Division of Geological Survey Bulletin 24, 155 p.

Converse, R. N., 1972, Flints used by Ohio's prehistoric Indians: Ohio Archaeologist, v. 22, no. 2, p. 36-39.

Coogan, A. H., and Parker, M. M., 1984, Six potential trapping plays in Ordovician Trenton limestone, northwestern Ohio: Oil and Gas Journal, v. 82, no. 48, p. 121-126.

Courter, E. W., 1974, Crystal Cave: Lapidary Journal, v. 28, p. 664-672.

Criss, R. E., Cooke, G. A., and Day, S. D., 1988, An organic origin for the carbonate concretions of the Ohio Shale: U.S. Geological Survey Bulletin 1836, 21 p.

Cross, A. T., Smith, W. H., and Arkle, Thomas, Jr., 1950, Field guide for the special field conference on the stratigraphy, sedimentation and nomenclature of the Upper Pennsylvanian and Lower Permian strata (Monongahela, Washington and Greene series) in the northern portion of the Dunkard basin of Ohio, West Virginia, and Pennsylvania: West Virginia Geological Survey, Ohio Division of Geological Survey, and Coal Research Committee, Society of Economic Geologists, 104 p.

Cumings, E. R., 1930, Silurian reefs near Tiffin, Carey and Marseilles, Ohio: Proceedings of the Indiana Academy of Science, v. 39, p. 199-204.

Cushing, H. P., Leverett, Frank, and Van Horn, F. R., 1931, Geology and mineral resources of the Cleveland district, Ohio: U.S. Geological Survey Bulletin 818, 138 p.

Dana, E. S., 1892, System of mineralogy (6th ed.): New York, John Wiley and Sons, 1,134 p.

———— 1932, The celestite locality near Clay Center, Ohio: American Journal of Science, v. 23, p. 383.

Dana, E. S., and Ford, W. E., 1932, A textbook of mineralogy (4th ed.): New York, John Wiley and Sons, 851 p.

Dana, J. D., 1858, A system of mineralogy (4th ed.): New York, D. Appleton and Co., pt. 2, 533 p.

———— 1868, A system of mineralogy (5th ed.): New York, John Wiley and Son, 827 p.

Dawson, J. W., 1871, Fossil land plants of the Devonian and Upper Silurian: Geological Survey of Canada, pt. 1, p. 1-92.

Dean, E. S., 1949, Additional analyses of coals of Ohio: Ohio Division of Geological Survey Report of Investigations 4, 17 p.

Delafield, James, 1822, Notices of the sulphate of strontian of Lake Erie and Detroit River: American Journal of Science, v. 4, p. 279-280.

Dellwig, L. F., and Evans, Robert, 1969, Depositional processes in Salina salt of Michigan, Ohio, and New York: American Association of Petroleum Geologists Bulletin, v. 53, p. 949-956.

DeLong, R. M., 1955, The Pittsburgh No. 8 and Redstone No. 8A coal beds in Ohio: Ohio Division of Geological Survey Report of Investigations 26, 49 p.

———— 1972, Bedrock geology of Flint Ridge area, Ohio: Ohio Division of Geological Survey Report of Investigations 84, map.

DeLong, R. M., and White, G. W., 1963, Geology of Stark County: Ohio Division of Geological Survey Bulletin 61, 209 p.

Denton, G. H., Collins, H. R., DeLong, R. M., Smith, B. E., Sturgeon, M. T., and Brant, R. A., 1961, Pennsylvanian geology of eastern Ohio: Guidebook for field trips, Cincinnati meeting, Geological Society of America, p. 133-205.

Dietz, R. S., 1946, Geological structures possibly related to lunar craters: Popular Astronomy, v. 54, p. 465-467.
——— 1960, Meteorite impact suggested by shatter cones in rock: Science, v. 131, p. 1781-1784.
Douglass, D. B., 1820, New locality of crystalized sulphat of Barytes: American Journal of Science, v. 2, p. 241.
——— 1821, Sulphat of Strontian: American Journal of Science, v. 3, p. 363-364.
Ehlers, E. G., and Stiles, D. V., 1965, Melanterite-rozenite equilibrium: American Mineralogist, v. 50, p. 1457-1461.
Ehlers, G. M., Stumm, E. C., and Kesling, R. V., 1951, Devonian rocks of southeastern Michigan and northwestern Ohio: Stratigraphy field trip, Detroit meeting, Geological Society of America, 40 p.
Espenshade, G. H., and Broedel, C. H., 1952, Annotated bibliography and index map of sulfur and pyrites deposits in the United States and Alaska: U.S. Geological Survey Circular 157, 48 p.
Explorer, The, 1961, Natural science notes (limestone concretions): Explorer, v. 3, no. 6, p. 5.
Farnsworth, Carolyn, 1961, About Ohio rocks and minerals: Ohio Division of Geological Survey Educational Leaflet 5, 30 p.
Farrington, O. C., 1915, Catalogue of the meteorites of North America to January 1, 1909: National Academy of Sciences Memoirs, v. 13, 513 p.
Farrington, O. C., and Tillotson, E. W., Jr., 1908, Notes on various minerals in the museum collection: Chicago, Field Columbian Museum, Geological Series, iii, no. 7, p. 131-163.
Feldmann, R. M., and Bjerstedt, T. W., 1987, Kelleys Island: giant glacial grooves and Devonian shelf carbonates in north-central Ohio, in Biggs, D. L., ed., North-Central Section of the Geological Society of America: Geological Society of America, Centennial Field Guide, v. 3, p. 395-398.
Feldmann, R. M., Coogan, A. H., and Heimlich, R. A., 1977, Field guide, the southern Great Lakes: Dubuque, Iowa, Kendall-Hunt Publishing Co., 256 p.
Fisher, H. H., 1975, Some sulfate minerals of Meigs County, Ohio: Rocks and Minerals, v. 50, p. 416-418.
——— 1976, Trapezohedral pyrite in Ohio: Rocks and Minerals, v. 51, p. 293.
——— 1977, Ohio celestine: Rocks and Minerals, v. 52, p. 411-414.
Fisher, Mildred, 1922, The geology of Kelley's Island: Ohio State University, M.S. thesis (unpublished), 60 p.
Fleischer, Michael, 1987, Glossary of mineral species (5th ed.): Tucson, Arizona, The Mineralogical Record, Inc., 227 p.
Flint, N. K., 1951, Geology of Perry County: Ohio Division of Geological Survey Bulletin 48, 234 p.
Floyd, J. C., 1971, Depositional environments of some Silurian rocks, northern Ohio: Bowling Green State University, M.A. thesis (unpublished), 231 p.
Foerste, A. F., 1891, On the Clinton oolitic iron ores: American Journal of Science, v. 41, p. 28-29.
——— 1919, Silurian fossils from Ohio, with notes on related species from other horizons: Ohio Journal of Science, v. 19, p. 367-404.
Ford, W. E., and Pogue, J. L., 1909, Calcite crystals from Kelley's Island, Lake Erie: American Journal of Science, v. 28, p. 186-187.
Forsyth, J. L., 1966a, The geology of the Bowling Green area, Wood County, Ohio: Compass, v. 43, p. 202-214.
——— 1966b, Glacial map of Licking County: Ohio Division of Geological Survey Report of Investigations 59, map.
——— 1971, Geology of the Lake Erie islands and adjacent shores: Guidebook for annual field excursion, Michigan Basin Geological Society, p. 1-18.
Foster, J. W., 1838, Report (on Muskingum County, and parts of Licking and Franklin Counties): Ohio Division of Geological Survey Second Annual Report, p. 74-107.
Foster, W. R., and Hoover, K. V., 1963, Hexahydrite (MgSO$_4$ · 6H$_2$O) as an efflorescence of some Ohio dolomites: Ohio Journal of Science, v. 63, p. 152-158.
Fowke, Gerard, 1894, Material for aboriginal stone implements: The Archaeologist, v. 2, p. 328-335.
——— 1902, Archaeological history of Ohio: Ohio State Archaeological and Historical Society, 760 p.
——— 1928, Archaeological investigations II: Smithsonian Institution Bureau of American Ethnology, Annual Report for 1926-1927, p. 399-540.

Frank, G. W., ed., 1969, Ohio intercollegiate field trip guides 1950-51 to 1969-70: Kent State University, Department of Geology, p. 1.1-20.27.
Frohman, C. E., 1971, Put-in-Bay, its history: Ohio Historical Society, 156 p.
Frondel, Clifford, 1962, The system of mineralogy, v. 3, silica minerals: New York, John Wiley and Sons, 334 p.
Frondel, Clifford, and Palache, Charles, 1950, Three new polymorphs of zinc sulfide: American Mineralogist, v. 35, p. 29-42.
Frye, Charles, ed., 1976, Local Pennsylvanian stratigraphy: Muskingum College, Twenty-seventh annual Ohio intercollegiate field trip, 3 p.
Fuchs, L. H., 1969, The phosphate mineralogy of meteorites: Meteorite Research, v. 12, p. 683-695.
Fuchs, L. H., Olsen, Edward, and Henderson, E. P., 1967, On the occurrence of brianite and panethite, two new phosphate minerals from the Dayton meteorite: Geochimica et Cosmochimica Acta, v. 31, p. 1711-1719.
Gait, R. I., 1980, Pyrite crystals from Duff's quarry, Huntsville, Ohio, U.S.A.: Mineralogical Record, v. 11, p. 97-99.
Galbraith, R. M., 1968, Peripheral deformation of the Serpent Mound cryptoexplosion structure in Adams County, Ohio: University of Cincinnati, M.S. thesis (unpublished), 47 p.
Garske, David, and Peacor, D. R., 1965, Refinement of the structure of celestite SrSO$_4$: Zeitschrift für Kristallographie, v. 121, p. 204-210.
Gettings, C. O., 1950, Ohio, in World news on mineral occurrences: Rocks and Minerals, v. 25, p. 600-601.
——— 1952a, Ohio, in World news on mineral occurrences: Rocks and Minerals, v. 27, p. 142-143.
——— 1952b, Ohio, in World news on mineral occurrences: Rocks and Minerals, v. 27, p. 493.
——— 1954, Ohio, in World news on mineral occurrences: Rocks and Minerals, v. 29, p. 259.
——— 1955, Ohio, in World news on mineral occurrences: Rocks and Minerals, v. 30, p. 485.
Gilbert, G. K., 1873, Reports on the surface geology of the Maumee Valley, and on the geology of Williams, Fulton, and Lucas Counties, and West Sister Island: Ohio Division of Geological Survey, v. 1, pt. 1, p. 535-590.
Gleason, Sterling, 1960, Ultraviolet guide to minerals: Princeton, New Jersey, Van Nostrand Co., 244 p.
Goldthwait, R. P., White, G. W., and Forsyth, J. L., 1961, Glacial map of Ohio: U.S. Geological Survey Miscellaneous Investigations Map I-316.
Good, C. W., and Taylor, T. N., 1974, Structurally preserved plants from Pennsylvanian (Monongahela Series) of southeastern Ohio: Ohio Journal of Science, v. 74, p. 287-290.
Goodwin, H. R., 1940, Geode locality in Ohio: Rocks and Minerals, v. 15, p. 260.
Green, D. A., 1957, Trenton structure in Ohio, Indiana, and northern Illinois: American Association of Petroleum Geologists Bulletin, v. 41, p. 627-642.
Green, Richard, 1970a, Ohio, still a mineral-producing state: Rocks and Minerals, v. 45, p. 584-585.
——— 1970b, Celestite: Rocks and Minerals, v. 45, p. 676-678, 687.
——— 1971, Ohio Lime, Woodville: Rocks and Minerals, v. 46, p. 280-281.
Greene, G. U., 1935, The occurrence of sphalerite at Ellsworth, Ohio: American Mineralogist, v. 20, p. 882-883.
——— 1937, Selenite crystals at Ellsworth, Ohio: Rocks and Minerals, v. 12, p. 272-273.
Gunn, C. B., 1968, A descriptive catalog of the drift diamonds of the Great Lakes region, North America: Gems and Gemology, v. 12, no. 12, p. 297-303, 333-334.
Gunnell, E. M., 1933, Luminescence of fluorite from Clay Center, Ohio: Rocks and Minerals, v. 8, p. 145-146.
Haden, J. M., 1977, Isotopic studies of sulfide and other mineralization from the Middle Paleozoic rocks of western Ohio: Ohio State University, M.S. thesis (unpublished), 117 p.
Hall, J. F., 1963, Distribution of salt in Ohio, in Bersticker, A. C., ed., Symposium on Salt: Cleveland, Northern Ohio Geological Society, p. 27-30.
Hall, J. F., and Alkire, R. L., 1956, The economic geology of

Crawford, Marion, Morrow, and Wyandot Counties: Ohio Division of Geological Survey Report of Investigations 28, 43 p.

Hamilton, H. V., 1953, Ohio, *in* World news on mineral occurrences: Rocks and Minerals, v. 28, p. 134-135.

Hansen, M. C., 1982, Diamonds from Ohio: Ohio Geology Newsletter, Fall, p. 1-3.

_____ 1983, Ohio meteorites: Ohio Geology Newsletter, Summer, p. 1-4.

_____ 1984, "Journey to the center of the earth"—the aeromagnetic anomaly map of Ohio: Ohio Geology Newsletter, Summer, p. 2-6.

_____ 1985a, Additional notes on diamonds: Ohio Geology Newsletter, Winter, p. 1-4.

_____ 1985b, Gold in Ohio: Ohio Geology Newsletter, Spring, p. 1-7.

_____ 1986, Rare arthrodire jaw found in Columbus: Ohio Geology Newsletter, Fall, p. 6-7.

Harness, C. L., 1942, Strontium minerals: U.S. Bureau of Mines Information Circular 7200, 17 p.

Hawes, G. W., 1884, Building stones of Ohio: Ohio Division of Geological Survey, v. 5, p. 577-642.

Hayes, P. D., 1969, Minerals of Ohio: University of Virginia, M.S. thesis (unpublished), 71 p.

Heimlich, R. A., Manus, R. W., and Jacoby, C. H., 1974, General geology of the International Salt Company Cleveland Mine, Cleveland, Ohio, *in* Heimlich, R. A., and Feldmann, R. M., eds., Selected field trips in northeastern Ohio: Ohio Division of Geological Survey Guidebook 2, p. 4-17.

Heinrich, E. W., and Vian, R. W., 1967, Carbonatitic barites: American Mineralogist, v. 52, p. 1179-1189.

Henderson, E. P., and Perry, S. H., 1946, New Westville, Preble County, Ohio, meteorite: Smithsonian Institution Miscellaneous Collections, v. 104, no. 17, Publication 3814, 9 p.

Herdendorf, C. E., 1963, The geology of the Vermilion quadrangle, Ohio: Ohio University, M.S. thesis (unpublished), 182 p.

Herdendorf, C. E., and Braidech, L. L., 1972, Physical characteristics of the reef area of western Lake Erie: Ohio Division of Geological Survey Report of Investigations 82, 90 p.

Herzer, Herman, 1893, A new tree from the Carboniferous rocks of Monroe County, Ohio: American Geologist, v. 11, p. 285-286.

_____ 1897, *Psaronius:* Ohio State Academy of Science, 5th Annual Report, p. 55-58.

Hey, M. H., 1966, Catalogue of meteorites with special reference to those represented in the collection of the British Museum (Natural History) (3rd ed.): London, British Museum of Natural History, 637 p.

Heyl, A. V., 1968, Minor epigenetic, diagenetic, and syngenetic sulphide, fluorite, and barite occurrences in the United States: Economic Geology, v. 63, p. 585-594.

Heyl, A. V., and Brock, M. R., 1962, Zinc occurrence in the Serpent Mound structure of southern Ohio: U.S. Geological Survey Professional Paper 450-D, p. D95-D97.

Heyl, A. V., and Van Alstine, R. E., 1976, Central and eastern United States, *in* Shawe, D. R., ed., Geology and resources of fluorine in the United States: U.S. Geological Survey Professional Paper 933, p. 62-81.

Hildreth, S. P., 1827, Notice of fossil trees near Gallipolis, Ohio: American Journal of Science, v. 12, p. 205-206.

_____ 1829, Miscellaneous notices of rocks and minerals in the State of Ohio: American Journal of Science, v. 16, p. 154-159.

_____ 1834, Ten days in Ohio: American Journal of Science, v. 25, p. 217-257.

_____ 1837, Miscellaneous observations made during a tour in May 1835 to the falls of the Cuyahoga, near Lake Erie: American Journal of Science, v. 31, p. 1-84.

_____ 1838, Report (on the coal measures): Ohio Division of Geological Survey First Annual Report, p. 25-63.

Hobbs, W. H., 1899, The diamond field of the Great Lakes: Journal of Geology, v. 7, p. 375-388.

Hodge, J. T., 1878, Report on the geology of Coshocton County: Ohio Division of Geological Survey, v. 3, p. 562-595.

Hoefs, Jochen, 1969, Natural calcium oxalate with heavy carbon: Nature, v. 223, p. 396.

Holden, W. F., and Carlson, E. H., 1979, Barite concretions from the Cleveland Shale in north-central Ohio: Ohio Journal of Science, v. 79, p. 227-232.

Hollenbaugh, D. W., 1979, Trace element geochemistry and mineralogy of septarian siderite concretions and enclosing shales in Columbiana County, Ohio: Kent State University, M.S. thesis (unpublished), 60 p.

Hollenbaugh, D. W., and Carlson, E. H., 1983, The occurrence of wurtzite polytypes in eastern Ohio: Canadian Mineralogist, v. 21, p. 697-703.

Holmes, W. H., 1919, Handbook of aboriginal American antiquities, part 1: Bureau of American Ethnology Bulletin 60, 380 p.

Hoover, K. V., 1960, Devonian-Mississippian shale sequence in Ohio: Ohio Division of Geological Survey Information Circular 27, 154 p.

Hopkins, R. M., 1954, A petrographic study of the Brassfield (Silurian) Limestone in southwestern Ohio: Ohio State University, M.S. thesis (unpublished), 91 p.

Horvath, A. L., and Sparling, Dale, 1967, Silurian geology of western Ohio—guide to forty-second annual field conference of the Section of Geology: Ohio Academy of Science, 25 p.

Hoskins, J. H., and Blickle, A. H., 1940, Concretionary *Callixylon* from the Ohio Devonian black shale: American Midland Naturalist, v. 23, p. 472-481.

Howard, C. L. H., 1959, Celestite and fluorite from Clay Center, Ohio: Cleveland Museum of Natural History Museum News, v. 1, no. 12, p. 125-130.

Hull, D. N., 1982, New Ohio mineral found in Coshocton County: Ohio Geology Newsletter, Summer, p. 6.

Hull, D. N., and Hansen, M. C., 1982, An occurrence of the mineral diadochite in Coshocton County, Ohio (abs.): Ohio Journal of Science, v. 82, no. 2, p. 31-32.

Hyde, C., and Landy, R. A., 1966, Whewellite from septarian concretions near Milan, Ohio: American Mineralogist, v. 51, p. 228-229.

Hyde, J. E., 1921, Geology of Camp Sherman quadrangle: Ohio Division of Geological Survey Bulletin 23, 190 p.

Hyde, J. E., and Marple, M. F., 1953, The Mississippian formations of central and southern Ohio: Ohio Division of Geological Survey Bulletin 51, 355 p.

Jacoby, C. H., 1969, Correlation, faulting and metamorphism of Michigan and Appalachian Basin salt: American Association of Petroleum Geologists Bulletin, v. 53, p. 136-154.

_____ 1970, Faults in salt mines, their impact on operations, *in* Rau, J. L., and Dellwig, L. F., ed., Third Symposium on Salt: Northern Ohio Geological Society, v. 2, p. 447-452.

Janssens, Adriaan, 1969, Devonian outcrops in Columbus, Ohio, and vicinity: Field trip guidebook, third annual meeting, North-Central Section, Geological Society of America, Ohio Division of Geological Survey, p. 1.1-1.22.

_____ 1970a, Middle Devonian formations in the subsurface of northwestern Ohio: Ohio Division of Geological Survey Report of Investigations 78, 22 p.

_____ 1970b, Guidebook to the Middle Devonian rocks of north-central Ohio: Ohio Geological Society, 30 p.

_____ 1971, Preliminary report on the stratigraphy of Upper Silurian rocks of western Ohio, *in* Forsyth, J. L., ed., Geology of the Lake Erie islands and adjacent shores: Guidebook for annual field excursion, Michigan Basin Geological Society, p. 30-36.

_____ 1974, The evidence for Lockport-Salina facies changes in the subsurface of northwestern Ohio, *in* Kesling, R. V., ed., Silurian reef-evaporite relationships: Guidebook for annual field excursion, Michigan Basin Geological Society, p. 79-88.

_____ 1977, Silurian rocks in the subsurface of northwestern Ohio: Ohio Division of Geological Survey Report of Investigations 100, 96 p.

Jolly, J. J., and Heyl, A. V., 1968, Mercury and other trace elements in sphalerite and wallrocks from central Kentucky, Tennessee and Appalachian zinc districts: U.S. Geological Survey Bulletin 1252-F, p. F1-F29.

Jones, V. E., 1935, Origin of the gypsum deposits near Sandusky, Ohio: Economic Geology, v. 30, p. 493-501.

Kahle, C. F., 1974, Nature and significance of Silurian rocks at Maumee quarry, Ohio, *in* Kesling, R. V., ed., Silurian reef-evaporite relationships: Guidebook for annual field excursion, Michigan Basin Geological Society, p. 31-54.

_____ 1978, Patch reef development and effects of repeated subaerial exposure in Silurian shelf carbonates, Maumee, Ohio, *in* Kesling, R. V., ed., Field excursions: North-Central Section Geological Society of America, University of Michigan, p. 63-115.

REFERENCES CITED

Kahle, C. F., and Floyd, J. C., 1968, Structures and fabrics in some middle and upper Silurian dolostones, northwestern Ohio—guidebook to forty-third annual field conference of the Section of Geology: Ohio Academy of Science, 40 p.

_____ 1971, Stratigraphy and environmental significance of sedimentary structures in Cayugan (Silurian) tidal flat carbonates, northwestern Ohio: Geological Society of America Bulletin, v. 82, p. 2071-2098.

_____ 1972, Geology of Silurian rocks, northwestern Ohio: Guidebook, first annual meeting, Eastern Section, American Association of Petroleum Geologists, Ohio Geological Society, 91 p.

Karhi, Louis, 1948, Cone-in-cone in the Ohio shale: Ohio State University, M.S. thesis (unpublished), 55 p.

Kepferle, R. C., Roen, J. B., de Witt, Wallace, Jr., Maynard, J. B., Ettensohn, F. R., and Barron, L. S., 1981, Chattanooga and Ohio Shales of the southern Appalachian Basin, in Roberts, T. G., ed., GSA Cincinnati '81 field trip guidebooks: Geological Society of America, American Geological Institute, v. 2, p. 259-361.

Kessen, K. M., Woodruff, M. S., and Grant, N. K., 1981, Gangue mineral $^{87}Sr/^{86}Sr$ ratios and the origin of Mississippi Valley-type mineralization: Economic Geology, v. 76, p. 913-920.

Kindt, E. A., 1952, Ohio, in World news on mineral occurrences: Rocks and Minerals, v. 27, p. 255-256.

King, P. B., 1977, The evolution of North America (revised ed.): Princeton, New Jersey, Princeton University Press, 197 p.

Klein, Cornelius, and Hurlbut, C. S., Jr., 1985, Manual of mineralogy (20th ed.): New York, John Wiley and Sons, 596 p.

Knille, R., and Gibbs, J., 1942, An interesting mineral trip in southwestern Ohio: Rocks and Minerals, v. 17, p. 318-320.

Koucky, F. L., ed., 1975, Serpent Mound cryptoexplosion structure: College of Wooster, Twenty-sixth annual Ohio intercollegiate field trip, 60 p.

Koucky, F. L., and Reidel, S. P., 1987, The Serpent Mound disturbance, south-central Ohio, in Biggs, D. L., ed., North-Central Section of the Geological Society of America: Geological Society of America, Centennial field guide, v. 3, p. 431-436.

Kraus, E. H., 1905a, Occurrence and distribution of celestite-bearing rocks: American Journal of Science, v. 19, p. 286-293.

_____ 1905b, On the origin of the caves of the island of Put-in-Bay, Lake Erie: American Geologist, v. 35, p. 167-171.

Kraus, E. H., and Hunt, W. F., 1906, The occurrence of sulphur and celestite at Maybee, Michigan: American Journal of Science, v. 21, p. 237-244.

Kraus, E. H., Hunt, W. F., and Ramsdel, L. S., 1959, Mineralogy (5th ed.): New York, McGraw-Hill Book Co., 686 p.

Kunz, G. F., 1892, Gems and precious stones of North America (2nd ed.): New York, Dover Publishing Inc., 367 p.

Kyte, D. J., 1962, Some notes on the findings of the multi-iridescent, double-generation fluorite of Paulding County, Ohio: Rocks and Minerals, v. 37, p. 27.

Lamb, G. F., 1910, Pennsylvanian limestones of northeastern Ohio below the Lower Kittanning coal: Ohio Naturalist, v. 10, p. 89-135.

Lamborn, R. E., 1927, The Olentangy shale in southern Ohio: Journal of Geology, v. 35, p. 708-722.

_____ 1929, Notes on the character and occurrences of the Olentangy shale in southern Ohio: Ohio Journal of Science, v. 29, p. 27-38.

_____ 1930, Geology of Jefferson County: Ohio Division of Geological Survey Bulletin 35, 204 p.

_____ 1942, The coal beds of western Carroll County and southeastern Mahoning County: Ohio Division of Geological Survey Bulletin 43, 33 p.

_____ 1951, Limestones of eastern Ohio: Ohio Division of Geological Survey Bulletin 49, 377 p.

_____ 1954, Geology of Coshocton County: Ohio Division of Geological Survey Bulletin 53, 245 p.

_____ 1956, Geology of Tuscarawas County: Ohio Division of Geological Survey Bulletin 55, 269 p.

Lamborn, R. E., Austin, C. R., and Schaaf, Downs, 1938, Shales and surface clays of Ohio: Ohio Division of Geological Survey Bulletin 39, 281 p.

Langlois, T. H., 1951, The caves on South Bass Island: Inland Seas, v. 7, p. 113-117.

La Rocque, Aurele, and Marple, M. F., 1955, Ohio fossils: Ohio Division of Geological Survey Bulletin 54, 152 p.

Leavens, P. B., 1968, New data on whewellite: American Mineralogist, v. 53, p. 455-463.

Leeds, A. R., 1875, On an asphaltic coal from the shale of the Huron River, Ohio, containing seams of sulphate of baryta: New York Academy of Sciences, Annals of the Lyceum of Natural History of New York, v. 11, p. 105-106.

Lesquereux, Leo, 1880, Description of the coal flora of the Carboniferous formation in Pennsylvania and throughout the United States: Pennsylvania Geological Survey, v. 1, p. 1-354.

Lintner, E. J., 1944, Gypsum, part 2 of Ohio's mineral resources: Ohio State University Engineering Experiment Station Circular 45, p. 10-30.

Locke, John, 1838, Geological report (on southwestern Ohio): Ohio Division of Geological Survey Second Annual Report, p. 201-286.

Lucius, J. E., and von Frese, R. R. B., 1988, Aeromagnetic and gravity anomaly constraints on the crustal geology of Ohio: Geological Society of America Bulletin, v. 100, p. 104-116.

Maslowski, Andy, 1986, Ohio gold: Rock and Gem, v. 16, no. 10, p. 20-22.

Mason, Brian, 1962, Meteorites: New York, John Wiley and Sons, Inc., 274 p.

_____ 1963, Olivine composition in chondrites: Geochimica et Cosmochimica Acta, v. 27, p. 1011-1023.

Mason, Brian, and Berry, L. G., 1968, Elements of mineralogy: San Francisco, W. H. Freeman and Co., 550 p.

Mason, Brian, and Wiik, H. B., 1961, The composition of the Ottawa, Chateau-Renard, Mocs, and New Concord meteorites: American Museum Novitates, no. 2069, p. 1-25.

McAllister, R. F., 1941, Digging fools gold in Ohio: The Mineralogist, v. 9, p. 203-204, 232-233.

McCall, G. J. H., ed., 1979, Astroblemes—cryptoexplosion structures: Stroudsburg, Pennsylvania, Dowden, Hutchinson and Ross, Inc., 437 p.

McCaughey, W. J., 1918, Copiapite in coal: American Mineralogist, v. 3, p. 162-163.

Medici, J. C., and Robinson, G. W., 1988, Three unusual habits of fluorite crystals from Delphos, Ohio (abs.): Rocks and Minerals, v. 63, p. 128.

Merrill, W. M., 1948, The geology of Green and Ward Townships, Hocking County, Ohio: Ohio State University, M.S. thesis (unpublished), 151 p.

_____ 1950, The geology of northern Hocking County, Ohio: Ohio State University, Ph.D. dissertation (unpublished), 444 p.

Mesolella, K. J., 1978, Paleogeography of some Silurian and Devonian reef trends, central Appalachian basin: American Association of Petroleum Geologists Bulletin, v. 62, p. 1607-1644.

Metzler, J. M., 1967, Bedrock and glacial geology of Bath Township, Summit County, Ohio: Kent State University, M.S. thesis (unpublished), 71 p.

Meyers, T. R., 1929, The geology of Jefferson and Bedford Townships, Coshocton County, Ohio: Ohio State University, M.S. thesis (unpublished), 85 p.

Miller, B. B., 1970, The Quaternary period, in Banks, P. O., and Feldmann, R. M., eds., Guide to the geology of northeastern Ohio: Northern Ohio Geological Society, p. 149-164.

Mills, W. C., 1917, Feurt mounds and village site: Ohio Archaeological and Historical Quarterly, v. 26, p. 304-449.

_____ 1921, Flint Ridge: Ohio Archaeological and Historical Quarterly, v. 30, p. 90-161.

Mitchell, R. H., 1951, Petrified wood in Ohio: Rocks and Minerals, v. 26, p. 253-255.

Mohr, E. B., 1931, The geology of the Bass Islands: Ohio State University, M.S. thesis (unpublished), 62 p.

Moody, J. D., Mooney, J. W., and Spivak, J., 1970, Giant oil fields of North America, in Halbouty, M. T., ed., Geology of giant petroleum fields: American Association of Petroleum Geologists Memoir 14, p. 8-17.

Moorbath, Stephen, 1977, The oldest rocks and the growth of continents: Scientific American, v. 236 (March), p. 92-104.

Moorehead, W. K., 1892, Primitive man in Ohio: New York, G. P. Putnam's Sons, 246 p.

Morgan, E. J., 1959, The morphology and anatomy of American species of the genus *Psaronius*: Illinois Biological Monographs, no. 27, 108 p.

Morgan, Richard, 1929, Geological aspects of Ohio archaeology:

Ohio State University, M.S. thesis (unpublished), 75 p.

Morningstar, Helen, 1922, Pottsville fauna of Ohio: Ohio Division of Geological Survey Bulletin 25, 312 p.

Morrison, R. B., 1934, Celestite and fluorite deposits in the upper Niagara dolomite at Clay Center, Ohio: Cornell University, M.S. thesis (unpublished), 48 p.

_____ 1935, The occurrence and origin of celestite and fluorite at Clay Center, Ohio: American Mineralogist, v. 20, p. 780-790.

Morton, James, and Carskadden, Jeff, 1972, Aboriginal flint quarrying activities in the Muskingum County area: Ohio Archaeologist, v. 22, no. 2, p. 15-21.

Moses, C. F., 1922, The geology of the Bellefontaine outlier: Ohio State University, M.S. thesis (unpublished), 88 p.

Murata, K. J., 1940, Volcanic ash as a source of silica for the silicification of wood: American Journal of Science, v. 238, p. 586-596.

Murphy, J. L., 1973, The aboriginal use of petrified wood in southeastern Ohio: Ohio Archaeologist, v. 23, no. 3, p. 29-30.

_____ 1976, The aboriginal use of fresh-water Monongahela chert in Ohio and West Virginia: Ohio Archaeologist, v. 26, no. 2, p. 23-26.

Murphy, J. L., and Blank, J. E., 1970, The Plum Run flint quarries: Ohio Archaeologist, v. 20, p. 198-200, 217.

Mychkovsky, George, 1978a, The origin of fluorite, sulfide and sulfate minerals in northwestern Ohio (abs.): Geological Society of America Abstracts with Programs, v. 10, no. 6, p. 279.

_____ 1978b, The origin of fluorite, sulfate and sulfide minerals in northwestern Ohio: Kent State University, M.S. thesis (unpublished), 74 p.

Napper, C. W., 1916, Occurrence of carbonaceous material in the Greenfield member of the Monroe formation: Ohio Journal of Science, v. 16, p. 155-159.

_____ 1917, Concretionary forms in the Greenfield limestone: Ohio Journal of Science, v. 18, p. 7-13.

Nelson, R. H., 1967, Mineralogy of the solution cavities in selected Devonian limestone areas of Ohio: Ohio University, M.S. thesis (unpublished), 91 p.

Newberry, J. S., 1868, On some remarkable fossil fishes discovered by Rev. H. Herzer in the black shale (Devonian) at Delaware, Ohio: American Association for the Advancement of Science Proceedings, v. 16, p. 146-147.

_____ 1870, Report on the progress of the Geological Survey of Ohio in 1869: Ohio Division of Geological Survey Report of Progress in 1869, p. 3-51.

_____ 1873a, The general geological relations and structure of Ohio: Ohio Division of Geological Survey, v. 1, pt. 1, p. 1-167.

_____ 1873b, Report on the geology of Cuyahoga County: Ohio Division of Geological Survey, v. 1, pt. 1, p. 170-200.

_____ 1874a, Surface geology of Ohio: Ohio Division of Geological Survey, v. 2, pt. 1, p. 1-80.

_____ 1874b, Report on the geology of Erie County and the islands; Lorain County: Ohio Division of Geological Survey, v. 2, pt. 1, p. 183-224.

_____ 1875, Note (on asphaltic coal from the shale of the Huron River, Ohio, containing seams of sulphate of baryta): New York Academy of Sciences, Annals of the Lyceum of Natural History of New York, v. 11, p. 105-106.

_____ 1878, Report on the geology of Jefferson County; Mahoning County: Ohio Division of Geological Survey, v. 3, p. 716-814.

_____ 1889, Devonian plants from Ohio: Journal of the Cincinnati Society of Natural History, v. 12, p. 48-56.

Nininger, H. H., 1942, The Enon, Ohio, meteorite (mesosiderite) (abs.): Popular Astronomy, v. 50, p. 563-565.

Nuhfer, E. B., 1967, Efflorescent minerals associated with coal: West Virginia University, M.S. thesis (unpublished), 74 p.

_____ 1972, Coal blooms: Earth Science, v. 25, p. 237-241.

Nussman, D. G., 1961, Ecology and pyritization of the Silica formation, Middle Devonian, of Lucas County, Ohio: University of Michigan, M.S. thesis (unpublished), 114 p.

Ohio Division of Geological Survey, 1990, 1988 Report on Ohio mineral industries: Ohio Department of Natural Resources, 118 p.

Ohle, E. L., 1959, Some considerations in determining the origin of ore deposits of the Mississippi Valley type: Economic Geology, v. 54, p. 769-789.

Orr, S. R., Faure, Gunter, and Botoman, George, 1982, Isotopic study of a siderite concretion, Tuscarawas County, Ohio: Ohio Journal of Science, v. 82, p. 52-54.

Orton, Edward, 1870, On the occurrence of a peat bed beneath deposits of drift in southwestern Ohio: American Journal of Science, v. 50, p. 54-57.

_____ 1871a, Report on geology of Montgomery County: Ohio Division of Geological Survey Report of Progress in 1869, p. 143-171.

_____ 1871b, The geology of Highland County: Ohio Division of Geological Survey Report of Progress in 1870, p. 255-309.

_____ 1873, Geology of Clermont County: Ohio Division of Geological Survey, v. 1, pt. 1, p. 435-449.

_____ 1874, Report on the geology of Ross County: Ohio Division of Geological Survey, v. 2, pt. 1, p. 642-658.

_____ 1878, Geology of Franklin County: Ohio Division of Geological Survey, v. 3, p. 596-646.

_____ 1884a, The coal seams of the lower coal measures of Ohio: Ohio Division of Geological Survey, v. 5, p. 129-300, 773-1058.

_____ 1884b, The iron ores of Ohio considered with reference to their geological order and geographical distribution: Ohio Division of Geological Survey, v. 5, p. 371-435.

_____ 1888a, Berea grit as a source of oil and gas in Ohio: Ohio Division of Geological Survey, v. 6, p. 311-409.

_____ 1888b, Gypsum or land plaster in Ohio: Ohio Division of Geological Survey, v. 6, p. 696-702.

_____ 1888c, The production of lime in Ohio: Ohio Division of Geological Survey, v. 6, p. 703-771.

Orton, Edward, Jr., and Peppel, S. V., 1906, The limestone resources and the lime industry in Ohio: Ohio Division of Geological Survey Bulletin 4, 365 p.

Outerbridge, W. F., Weiss, M. P., and Osborne, R. H., 1973, Geologic map of the Higginsport quadrangle, Ohio-Kentucky, and part of the Russellville quadrangle, Mason County, Kentucky: U.S. Geological Survey Map GQ-1065.

Palache, Charles, Berman, Harry, and Frondel, Clifford, 1944, 1951, The system of mineralogy (7th ed.): New York, John Wiley and Sons, v. 1 (1944), 834 p.; v. 2 (1951), 1,124 p.

Palmer, A. R., 1983, The Decade of North American Geology 1983 geologic time scale: Geology, v. 11, p. 503-504.

Parr, D. F., and Chang, L. L. Y., 1977, Descriptive mineralogy of Pugh Quarry, northwestern Ohio: marcasite and pyrite: Ohio Journal of Science, v. 77, p. 213-222.

_____ 1978, Descriptive mineralogy of Pugh Quarry, northwestern Ohio: sphalerite: Ohio Journal of Science, v. 78, p. 272-279.

_____ 1979, Descriptive mineralogy of Pugh Quarry, northwestern Ohio: calcite, dolomite, and fluorite: Ohio Journal of Science, v. 79, p. 24-31.

_____ 1980, Descriptive mineralogy of Pugh Quarry, northwestern Ohio: barite and celestite: Ohio Journal of Science, v. 80, p. 20-29.

Pearl, R. M., 1980, Cleaning and preserving minerals (5th ed.): Colorado Springs, R. M. Pearl Books, 87 p.

Peppel, S. V., 1904, Gypsum deposits of Ohio, *in* Adams, G. I., and others, Gypsum deposits in the United States: U.S. Geological Survey Bulletin 223, p. 38-44.

Phalen, W. C., 1914, Celestite deposits in California and Arizona: U.S. Geological Survey Bulletin 540, p. 521-533.

Porter, Jacob, 1823, Miscellaneous localities of minerals: American Journal of Science, v. 6, p. 247.

Prosser, C. S., 1912, Devonian and Mississippian formations of northeastern Ohio: Ohio Division of Geological Survey Bulletin 15, 574 p.

_____ 1913, The Huron and Cleveland shales of northern Ohio: Journal of Geology, v. 21, p. 323-362.

Prufer, O. H., 1963, The McConnell site, a late paleo-Indian workshop in Coshocton County, Ohio: Cleveland Museum of Natural History Scientific Publications, new series, v. 2, no. 1, 51 p.

Quick, Lelande, Leiper, Hugh, and Kraus, P. D., 1977, Gemcraft, how to cut and polish gemstones (2nd ed.): Radnor, Pennsylvania, Chilton Book Co., 195 p.

Quinn, M. J., and Goldthwait, R. P., 1985, Glacial geology of Ross County, Ohio: Ohio Division of Geological Survey Report of Investigations 127, 42 p.

Ramdohr, Paul, 1973, The opaque minerals in stony meteorites: Amsterdam, Elsevier Publishing Co., 244 p.

REFERENCES CITED

Read, M. C., 1871, Sketches of the geology of Geauga and Holmes Counties: Ohio Division of Geological Survey Report of Progress in 1870, p. 463-484.

_____ 1878a, Report on the geology of Huron, Richland, Knox, and Licking Counties: Ohio Division of Geological Survey, v. 3, p. 289-361.

_____ 1878b, Report on the geology of Ashland County: Ohio Division of Geological Survey, v. 3, p. 519-528.

Reidel, S. P., 1972, Geology of the Serpent Mound cryptoexplosion structure: University of Cincinnati, M.S. thesis (unpublished), 150 p.

_____ 1975, Bedrock geology of the Serpent Mound cryptoexplosion structure, Adams, Highland, and Pike Counties, Ohio: Ohio Division of Geological Survey Report of Investigations 95, map.

Reidel, S. P., Koucky, F. L., and Stryker, J. R., 1982, The Serpent explosion structure, southwestern Ohio, in Roberts, T. G., ed., GSA Cincinnati '81 field trip guidebooks: Geological Society of America, American Geological Institute, v. 2, p. 391-403.

Reidel, S. P., and Koucky, F. L., and Stryker, J. R., 1982, The Serpent Mound disturbance, southwestern Ohio: American Journal of Science, v. 282, p. 1343-1377.

Rexroad, C. B., Branson, E. R., Smith, M. O., Summerson, Charles, and Boucot, A. J., 1965, The Silurian formations of east-central Kentucky and adjacent Ohio: Kentucky Geological Survey Bulletin 2, series 10, 34 p.

Rexroad, C. B., and Kleffner, M. A., 1984, The Silurian stratigraphy of east-central Kentucky and adjacent Ohio: Field trip guide for the Geological Society of America North-Central and Southeastern Sections, Lexington, Kentucky, p. 44-65.

Richards, R. P., 1985, Whiskers and other distorted pyrite and marcasite crystals from Devonian septarian concretions from Ohio (abs.): Rocks and Minerals, v. 60, p. 289.

Richards, R. P., and Chamberlain, S. C., 1987, Pyrite crystals from the Duff quarry: Mineralogical Record, v. 18, p. 391-398.

Robbins, M. A., 1983, The collector's book of fluorescent minerals: New York, Van Nostrand Reinhold Co., 288 p.

Roberts, W. L., Rapp, G. R., Jr., and Weber, Julius, 1974, Encyclopedia of minerals: New York, Van Nostrand Reinhold Co., 848 p.

Robinson, Samuel, 1825, Catalogue of American minerals with their localities: Boston, Cummings, Hilliard and Co., 316 p.

Roedder, Edwin, 1967, Environment of deposition of stratiform (Mississippi Valley-type) ore deposits, from studies of fluid inclusions, in Brown, J. S., ed., Genesis of stratiform lead-zinc-barite-fluorite deposits - a symposium: Society of Economic Geologists Monograph 3, p. 349-362.

_____ 1969, Varvelike banding of possible annual origin in celestite crystals from Clay Center, Ohio, and in other minerals: American Mineralogist, v. 54, p. 796-810.

_____ 1979, Fluid inclusion evidence on the environment of sedimentary diagenesis, a review, in Scholle, P. A., and Schluger, P. P., eds., Symposium on determination of diagenetic paleotemperatures: Society of Economic Paleontologists and Mineralogists Special Publication 26, p. 89-107.

_____ 1984, Fluid inclusions: Mineralogical Society of America Reviews in Mineralogy, v. 12, 644 p.

Rogers, J. K., 1936, Geology of Highland County, Ohio: Ohio Division of Geological Survey Bulletin 38, 148 p.

Rogers, Maynard, 1935, Large concretions of the Ohio Black Shale: Compass, v. 15, p. 167-169.

Roudebush, J. L., 1880, The geology and mineralogy of Clermont County, Ohio, in Rockey, J. L., and Bancroft, R. J., History of Clermont County, Ohio: Louis H. Everts, Publisher, p. 12-23.

Runkle, D. M., 1951, Celestite: Industrial Development Department, Ohio Chamber of Commerce, Publication 11, 6 p.

Sanford, Samuel, and Stone, R. W., 1914, Useful minerals of the United States: U.S. Geological Survey Bulletin 585, 250 p.

Sarles, E. H., 1951, Ohio, in World news on mineral occurrences: Rocks and Minerals, v. 26, p. 41.

Scheihing, M. H., Gluskoter, H. J., and Finkelman, R. B., 1978, Interstitial networks of kaolinite within pyrite framboids in the Meigs Creek Coal of Ohio: Journal of Sedimentary Petrology, v. 48, p. 723-732.

Schmidt, R. G., McFarlan, A. C., Nosow, Edmund, Bowman, R. S., and Alberts, Robert, 1961, Examination of Ordovician through Devonian stratigraphy and the Serpent Mound chaotic structure area: Guidebook for field trips, Cincinnati meeting, Geological Society of America, p. 261-293.

Schreck, A. E., and Arundale, J. C., 1959, Strontium, a materials survey: U.S. Bureau of Mines Information Circular 7933, 45 p.

Seaman, D. M., and Hamilton, H. V., 1950, Occurrence of polymorphous wurtzite in western Pennsylvania and eastern Ohio: American Mineralogist, v. 35, p. 43-50.

Seyfried, C. K., 1953, Concretions as indicators of compaction of the Ohio black shale, southern Ohio: University of Cincinnati, M.S. thesis (unpublished), 57 p.

Shaver, R. H., 1974, Structural evolution of northern Indiana during Silurian time, in Kesling, R. V., ed., Silurian reef-evaporite relationships: Guidebook for annual field excursion, Michigan Basin Geological Society, p. 55-77, 89-109.

_____ 1977, Silurian reef geometry - new dimensions to explore: Journal of Sedimentary Petrology, v. 47, p. 1409-1424.

Shaver, R. H., Wayne, W. J., Gutschick, R. C., Alberts, Robert, Pope, J. K., Forsyth, J. L., Durrell, R. H., and Summerson, C. H., 1961, Geology from Chicago to Cincinnati: Guidebook for field trips, Cincinnati meeting, Geological Society of America, p. 1-44.

Shepard, C. U., 1860, Notices of several American meteorites: American Journal of Science, 2nd series, v. 30, p. 204-208.

Shetrone, H. C., 1926, Explorations of the Hopewell Group: Ohio Archaeological and Historical Quarterly, v. 35, p. 5-227.

Silliman, Benjamin, 1821, Crystallized gypsum: American Journal of Science, v. 4, p. 51-52.

_____ 1822a, Miscellaneous notices in mineralogy and geology: American Journal of Science, v. 5, p. 39-42.

_____ 1822b, Miscellaneous localities of minerals: American Journal of Science, v. 5, p. 254-255.

_____ 1824, Localities of minerals: American Journal of Science, v. 7, p. 45-49.

Sinkankas, John, 1972, Gemstone and mineral data book: New York, Winchester Press, 346 p.

Smith, C. M., 1885, A sketch of Flint Ridge, Licking County, Ohio: Report of the Smithsonian Institution for 1884, p. 851-873.

Smith, G. E., 1951, Geology of Ames Township, Athens County, Ohio, and adjacent Federal Creek coal field: West Virginia University, M.S. thesis (unpublished), 66 p.

Smith, J. L., 1861, The Guernsey County, Ohio, meteorites: American Journal of Science, 2nd series, v. 31, p. 87-98.

_____ 1864, A new meteoric iron from Wayne County, Ohio: American Journal of Science, 2nd series, v. 38, p. 385-387.

Smith, O. C., 1953, Identification and qualitative chemical analysis of minerals (2nd ed.): Princeton, New Jersey, D. Van Nostrand Co. Inc., 385 p.

Smyth, Pauline, 1957, Fusulinids from the Pennsylvanian rocks of Ohio: Ohio Journal of Science, v. 57, p. 257-283.

Sparling, D. R., 1965, Geology of Ottawa County, Ohio: Ohio State University, Ph.D. dissertation (unpublished), 265 p.

_____ 1970, The Bass Islands Formation in its type region: Ohio Journal of Science, v. 70, p. 1-33.

_____ 1971, Bedrock geology of Ottawa County, in Forsyth, J. L., ed., Geology of the Lake Erie islands and adjacent shores: Guidebook for annual field excursion, Michigan Basin Geological Society, p. 19-29.

Stansbery, D. H., 1965, The indigenous minerals of South Bass Island in western Lake Erie: Wheaton Club Bulletin, v. 10, p. 18-21.

Stauffer, C. R., 1909, The Middle Devonian of Ohio: Ohio Division of Geological Survey Bulletin 10, 204 p.

_____ 1916, The relationships of the Olentangy shale and associated Devonian deposits of northern Ohio: Journal of Geology, v. 24, p. 476-487.

Stauffer, C. R., Bownocker, J. A., and Hubbard, G. D., 1911, Geology of the Columbus quadrangle: Ohio Division of Geological Survey Bulletin 14, 133 p.

Stauffer, C. R., and Schroyer, C. R., 1920, The Dunkard series of Ohio: Ohio Division of Geological Survey Bulletin 22, 167 p.

Stevenson, J. J., 1878, Report on the geology of Carroll, Harrison, Guernsey, Muskingum, and Belmont Counties: Ohio Division of Geological Survey, v. 3, p. 177-287.

Stewart, G. A., 1927, Fauna of the Silica shale of Lucas County: Ohio Division of Geological Survey Bulletin 32, 76 p.

Stieglitz, R. D., 1975, Sparry white dolomite and porosity in Trenton Limestone (Middle Ordovician) of northwestern Ohio: American Association of Petroleum Geologists Bulletin, v. 59, p. 530-533.

Stith, D. A., 1983, Physical properties of carbonate aggregate from Ohio: Ohio Division of Geological Survey Report of Investigations 121, 17 p.

Stothers, D. M., and Rutter, William, 1978, Pipe Creek chert: newly discovered aboriginal quarry source: Ohio Archaeologist, v. 28, no. 3, p. 13.

Stout, W. E., 1916, The geology of southern Ohio: Ohio Division of Geological Survey Bulletin 20, 723 p.

─────── 1918, Geology of Muskingum County: Ohio Division of Geological Survey Bulletin 21, 351 p.

─────── 1927, Geology of Vinton County: Ohio Division of Geological Survey Bulletin 31, 402 p.

─────── 1940, Marl, tufa rock, travertine, and bog ore in Ohio: Ohio Division of Geological Survey Bulletin 41, 56 p.

─────── 1941, Dolomites and limestones of western Ohio: Ohio Division of Geological Survey Bulletin 42, 468 p.

─────── 1944, The iron-ore bearing formations of Ohio: Ohio Division of Geological Survey Bulletin 45, 230 p.

─────── 1945, Some localities for fossil plants in Ohio: Ohio Journal of Science, v. 45, p. 129-161.

─────── 1946, Mineral resources of Ohio (revised ed.): Ohio Division of Geological Survey Information Circular 1, 33 p.

Stout, W. E., and Lamborn, R. E., 1924, Geology of Columbiana County: Ohio Division of Geological Survey Bulletin 28, 408 p.

Stout, W. E., and Schoenlaub, R. A., 1945, The occurrence of flint in Ohio: Ohio Division of Geological Survey Bulletin 46, 110 p.

Stout, W. E., Ver Steeg, Karl, and Lamb, G. F., 1943, Geology of water in Ohio: Ohio Division of Geological Survey Bulletin 44, 694 p.

Strogonoff, R. F., 1966, The common minerals of northwestern Ohio and their geologic occurrence: Bowling Green State University, M.A. thesis (unpublished), 67 p.

Sturgeon, M. T., and associates, 1958, The geology and mineral resources of Athens County, Ohio: Ohio Division of Geological Survey Bulletin 57, 600 p.

Sturgeon, M. T., and Smith, G. E., 1954, Some geologic features of Athens County—guide to twenty-ninth annual field conference of the Section of Geology: Ohio Academy of Science, 26 p.

Summerson, C. H., 1959, Evidence of weathering at the Silurian-Devonian contact in central Ohio: Journal of Sedimentary Petrology, v. 29, p. 425-429.

─────── 1966, Crystal molds in dolomite — their origin and environmental interpretation: Journal of Sedimentary Petrology, v. 36, p. 221-224.

Summerson, C. H., Forsyth, J. L., Hoover, K. V., and Ulteig, J. R., 1963, Stratigraphy of the Silurian rocks in western Ohio: Guidebook for annual field excursion, Michigan Basin Geological Society, 71 p.

Summerson, C. H., Jackson, R. R., Moore, C. V., and Struble, R. A., 1957, Insoluble residue studies of the Columbus and Delaware limestones in Ohio: Ohio Journal of Science, v. 57, p. 43-61.

Swemba, M. J., 1974, The relationship between cell dimensions, trace element analysis and color of northwest Ohio fluorites: University of Toledo, M.S. thesis (unpublished), 43 p.

Szmuc, E. J., 1957, Stratigraphy and paleontology of the Cuyahoga Formation of northern Ohio: Ohio State University, Ph.D. dissertation (unpublished), 623 p.

Textoris, D. A., and Carozzi, A. V., 1966, Petrography of a Cayugan (Silurian) stromatolite mound and associated facies, Ohio: American Association of Petroleum Geologists Bulletin, v. 50, p. 1375-1388.

Thorndale, Theresa, 1898, Sketches and stories of the Lake Erie islands: Sandusky, Ohio, I. F. Mack and Brother Publishers, 379 p.

Totten, S. M., 1973, Glacial geology of Richland County, Ohio: Ohio Division of Geological Survey Report of Investigations 88, 55 p.

─────── 1976, The "up-in-the-air" late Pleistocene beaver pond near Lodi, Medina County, northern Ohio (abs.): Geological Society of America Abstracts with Programs, v. 8, no. 4, p. 514.

Treesh, M. I., 1970, Sedimentary structures and brecciation in Cayugan (Upper Silurian) dolomites on Catawba and South Bass Islands, Ohio: Bowling Green State University, M.A. thesis (unpublished), 79 p.

Troost, Gerard, 1822, Description of some crystals of sulphate of strontian from Lake Erie: Academy of Natural Sciences of Philadelphia Journal, v. 2, p. 300-302.

Tucker, W. M., 1919, Pyrite deposits in Ohio coal: Economic Geology, v. 14, p. 198-219.

Ulteig, J. R., 1964, Upper Niagaran and Cayugan stratigraphy of northeastern Ohio and adjacent areas: Ohio Division of Geological Survey Report of Investigations 51, 48 p.

Van Horn, F. R., 1910, Local anticlines in the Chagrin shales at Cleveland, Ohio: Geological Society of America Bulletin, v. 21, p. 771-773.

Van Horn, F. R., and Van Horn, K. R., 1933, X-ray study of pyrite or marcasite concretions in the rocks of the Cleveland, Ohio, quadrangles: American Mineralogist, v. 18, p. 288-294.

Van Winkle, W. L., 1953, Ohio, in World news on mineral occurrences: Rocks and Minerals, v. 28, p. 35.

Ver Steeg, Karl, 1940, Sphalerite and galena in sedimentary rocks in Ohio: Science, v. 92, p. 259.

─────── 1942, Galena in concretions of Pottsville age: Science, v. 95, p. 223.

─────── 1948, Mississippian disconformity and compaction: Ohio Journal of Science, v. 48, p. 185-188.

Verber, J. L., and Stansbery, D. H., 1953, Caves in the Lake Erie islands: Ohio Journal of Science, v. 53, p. 358-362.

Vierthaler, A. A., 1961a, There are diamonds in Wisconsin: Lapidary Journal, v. 15, p. 18, 20, 22, 25.

─────── 1961b, Wisconsin diamonds: Gems and Gemology, v. 10, p. 210-215.

Wasson, J. T., and Sedwick, S. P., 1969, Possible sources of meteoric material from Hopewell Indian burial mounds: Nature, v. 222, p. 22-24.

Weber, J. N., Williams, E. G., and Keith, M. L., 1964, Paleoenvironmental significance of carbon isotopic composition of siderite nodules in some shales of Pennsylvanian age: Journal of Sedimentary Petrology, v. 34, p. 814-818.

Wedow, Helmuth, Jr., Heyl, A. V., and Sweeney, J. W., 1968, Zinc and lead, in Mineral resources of the Appalachian region: U.S. Geological Survey Professional Paper 580, p. 450, 452-466.

Wells, J. W., 1944a, Fish remains from the middle Devonian bone beds of the Cincinnati arch region: Paleontographica Americana, v. 3, no. 16, p. 1-62.

─────── 1944b, Middle Devonian bone beds of Ohio: Geological Society of America Bulletin, v. 55, p. 273-302.

Westgate, L. G., 1926, Geology of Delaware County: Ohio Division of Geological Survey Bulletin 30, 147 p.

White, G. W., 1926, The limestone caves and caverns of Ohio: Ohio Journal of Science, v. 26, p. 73-116.

─────── 1949, Geology of Holmes County: Ohio Division of Geological Survey Bulletin 47, 373 p.

─────── 1953, The character and distribution of the glacial and alluvial deposits, in Smith, R. C., The ground-water resources of Summit County, Ohio: Ohio Division of Water Bulletin 27, p. 18-24.

─────── 1971, Glacial geology of Trumbull County, Ohio: Ohio Division of Geological Survey Report of Investigations 80, map with text.

─────── 1982, Glacial geology of northeastern Ohio: Ohio Division of Geological Survey Bulletin 68, 75 p.

White, J. S., 1975, What's new in minerals? Celestine from Ohio: Mineralogical Record, v. 6, p. 38.

─────── 1977, Calcite on celestine: Mineralogical Record, v. 8, p. 60-61.

Whitlock, H. P., 1910, Crystallographic notes: School of Mines Quarterly (Columbia University), v. 31, p. 225-234.

Whittlesey, Charles, 1838, Geological report: Ohio Division of Geological Survey Second Annual Report, p. 41-73.

Wiese, R. G., Jr., and Fyfe, W. S., 1986, Occurrences of iron sulfides in Ohio coals: International Journal of Coal Geology, v. 6, p. 251-276.

Wiese, R. G., Jr., Powell, M. A., and Fyfe, W. S., 1987, Spontaneous formation of hydrated iron sulfates on laboratory samples of pyrite- and marcasite-bearing coals: Chemical Geology, v. 63, p. 29-38.

Wilson, Thomas, 1899, Arrowpoints, spearheads, and knives of prehistoric times: Annual Report of the Smithsonian Institution for 1897, pt. II, p. 811-988.

Wilson, W. E., 1986, What's new in minerals?: Mineralogical Record, v. 17, p. 147.

─────── 1987, What's new in minerals?: Mineralogical Record, v. 18, p. 361.

Winchell, N. H., 1873, Reports on the geology of Sandusky, Seneca, Wyandot, and Marion Counties: Ohio Division of Geological

REFERENCES CITED

Survey, v. 1, pt. 1, p. 591-645.

Winchell, N. H., 1874, Reports on the geology of Ottawa, Crawford, Morrow, Delaware, Van Wert, Union, Paulding, Hardin, Hancock, Wood, Putnam, Allen, Auglaize, Henry, Mercer, and Defiance Counties: Ohio Division of Geological Survey, v. 2, pt. 1, p. 227-438.

Winslow, J. D., and White, G. W., 1966, Geology and ground-water resources of Portage County, Ohio: U.S. Geological Survey Professional Paper 511, 80 p.

Withington, C. F., 1962, Gypsum and anhydrite in the United States, exclusive of Alaska and Hawaii: U.S. Geological Survey Mineral Investigations Resource Map MR-33, 18 p.

Wittine, A. H., 1970, A study of a late Pleistocene lake in the Cuyahoga Valley, Summit County, Ohio: Kent State University, M.S. thesis (unpublished), 64 p.

Worl, R. G., Van Alstine, R. E., and Heyl, A. V., 1974, Fluorite in the United States: U.S. Geological Survey Mineral Investigations Resources Map MR-60, 13 p.

Wright, G. F., 1890, The glacial boundary in western Pennsylvania, Ohio, Kentucky, Indiana, and Illinois: U.S. Geological Survey Bulletin 58, 112 p.

_____ 1898, A recently discovered cave of celestite crystals at Put-in-Bay, Ohio: Science, v. 8, p. 502-503.

Wuestner, Herman, 1938, Collecting minerals in southwestern Ohio: Rocks and Minerals, v. 13, p. 259-268.

Zubovic, Peter, Stadnichenko, Taisia, and Sheffey, N. B., 1966, Distribution of minor elements in coals of the Appalachian region: U.S. Geological Survey Bulletin 1117-C, 37 p.

APPENDIX A.—INDEX OF OHIO MINERALS BY COUNTY

Adams: barite, calcite, celestite, dolomite, fluorite, hematite, hemimorphite, hexahydrite, hydrozincite, manganese oxides, melanterite, pyrite, quartz, smithsonite, sphalerite, sulfur
Allen: calcite, dolomite, fluorite, pyrite, sphalerite
Ashtabula: pyrite
Athens: calcite, gypsum, hematite, melanterite, pyrite, quartz, sphalerite, wurtzite
Auglaize: calcite, pyrite, quartz, sphalerite
Belmont: barite, pyrite, quartz, szomolnokite
Brown: celestite, gold, vivianite
Carroll: barite, gold, melanterite, pyrite, rozenite, sphalerite, szomolnokite, wurtzite
Champaign: calcite
Clermont: diamond, gold
Clinton: hematite
Columbiana: barite, calcite, chalcopyrite, copiapite, gypsum, hematite, melanterite, pyrite, sphalerite, wurtzite
Coshocton: diadochite, galena, manganese oxides, pyrite, quartz
Crawford: calcite, fluorite
Cuyahoga: anhydrite, barite, calcite, diamond, gypsum, halite, halotrichite-pickeringite, hexahydrite, melanterite, pyrite, sphalerite
Delaware: barite, calcite, galena, gypsum, marcasite, melanterite, pyrite
Erie: aragonite, barite, calcite, celestite, dolomite, ferroan dolomite, fluorite, gypsum, halotrichite-pickeringite, pyrite, quartz, sphalerite, whewellite
Fayette: calcite, pyrite, quartz, sphalerite
Franklin: barite, calcite, opal, pyrite, whewellite
Gallia: galena, hematite, pyrite, quartz
Geauga: manganese oxides, quartz
Greene: calcite, dolomite, marcasite, pyrite, quartz
Guernsey: pyrite, quartz, sphalerite
Hamilton: diamond, manganese oxides, vivianite
Hancock: barite, calcite, celestite, fluorite, gypsum, hexahydrite, pyrite, sphalerite
Hardin: calcite, dolomite, fluorite, pyrite, sphalerite
Harrison: pyrite
Henry: calcite, pyrite
Highland: barite, calcite, hematite, hexahydrite, melanterite, pyrite, quartz, sphalerite
Hocking: pyrite, quartz
Holmes: quartz
Huron: aragonite, barite, calcite, dolomite, ferroan dolomite, fluorite, gypsum, halotrichite-pickeringite, pyrite, quartz, sphalerite
Jackson: pyrite, quartz
Jefferson: barite, calcite, pyrite, quartz, sphalerite, wurtzite
Knox: gold
Lake: anhydrite, gypsum, halite
Lawrence: hematite, pyrite, quartz
Licking: barite, calcite, galena, gold, manganese oxides, quartz
Logan: calcite, dolomite, fluorite, pyrite, quartz, sphalerite
Lorain: barite, calcite, halotrichite-pickeringite, melanterite, pyrite, quartz, rozenite

Lucas: barite, calcite, celestite, dolomite, fluorite, gypsum, halite, pyrite, sphalerite, strontianite, sulfur
Madison: calcite
Mahoning: barite, calcite, chalcopyrite, diamond, gold, gypsum, pyrite, quartz, sphalerite
Marion: calcite, celestite, dolomite, fluorite, marcasite, pyrite, sphalerite, strontianite
Medina: vivianite
Meigs: alunogen, botryogen, copiapite, halotrichite-pickeringite, hematite, pyrite, quartz
Mercer: calcite, dolomite, pyrite, quartz, sphalerite
Miami: calcite, dolomite, glauconite, pyrite, sphalerite
Monroe: calcite, quartz
Montgomery: vivianite
Morgan: hematite, pyrite, quartz
Muskingum: barite, calcite, galena, hematite, pyrite, quartz, sphalerite
Noble: hematite, pyrite
Ottawa: anhydrite, barite, calcite, celestite, dolomite, fluorite, galena, gypsum, halite, hexahydrite, marcasite, pyrite, sphalerite, sulfur
Paulding: calcite, fluorite, pyrite, quartz, sphalerite
Perry: copiapite, hematite, melanterite, pyrite, quartz
Pickaway: calcite, dolomite, marcasite, pyrite
Pike: gypsum, sphalerite
Portage: barite, calcite, chalcopyrite, gypsum, sphalerite
Preble: calcite, hematite, pyrite, sphalerite
Putnam: calcite, fluorite, pyrite, sphalerite
Richland: gold
Ross: barite, calcite, dolomite, gold, gypsum, halotrichite-pickeringite, melanterite, pyrite, quartz, sphalerite
Sandusky: barite, calcite, celestite, dolomite, fluorite, galena, hexahydrite, pyrite, sphalerite, strontianite
Scioto: hematite, potash alum
Seneca: calcite, celestite, dolomite, fluorite, galena, gold, marcasite, pyrite, sphalerite, strontianite, sulfur
Stark: barite, calcite, halotrichite-pickeringite, pyrite, sphalerite, wurtzite
Summit: calcite, chalcopyrite, diamond, epsomite, gypsum, potash alum, pyrite, sphalerite, thenardite
Trumbull: pyrite, quartz, sphalerite
Tuscarawas: barite, calcite, pyrite, sphalerite, wurtzite
Union: calcite, fluorite, marcasite, pyrite
Van Wert: calcite, dolomite, fluorite, pyrite, sphalerite
Vinton: calcite, galena, gypsum, halotrichite-pickeringite, melanterite, pyrite, quartz, rozenite, sphalerite
Warren: gold, vivianite
Washington: gypsum, hematite, pyrite
Wayne: aragonite, barite, calcite, chalcopyrite, galena, pyrite, sphalerite
Wood: aragonite, barite, calcite, celestite, dolomite, fluorite, galena, glauconite, gypsum, hexahydrite, marcasite, pyrite, sphalerite, strontianite, sulfur
Wyandot: calcite, celestite, dolomite, fluorite, gypsum, halite, hexahydrite, pyrite, sphalerite, strontianite, sulfur

APPENDIX B.—MUSEUMS IN OHIO WITH MINERALOGY COLLECTIONS[1]

CINCINNATI

Cincinnati Museum of Natural History
1720 Gilbert Avenue
Cincinnati, Ohio 45202
(Note: the Cincinnati Museum is scheduled to move to Union Terminal in the fall of 1991)

University of Cincinnati Geology Museum
Department of Geology
University of Cincinnati
Cincinnati, Ohio 45221

CLEVELAND

Cleveland Museum of Natural History
Wade Oval, University Circle
Cleveland, Ohio 44106

COLUMBUS

Center of Science and Industry (COSI)
280 E. Broad Street
Columbus, Ohio 43215

Ohio Historical Center
1982 Velma Avenue
Columbus, Ohio 43211

Orton Museum
Orton Hall
Department of Geological Sciences
The Ohio State University
155 S. Oval Drive
Columbus, Ohio 43210

DAYTON

Dayton Museum of Natural History
2629 Ridge Avenue
Dayton, Ohio 45414

FLINT RIDGE

Flint Ridge State Memorial
Brownsville, Ohio 43721

LIMA

Allen County Historical Society
620 W. Market Street
Lima, Ohio 45801

OXFORD

Geology Museum
Room 8 Shideler Hall
Miami University
Oxford, Ohio 45056

TIFFIN

Biology Museum
Laird Science Hall
Heidelberg College
Greenfield Street
Tiffin, Ohio 44883

Seneca County Historical Museum
28 Clay Street
Tiffin, Ohio 44883

TOLEDO

Toledo Museum of Health and Natural History
2700 Broadway
Toledo, Ohio 43609

WOOSTER

Wayne County Historical Society
546 E. Bowman Street
Wooster, Ohio 44691

[1]Other universities and county historical societies may also have mineral displays.